Making Things Grow

Making Things Grow

THE STORY OF

MISSISSIPPI CHEMICAL
CORPORATION

by Jo G. Prichard

with essays by Willie Morris and art by William Dunlap

MISSISSIPPI CHEMICAL CORPORATION / YAZOO CITY, MISSISSIPPI

Copyright © 1998
by Mississippi Chemical Corporation

Printed in Japan
Library of Congress Catalog number:
98-67044

Produced by Prichard & Associates
Jackson, Mississippi
Jo G. Prichard, president; JoAnne Prichard
Morris, editorial director; John Langston,
designer and production coordinator;
and Anne Stascavage, editor.

Distributed by
University Press of Mississippi
3825 Ridgewood Road
Jackson, Mississippi 39211

ISBN: 1-57806-109-1

CONTENTS

FOREWORD

This book is dedicated to the very special people who, over the last fifty years, created the commercial enterprise called Mississippi Chemical Corporation and also to the equally special people who have perpetuated the company since its founding. I am completely convinced that the success of this company is principally attributable to the character of these people, and its culture today clearly reflects the enduring values of its founders. The company was created as an economic entity and continues to be primarily responsive to the financial interests of its owners, yet its spirit also reflects its roots in the very Mississippi soil it was created to feed. The company was a vital part of the social fabric of the state from its inception, both as a consequence of the broad base of farmer-shareholders, who wielded substantial political influence in an agrarian region, and of the leadership role played by Owen Cooper and others associated with the company in promoting social change in the state and South. A major challenge of each successive generation of employees has been to sustain the collective conscience of the company while generating a healthy return on investment for our owners. Thus far, we have been able to do that and I am optimistic about our future in this regard.

In talking with the authors, we made it very clear that we did not want to publish a superficial exclamation of self-promotion, nor did we want a sterile chronology. To do justice to the people who have been involved with the company through the years, it was very important to us to capture the personality and character of these people and to set forth the sequence of principal events with candor and in appropriate context.

Jo G. Prichard, himself a former employee and shareholder, researched Mississippi Chemical's history. From the fruits of his effort, I have developed an even deeper appreciation for the generations of employees of Mississippi Chemical and each of its subsidiaries. We regret that not every person who helped build and preserve the company can be mentioned, that no telling of events can include all the details vividly recalled by the participants, and that some of the company's most beloved figures cannot possibly be captured on paper. Nevertheless, within the inherent limits of this endeavor, the authors have, I think, caught the spirit of the company—a spirit created by many but ultimately larger than any one of us.

My sincerest thanks to all those who have been a part of Mississippi Chemical's story.

Charles O. Dunn, President & CEO
Yazoo City
October 1, 1998

PREFACE

Without roots, plants perish. Without roots in the stories that convey its history and core of values, organizations perish. For fifty years Mississippi Chemical Corporation has been anchored by a hardy purpose and guided by a clear core of values that have been passed on from person to person, from generation to generation through vivid stories. This fiftieth anniversary history attempts to record not only the events that define the company's progress but also the shared stories that embody the spirit of Mississippi Chemical and its people.

For half a century, my own life and Mississippi Chemical's have been intimately linked. In 1940, a year before I was born, my grandfather Jo Prichard, Sr., was a member of the Mississippi Farm Bureau board of directors that hired Owen Cooper to bring new economic lifeblood to farm families. Mississippi Chemical was their most courageous and ambitious undertaking. On March 26, 1948, six months before Mississippi Chemical was chartered, my father Jo Prichard, Jr., attended the first county meeting ever held to sell MCC stock; he volunteered to lead a group of Sunflower County farmers to enlist their neighbors' support for the radical idea of the world's first farmer-owned nitrogen fertilizer plant. He was one of MCC's original shareholders and a passionately faithful customer. Shortly before his death in 1984, he advised my mother, Nona Mae Prichard, "Whatever you do, don't sell the MCC stock. It's the most valuable investment we have."

When I was a junior in high school, my dad persuaded me to invest a hundred dollars in the new venture Owen Cooper had started, called First Mississippi Corporation. "If it's anything like Mississippi Chemical," he said, "it'll be the best investment you'll ever make." And it was. Eventually that one hundred dollars grew to be worth more than ten thousand dollars and helped send my son Gibson through Mississippi State University.

In 1965, when I sought Owen Cooper's counsel about job opportunities in Mississippi, he invited me to come to Mississippi Chemical as his personal assistant. I accepted this offer, and for the next eighteen years was fortunate to work with the remarkable people who make up the Mississippi Chemical Corporation community. I was nurtured and given a sense of place by the company and by the town of Yazoo City, which has profoundly shaped both the company and my family's lives. I count the good people of Mississippi Chemical and Yazoo County among the greatest blessings of my life.

Because of this long affiliation with Mississippi Chemical, I was gratified when the company commissioned me to write this history. In this endeavor I have searched the written, oral, and photographic archives of the state of Mississippi as well as of the company itself. I have interviewed dozens of employees, board members, and community witnesses to Mississippi Chemical's inception and growth, struggles and successes. I hope this history honors the individual stories entrusted to me. That is my aim.

While each person voiced a multitude of memories about Mississippi Chemical, two things were universally cited. The first is the integrity of the company and its people. From the board room to the boiler room, from the towers of Wall Street to the mines of Carlsbad, Mississippi Chemical is known and revered for its honesty. It is a legacy of Owen Cooper, LeRoy Percy, and countless others and an undeviating hallmark of the company today. The second keystone of MCC is the warm respect, friendship, and sense of family shared by the company's employees, and this in many cases extends to the suppliers, customers, and communities with whom they work. "When I walk in the front door of Mississippi Chemical and am greeted like a long lost friend," company consultant Alec Van Ryan once said, "I know this is the most exceptional workplace on earth."

While it is impossible to acknowledge everyone who helped with this project, those who made especially generous and important contributions include David Arnold, Marion Brown, Harold Capello, Harold Fisher, Emery Gregory, Blanche Hester, Glen Moore, John Rednour, and Sue Tatum. I particularly appreciate the support of Melinda Hood and Wendy Weathersby, who coordinated this project for the company, and the following persons who assisted them: Ethel Truly, Pamela Deer, Mary Johnston, Rosalyn Glascoe, BeLinda Sanders, Bill Stewart, Glen Moore, Danny Hood, and Maris, West & Baker. I also salute Bill Dunlap and Willie Morris for their invaluable contributions.

Finally I wish to thank my son David and my wife Mary Nell for their support and understanding, which enabled me to chronicle this story.

Jo G. Prichard

Making Things Grow

The Place, the People, and the Vision

In 1948, the year Mississippi Chemical Corporation was formally incorporated, Yazoo City, Mississippi, was a somnolent river town of some nine thousand souls. Providence had placed us half on the hills, half in the great Delta, but in quintessential élan we were really flatland people, I recognize now. The town was roughly half Aryan and half African, with an additional leavening of Italian, Lebanese, Jewish, and Chinese; it took its name from the Yazoo River, which meandered in its ineluctable twists and turns all the way to the foot of Main Street before proceeding southward to enter the Mississippi just north of Vicksburg. Historically, then, it had been in every sense a port town, with connections to Vicksburg, Natchez, and New Orleans. "Yazoo" was an Indian name, which local legend translates "death," or "Waters of the Dead," and the Indians' spooky burial mounds, resembling miniature grassy hills, were the only rises in the Delta.

We were so isolated in my growing up. It was a lazy town, I would write in North Toward Home, "a lethargic dreamy place, green and lush all year except for those four stark months at the end and the beginning, heavy with leafy smells, at night full of rumblings and lost ghosts—the Yankees in the sunken gunboat down in the river, the witch in the cemetery who broke out of the sturdy link chains surrounding her grave and burned down the whole town in 1904, Casey Jones crashing headlong into that unfortunate Illinois Central freight." A five-hundred-watt radio station arrived in town about then to considerable excitement, and as a teenaged disk jockey I contrived the station sign-on: "This is WAZF, 1230 on your dial, in downtown Yazoo City, with studios high atop the Taylor-Roberts Feed and Seed Store." (We were on the second floor.) Our high school graduation class would be the largest in the town's history, fifty-two strong, and after our commencement exercises at the Midnight to Dawn Dance at the country club, a mile or so from the site of MCC, we mindlessly Memphis-shuffled with our double-named girlfriends to a beloved black ensemble called the Red Tops, which peregrinated throughout the Mississippi Delta and whose favorite song went:

When it's darkness on the Delta,
That's the time my heart is light,
When it's darkness on the Delta,
Let me linger in the shelter of the night.

When I was a little boy, in 1939, they discovered oil out around Tinsley in Yazoo County, and overnight the town was descended upon by outlanders with unfamiliar license plates from Texas, Oklahoma, Arkansas, Kansas, and other exotic venues. At age five I was the young "Oil King," outfitted with a cardboard golden crown in the lead float in a celebrative parade down Main Street, with my contemporary Esme Jean North as Queen. We both waved official wands, which were painted coat hangers. The Tinsley strike was lucrative, but the oil did not last in any overwhelming abundance all that long, although in 1941 the Southland Company built the state's first oil refinery halfway between the oil fields and the town. Yet Yazoo had an experience then of an influx of ambitious outlanders who briefly pierced our isolation and brought resourceful and unexpected elements to the town, which later would hold it in good stead with the MCC invasion.

Many interesting new people were converging on my town again from all over America a decade after the oil boomlet, attendant to the risky and visionary "chemical plant," as everyone would call it. These émigrés would be intrigued by the town and its people, by its extravagant humor and storytelling, by its climactic contrasts of white and black, of hills and Delta, of prosperous and poor, for Yazoo had forever been nothing if not beguilingly different, and by the vast and peremptory alluvial flatness that engulfed it from the north and west. Yazoo City indeed was known as "the Gateway to the Delta"; there would not be a hill from here almost to Memphis, more than two hundred miles away. When you see the sultry little churches and juke joints and shotgun shacks, you realize—blues. It is the richest land in the world, Old Testament to me in its ageless rhythms and despairs. James C. Cobb, the historian, calls the Delta "the most Southern place on earth." Richard Ford, the novelist, identifies it as "the South's South."

Some would cite Main Street as the first street in the Delta, but never I. Grand Avenue, my neighborhood, was the first one, and the precipitous hills began to loom a mere hundred yards or so from the house where I grew up. Two blocks from my house was that of Haley Barbour, someday to be the chairman of the national Republican party. Directly across the street from Haley was Dora Lee Livingston, future runner-up to Miss America. Half a block in the other direction from my boyhood house was the dwelling of Mike Espy, destined to be the first black congressman from Mississippi since Reconstruction and later U.S. secretary of agriculture. One block east was the humble domicile of Zig Ziglar, whose motivational books would be enormous bestsellers. And not far from here, in the black precincts of Brickyard Hill, was the home of Willie Brown, fated to be the greatest defensive back in the history of American football.

In Yazoo in those times we middle-class kids and planters' sons started driving cars at twelve or thirteen, and I remember as graphically as yesterday cruising in my father's green Desoto sedan past the cornfield off Highway 49E, where they were slowly and painstakingly putting together the new chemical plant. Rail cars from all over the nation were bringing in the basic components. It was a bizarre spectacle, dozens of anonymous men working mysteriously in the muddy field with esoteric pieces of equipment lying about, and wheelbarrows and small tractors being scurried around. The words "nitrogen" and "ammonia" and "ammonium nitrate" were just then coming into the parlance of the town, and since these were the early years of the horrendous thermonuclear age, my friend "Muttonhead" Shepherd in the Desoto with me one day suddenly exclaimed, "My God, do you think they're buildin' an A-Bomb factory?"

The formative years of Mississippi Chemical were bellwethers of important and critical milestones in American and Mississippi history. In 1947, only a few months before MCC's incorporation, at Delta State Teachers College in Cleveland, Mississippi, only eighty miles from Yazoo City in the middle Delta, Under Secretary of State Dean Acheson, substituting for the ailing Secretary George Marshall, first disclosed to a public audience the concept of the Marshall Plan. The recent cruel winter in war-ravaged Europe had threatened the people of that continent with extinction, Acheson warned; Winston Churchill would call the Plan "the most unsordid act in history." Soon the United States was committed to sending a substantial portion of its precious fertilizer to aid our European allies. This generosity would compound the already dire shortage of fertilizer in the United States in the late 1940s and lend significance and drama to the forming of MCC.

In Mississippi the late 1940s were marked by a burgeoning revolution in agriculture, which changed the contours of the state and the larger South. Cotton began to shift from sharecropping and from hoes to tractors with flame-burners; cross-plowing, herbicides, and mechanical cotton-pickers were coming into use. The first mechanical picker was made by International Harvester and had been tested in 1944 at Hopson Plantation just south of Clarksdale in the Delta. One two-row mechanical picker could replace 140 hand pickers. The familiar vista of hundreds of black people of all ages chopping and picking cotton in the fields was disappearing. This led to the largest ethnic migration in American history: Mississippi and other Southern blacks departing for the great cities of the North and Midwest.

Beginning in 1950 the state's soybean acreage first surpassed cotton. A Dr. Hartwig at the Stoneville Experiment Station would lead the world in developing soybean varieties, which he named for Confederate generals—Jackson, Hood, Hill, and, of course, Lee; he also named a newly developed wet-soils bean "Semmes" in honor of the Confederate admiral. In 1956 deadly methyl parathion was introduced to the cotton industry to control the boll weevil, and for years it and DDT would be the mainstays against that wily predator.

From the end of World War II to the early 1950s the principal impetus in Mississippi itself was economic development as represented by MCC and progressive Governor Hugh White's Balance Agriculture with Industry (BAWI) programs, accompanied by the creation of the industrial bond concept, which was subsequently imitated by every state in the nation. Then the resistance against racial integration took center stage. There were already rumblings of this in the state in 1948 when legislators, infuriated by President Truman's Commission on Civil Rights, urged Mississippians to leave the Democratic party over the race issue. Some five thousand Democratic leaders met in Jackson that year to craft a Southern battle plan calling for a convention of "true, white Jeffersonian Democrats." In 1948 delegates from Mississippi and other Southern states walked out of the National Democratic Convention when a strong civil rights plank was adopted. In the subsequent Dixiecrat, or States' Rights, Convention Governors J. Strom Thurmond of South Carolina and Fielding L. Wright of Mississippi were nominated for president and vice president. In November the state voted 87 percent for the Dixiecrat ticket. Harry Truman upset Thomas E. Dewey anyway.

Measured by history's sweep, the emergence of the United States as the dominant world power had been swift. "In 1940 the representative

American statesman was still an isolationist," Haynes Johnson has observed. "By 1950 the United States was garrisoning its defeated enemies, Germany and Japan, and willingly assuming global burdens and responsibilities on a scale undreamed of by the Greeks or Romans." In 1948 and 1949 the Cold War with the Soviets had intensified. Josef Stalin seized Czechoslovakia and imposed his blockade on Berlin, leading to the daring Truman airlift which terminated the siege after fifteen months. The NATO Alliance was signed, and Alger Hiss went on trial for perjury. The Kinsey Report on sex in America came out to much shock and titillation. In its deepening Indian summer, Hollywood was making some of its finest movies: All About Eve, Born Yesterday, Twelve O'Clock High.

The early 1950s were marked by singularly turbulent times for Mississippi and the nation—a desperate war halfway around the world, a watershed U.S. Supreme Court decision, and the television revolution— all of which profoundly touched everyday life in Yazoo. I recall the very first time I ever saw television, in the Sears-Roebuck store on Main Street, which had just received its first shipment. "Ain't it somethin'?" the clerk said, but one could hardly see the wrestlers for the snowy interference. Mr. Hibbie Barrier, father of my surrogate brothers Jerry, Bubba, and Bee, was one of the first owners of one of these new contraptions in Yazoo, and naturally we kids congregated at the Barrier domicile on Second Street to watch, still unable, however, to discern Kukla, Fran, and Ollie or Liberace himself from the humanoid blizzards on the little screen. We were mesmerized nonetheless.

In March 1951 there was a histrionic moment in the former cornfield, one which everyone there would always remember, a small group of men bent over a big glass flask in the nitric acid plant waiting on the first drops of the vibrant amber acid. What followed was the initial modest production of the solid ammonium nitrate fertilizer and a tense and worrisome period in which aggravating technical problems threat-

ened to close down the whole company before it really started. MCC was a gamble from the beginning.

I remember, when I was in the eleventh grade, seeing the first big bags of fertilizer displayed in store windows downtown. I was back in the composing room of the old Herald office on Main Street working on the school newspaper, The Flashlight, when I heard a small commotion up front. I rushed out just in time to help drag in the bulging one-hundred-pound MCC bag.

It was a time of tail fins and white bucks, of "the silent generation." Women's skirts rose to mid-calf. In Oxford, Mississippi, 150 miles away, William Faulkner learned he had been awarded the Nobel Prize for literature. "I decline to accept the end of man," he said in his Stockholm acceptance speech. "I believe that man will not merely endure, he will prevail." This declaration would be assiduously tested in the Korean War, when the United States and Red China poised perilously at the brink of all-out conflict. All over the country people were constructing backyard bomb shelters, and schools were staging drills against atomic attacks, although we never saw either of these phenomena in Yazoo itself.

More than most, the town and the state were viscerally enveloped by Korea; the Dixie Division of the National Guard, which included the local unit, had been activated and was soon dispatched to combat. My pals Ralph Atkinson, Henjie Henick, and I played Taps on our trumpets for the military funerals of the returning dead, moments of terrible sorrow and grief. The words we were hearing in those days were Yaks and Stormoviks, Porkchop Hill and Inchon, Pusan and the Yangtze River, and Douglas MacArthur's farewell after Truman fired him: "Old soldiers never die; they just fade away." In that year I caught a faraway glimpse of the general during his triumphant visit to Jackson.

Several of my friends and I were hired to "take inventory" at the chemical plant. It was oppressively hot in the warehouse in those high Dixie summers, and none of us wished to make counting bolts and nuts a life's commitment, but I think we did feel fine about our minuscule contribution to the cooperative yet still unproven endeavor of which all Yazooans were beginning to feel proud. Not long thereafter, MCC's stockholders voted to double the size of the company's production facilities.

In 1952, Yazoo County voted "wet" for the first time in its history—one of eleven Mississippi counties voting to legalize liquor sales. But because the issue failed statewide, alcohol would remain illegal in the state. On the same ballot John Stennis was elected to his first full term in the United States Senate.

Later that year in a special session the state legislature approved a substantial program to upgrade black schools in a last-minute effort to strengthen "separate but equal" education. But it was too late. On May 17, 1954, the Supreme Court in a unanimous decision, joined in by three justices from the South, ruled in Brown v. the Board of Education of Topeka, Kansas, declaring school segregation unconstitutional and ordering the integration of all public schools. I was a student at the University of Texas then, where I read the newspaper reports in a campus cafeteria. I remembered the black children I had known who passed by my house every day to their school, known colloquially as Yazoo High Number Two, and the Black Panthers' football games in which they played in our discarded uniforms. I pondered that day where the future might lead back home.

Soon the Citizens Council was organized to resist implementation of the court order. By 1956 this organization grew to a statewide membership of eighty thousand. I was on vacation from college and attended the organizational meeting of the Yazoo chapter and was as shocked as some others were by the methods then announced to be used by the Yazoo chapter. Mississippi launched massive legal resistance for the next decade with "states' rights" and "maintenance of racial integrity" the bywords. The legislature made abolition of all public schools a county option, and the state's voters approved this in a referendum.

On my walks down the streets of town I could hear from almost every house radio the voice of Senator Joe McCarthy in his hearings in Washington on Communist infiltration. National television was starting to dramatize differences between the South and the rest of the nation. In Montgomery, Alabama, a black woman named Rosa Parks refused to take a back seat in a public bus. People across America were beginning to hear about a gyrating young performer who had been galvanizing small audiences on his Delta road tours. His name was Elvis.

If the boy from Tupelo could in the Lord's appropriate time become an enduring presence on the cultural landscape, might not also the ambitious and hazardous enterprise that had risen from the muddy Yazoo Delta cornfield?

W. M.

CHAPTER ONE

A Compelling Cause

The story of Mississippi Chemical Corporation begins in the rising desperation among American farmers in the months following World War II, a desperation born of circumstances that seemed almost insurmountable at the time. After patiently watching the nation's nitrogen output from 1942 to 1945 go into the production of bombs and ammunition, farmers were now demanding synthetic nitrogen fertilizers to increase their yields and profits. Researchers like Mississippi's W. B. Andrews were proving that heavy applications of nitrogen could produce increases in cotton and corn yields of between

Farmers in town, 1930s. Photo by Eudora Welty. From Reconstruction to Mississippi Chemical's formation about seventy-five years later, Southern farmers banded together to seek solutions to the challenges they faced. In 1947 the Mississippi Farm Bureau Federation took the lead in organizing Mississippi Chemical Corporation.

four- and tenfold, but in the aftermath of the war, supplies of this miracle-working element were practically nonexistent.

Federal acreage controls applied stringent limits on the number of acres farmers could plant. Since the only way to improve production and profits was to fertilize heavily, farmers were furious when they could not get the fertilizers they needed. With the advent of peace, farmers appealed to Washington for help in overcoming shortages caused by the war but were disappointed in their efforts. In 1945 and 1946 they pressed Congress to pass a national fertilizer program, but to no avail. In 1946 Southerners urged the U.S. House of Representatives to appropriate three million dollars to build a phosphate fertilizer plant at Mobile, Alabama, but the measure failed, 201 to 136.

Ironically, the dwindling supplies of nitrogen remaining after the war were further de-

pleted by the Allied victory and peacetime efforts to rebuild Europe. Because nitrogen is used to make munitions, Allied bombers had destroyed much of the nitrogen capacity in Germany, Italy, Japan, and Eastern Europe. This compounded the postwar nitrogen scarcity. "Europe is devastated," Mississippi Farm Bureau President Ransom Aldrich declared on returning from a tour of the continent. "Their nitrogen plants are virtually wiped out. Millions are starving. They urgently need U.S. food and fertilizers. I predict a severe worldwide shortage of nitrogen." And the shortage in America worsened when Under Secretary of State Dean Acheson, in a speech at the Delta Council in Cleveland, Mississippi, in May 1947, proposed a plan of unilateral aid to Europe that would become known as the Marshall Plan. Soon the United States was committed to sending a substantial portion of its precious fertilizers to aid European nations. The U.S.

Unlocking the Key to Life

THE NOBEL PRIZE EFFORT TO TAKE NITROGEN FROM THE AIR AND PRODUCE AMMONIA TO FEED THE WORLD

Adapted from "Global Population and the Nitrogen Cycle,"
by Vaclav Smil, *Scientific American*, July 1997.

Nitrogen is a basic component of DNA and RNA, our genetic molecular structure, and is critical in making all proteins, and thus all plant and animal life.

Unlike carbon, hydrogen, and oxygen, all readily available to sustain plant and human life, nearly all of the world's nitrogen is "locked" in the air and inaccessible to humans and most plants. Why? While most common gases exist in the atmosphere as paired atoms, nitrogen's peculiar chemistry results in pairs that are more tightly bound than those in other gases (oxygen, for example) and much harder to separate.

In the nineteenth century, scientists began to understand that if they could find a way to access the nitrogen in the air, they could increase the world's food production. Unless they could unlock this key element, population growth would be forever limited by natural plant processes for taking tiny amounts of nitrogen from the air. They were aware that plant life required nitrogen, phosphorus, and potash. The latter two elements were relatively easy to supply from the earth's deposits, but the only known sources of nitrogen besides manures were Chilean nitrate, found in the deserts of Chile, and guano left by the birds in Peru's rainless Chincha Islands. These sources were quickly depleted. Unless scientists could find a way to take nitrogen out of the air to nourish plants, the earth could support a population of only about two people per acre of cultivatable land. The limited availability of nitrogen foreshadowed a crisis; the world's population would eventually quadruple in the twentieth century.

Fortunately, two brilliant Germans invented a way to take nitrogen from the air and make ammonia and other fertilizers rich in nitrogen. The breakthrough came early in the twentieth century when Carl Bosch of Germany's BASF Corporation and scientist Fritz Haber invented a synthetic process for making ammonia and then developed it on a commercial scale. Haber won the Nobel Prize in 1919 for his laboratory work from 1900 to 1910 to devise a workable scheme to synthesize ammonia from nitrogen and hydrogen under high temperatures. Then Bosch successfully undertook the challenge of transferring the concept from Haber's lab to a commercial factory that could handle the huge pressures and temperatures required to make ammonia. Soon the world's first commercial ammonia factory—opened in 1913 at Oppau, Germany—was making 170 tons of ammonia a day, about 10 percent of the output of modern ammonia plants in 1998 but enough to serve as an ingredient in all of Germany's explosives in World War I.

Explosives were not the only deadly device Haber engineered. As director of the Kaiser Wilhelm Institute of Physical Chemistry during World War I, he developed the use of chlorine gas for the German general staff. While he hoped it would speed the end of the war, his wife, tormented by her husband's horrific contribution to the war, committed suicide on the eve of its first use against the Allies. After the war, the Allies branded Haber a war criminal. When Hitler, with his anti-Semitism, rose to power in Germany, Jewish Haber fled to England and then Switzerland.

It is ironic that Fritz Haber's synthetic ammonia quickly became a powerful force for both sustaining and destroying life. The presentation of his 1919 Nobel prize for synthesizing ammonia noted, "He created an exceedingly important means of improving the standards of agriculture and the well-being of humankind." Today, that praise seems inadequate. For without the synthetic production of ammonia, the primary ingredient in all manufactured nitrogen fertilizers, 75 percent of today's world population would likely starve.

20 PART ONE: 1948–1956

Farmers lined up to purchase scarce ammonia fertilizer from the Valley Fertilizer Company storage spheres near Greenville, Mississippi, in the spring of 1947. The extreme shortage of ammonia led to efforts to organize Mississippi Chemical Corporation.

was slow to rebuild the German nitrogen plants, however, fearful they might be seized by the Soviets and used to make munitions.

Aldrich's predictions were all too accurate. "Farmers woke up in 1947 without a single pound of nitrogen to put on their cotton," *Fortune* magazine reported in August 1948. They were so concerned that they leaped at the new idea of using anhydrous ammonia—pure ammonia undiluted by water—just perfected by W. B. Andrews at Mississippi State College and first published in his initial research bulletin of March 1947. Andrews's twenty-two-page bulletin was the culmination of four years of extensive experiments. "Anhydrous ammonia and solutions of ammonia," it reported, "have been found to

have crop producing value equal to or superior to ammonium nitrate for row crops." Andrews's disclosure also emphasized that ammonia cost only six cents per pound while solid nitrogen fertilizers like ammonium nitrate cost from ten to sixteen cents per pound. The brochure contained detailed instructions on how to make the six-inch-long ammonia knife required to inject the gas into the soil, along with descriptions of the equipment necessary for hauling, storage, and application of the new ammonia product. The stampede began.

"Planters are being seized with a strange malady called 'anhydrophobia' or 'ammonia-mania,'" *Fortune* magazine reported. "The virus is a new method of injecting the most

concentrated nitrogen compound in Delta soil. Though seldom fatal, the malady can be violent: arguments, lawsuits, and even near riots have occurred when sufferers were deprived of the liquor they craved. The liquor is anhydrous ammonia used for fertilizer and its sweep across the Delta is the hottest news in the fertilizer industry today."

Andrews surmised that ammonia would be applied to a hundred thousand acres in 1947. But he underestimated the farmers' confidence in his findings. That first year, two hundred thousand acres of cotton in the Mississippi Delta received ammonia fertilizer, although the farmers had little or no idea how the gas would actually work. When a researcher called one farmer to ask how

Ammonia Pioneers Pave Way for MCC

Ammonia (NH3)—also called anhydrous ammonia, meaning literally "without water"—is a gas at atmospheric pressure, much like butane or propane, which will dissipate into the air. However, if cooled to temperatures below -28 degrees F. at atmospheric pressure, it becomes a liquid and remains so when stored under pressure. The work in the mid-1940s of W. B. Andrews, Mississippi State College agronomist, and his associates at the Mississippi Agricultural Experiment Station in Stoneville, Mississippi, centered around perfecting special high pressure equipment for storing, hauling, and injecting ammonia into the soil. The pressurized liquid ammonia had to be stored and hauled in thick steel tanks, which at the time were scarce because the war effort had consumed most available steel. Andrews's team placed a small steel tank holding the ammonia on the back of a tractor. The liquid ammonia moved from the tank through sealed rubber hoses into curved six-inch-long hollow steel "knives," which injected ammonia into the soil. Andrews designed and attached a series of these knives behind this experimental application rig—one for each row of cotton or corn the tractor could service. As the tractor drove slowly over a field, the knives plunged into the soil and the driver flipped a switch to discharge the ammonia through the hoses, through the submerged knives, and into the soil itself. No longer under high pressure, the ammonia became a gas when released six inches deep into the soil.

Andrews's developments built upon the innovative work of J. O. Smith of Greenville, who first applied ammonia as a fertilizer in 1932, using a crude rig pulled by a mule named Ike. He borrowed a tiny canister of ammonia from the Leland ice house, attached it to a modified mule-pulled plow, and then knifed it into the soil. When bystanders complained that they could not see the ammonia going into the soil, Smith pulled up the plow and the cloud of ammonia enveloped Ike and the onlookers, causing the men to cough profusely and Ike to race off with his rig in tow. Smith, who spent his life devising ways to convert farming from mules to mechanical equipment, conducted his pioneering work at the Stoneville research center. (Smith has strong ties to MCC: his son Ephraim is an engineer with the company, his daughter-in-law Glenda is a business systems analyst for the company, and his daughter Melanie is the widow of former Mississippi Chemical engineer, Philip Gousset.)

Six-inch-long steel "knives," above, were used to inject gaseous ammonia directly into soils where it increased yields three- to tenfold. J. O. Smith, father of Mississippi Chemical engineer Ephraim Smith, is credited with making the first applications of ammonia at the Delta Branch Experiment Station near Stoneville, Mississippi in the early 1930s, using a mule-drawn rig like the one shown above.

things were with his ammonia, the farmer replied: "How the hell do I know? All I see is some smoke going into the ground. Ask me next August if it works."

There was not nearly enough of Andrews's ammonia fertilizer for the thousands of farmers clamoring to try it. Farmers in Greenville, Mississippi, were so angry over not being able to get even limited shipments that the Mississippi Highway Patrol had to be called in to quiet the dispute. "These farmers are so mad I've been called fifty-seven kinds of S.O.B. in one day," said Peter Generelly, whose Valley Fertilizer Company of Greenville was the primary distributor. "My phone rings all hours of the night and day and I've even had one man call from Chicago and he wants to drive all the way to Mississippi to buy one tank of nitrogen."

Something had to be done to get fertilizer to the farmers. The Mississippi Farm Bureau and its energetic young executive director Owen Cooper accepted the challenge. Responding to the alarm of its farmer-members, the Farm Bureau board voted on June 27, 1947, to name a committee to study the idea of farmers' building their own nitrogen fertilizer facility. Sue Tatum, Cooper's secretary at the Farm Bureau (and later a corporate officer at MCC), was present at that meeting and recalls her reaction: "I remember thinking to myself, 'These folks are whistling in the dark. Farmers are not going to do this.' After all, farmers didn't have much money, and most of them were not open to new ideas. I couldn't believe farmers could be moved to do something of this magnitude for themselves."

∾

Although no farmers in Mississippi—or anywhere else—had ever undertaken such a bold and costly innovation, they did have a history of banding together to attack the economic forces and markets that threatened to defeat them. Soon after the Civil War ended, leaving the South's cotton economy in ruin, Mississippi farmers first organized to seek the political, economic, and agronomic solutions necessary to recover from the upheaval and survive the traumas of Reconstruction.

The Grange, a national farmers' movement, was established in Mississippi in 1871 and lasted more than a quarter of a century. During those years, the Mississippi Grange, with a membership of thirty thousand farm families, convinced the legislature to open Mississippi A & M College in Starkville as a nexus for agricultural education (and also to found the nation's first state-supported college for women twenty miles away in Columbus). The Grange also organized twenty-five supply cooperatives, through which farmers could collectively purchase farm supplies, and fought against outrageous railroad fees and abuse by commodity brokers and merchants. In an 1890 article attacking what they termed economic abuse of the farmers, the Grange claimed "three primary crops in the state: cotton, freight rates, and interest fees. The first is produced by the farmers' sweat and toil. The other two by men who sit in comfortable offices and farm the farmers."

From the turn of the century to World War I, the Mississippi Farmers Union, which had sixty-five thousand members, helped build an agricultural infrastructure that would later contribute considerably to Mississippi Chemical's founding and success. It persuaded the legislature to form a Mississippi Department of Agriculture and Commerce in 1906 and two years later to fund county departments of agriculture, forerunners of the county agent system.

In the 1920s farmers, encouraged by their county agents, organized local Farm Bureau chapters in every county in the state, and most counties in the South, to help farmers make collective sales of their crops and joint purchases of essential supplies like fertilizer and seeds. The first major collective fertilizer purchase occurred in 1921, when Laurel farmer C. L. Neill bought for the Farm Bureau two ocean-going shiploads of Chilean nitrate, some fifty thousand tons. This natural source of essential nitrogen plant food was mined in the Chilean desert by Du Pont and traversed America's new Panama Canal to Gulfport, Mississippi.

During the 1920s a new state Farm Bureau organized numerous cooperative, or farmer-owned, business ventures to buy fertilizers, gin cotton, purchase auto insurance, and market pigs, truck crops, and cotton. As cooperatives these businesses returned all profits to the pockets of their farmer-owners. Mississippi led the nation in the percentage of cotton marketed by farmer-owned cooperatives. During the booming 1920s, the state's farmers sold over eleven million bales for $1.25 billion, with cooperatives marketing over two million bales of that total for $230 million.

Previously Mississippi had been so completely dependent on agriculture that it had very few laws governing corporations or co-operatives. Because Mississippi law did not permit growers to form a cooperative for selling their products, the first such organization doing business in the state, Staple Cotton Cooperative (later known as Staplcotn), was forced to incorporate in Nashville, Tennessee, on May 23, 1921. Shortly thereafter the Farm Bureau corrected the situation by successfully pushing legislation permitting such cooperatives through the Mississippi legislature.

Soon, however, the Great Depression descended, nearly obliterating Mississippi's cotton-based economy. By 1932 more than half of the state's farmers faced bankruptcy. Mississippi's income from cotton sales had drastically plummeted from $181 million a year in 1929 to only $46 million in 1932. Eighty-five percent of the state's workers were farmers, farm laborers, or workers employed in farm supply or other farm-related businesses. This was the South's and its farmers' darkest hour since Reconstruction.

In 1933 President Franklin D. Roosevelt created the New Deal Agricultural Adjustment Act (known as the "Triple A") to rescue farm families by paying them to plow under "excess" acreage—ten million acres of cotton alone—and guaranteeing farm prices on a parity with the cost of supplies. So began federal government acreage controls on key commodities: cotton, corn, wheat, rice, and peanuts. (This program would continue for sixty-two years, until after Mississippi Chemical director and Yazoo City native

Owen Cooper, executive director of the Mississippi Farm Bureau Federation, coordinated the daunting task of organizing thousands of Southern farmers to build the world's first farmer-owned nitrogen fertilizer facilities. Left, Cooper is shown in his office at the Farm Bureau in Jackson. In 1948 Cooper was hired as Mississippi Chemical's first executive officer.

Haley Barbour, then chairman of the Republican National Committee, engineered a Republican takeover of the U.S. Congress in 1994.) FDR's Triple A appeared to be a stunning success. Mississippi's total farm income rose steadily from $69 million in 1932 to $177 million in 1937, and the state's farmers received an additional $80 million in payments for unplanted acres. As they concentrated on fewer acres, yields of lint cotton per acre doubled from 185 pounds to 372 pounds. Scant wonder that in a 1938 national referendum 96 percent of American farmers voted to make the Agricultural Adjustment Act a continuing program. This quadrupling of farm income in five years suggests why a Walthall County, Mississippi, farmer returned from a debate over Roosevelt's farm policy and proudly told his wife he was a Communist. "What's a Communist?" she asked. "I ain't got no idea," the farmer

replied. "But they called Mr. Roosevelt a Communist today. If Mr. Roosevelt's a Communist, then I am too."

In 1940 a far less noticed government action would eventually give Mississippi Chemical its founder. Less than a week after Governor Paul B. Johnson was sworn into office, he fired thirty-two-year-old Owen Cooper as deputy director of the Mississippi Planning Commission and gave the job to a political associate. "I thank Governor Johnson almost every morning," Cooper would later recall. "He saved me from becoming a government bureaucrat."

Cooper was hired in 1940 as executive director of the Mississippi Farm Bureau Federation. During the ensuing decade he teamed with its president, Ransom Aldrich, to launch a series of ambitious programs to aid farmers and their families. But when World War II erupted, Cooper and the Farm

Bureau gave their support to the war effort. Mississippi and American farmers were unstinting in boosting the production of food and cotton for the Allies. They were handicapped, however, by the lack of nitrogen fertilizers.

Ten days after Pearl Harbor, the Farm Bureau board discussed the nitrogen fertilizer shortage and, throughout the duration of the war, sent delegations and resolutions to Washington urging the government to build additional nitrogen fertilizer plants. (Cooper and the Mississippi Farm Bureau also sent Washington $2.8 million in savings bond sales to buy nine B-17 Flying Fortresses. The nine bombers eventually flew into battle bearing names like "The Kemper County Killer" and "The Meridian Mauler.")

After the Allies successfully invaded Normandy on D-day, 1944, Owen Cooper and the Farm Bureau began their own massive drive for better rural hospitals and affordable health insurance for rural Mississippians. By 1946 they had convinced the legislature to establish the Mississippi Hospital Commission and to match federal Hill-Burton funds to build rural hospitals. With Cooper as chairman, the commission built dozens of rural hospitals across the state. During the same period Cooper and the Farm Bureau organized the state's health care company, Blue Cross & Blue Shield of Mississippi, to provide inexpensive health insurance for all its citizens. The first policies would be issued in 1948. As World War II was ending in 1945, the Farm Bureau and Cooper addressed the lack of affordable life and casualty insurance for Southern farm families. The Bureau

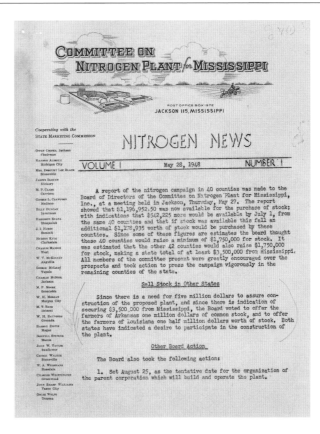

raised four hundred thousand dollars in Alabama, Arkansas, Kentucky, Texas, and Mississippi to form the Southern Farm Bureau Life and Casualty Insurance Company; charter policies were issued in January 1947. (Because of this company's success, no premiums have been required on charter policies for more than four decades.) The Bureau soon started its own casualty insurance company, and a mutual insurance company for fire protection shortly followed.

Even with these innovative programs to its credit, building a nitrogen plant was a singularly daunting challenge for the Mississippi Farm Bureau. Nowhere in all of America had farmers constructed a complicated,

costly plant to take nitrogen from the air to make fertilizer; such a plant would require ten times the capital the Farm Bureau had raised to found its insurance companies. Yet this was the proposal being considered in the poorest state in the Union. When the Farm Bureau board met on that June day in 1947 and voted to appoint a committee to study the possibility of farmers' building their own fertilizer plant, few in the meeting could have guessed that Mississippi Chemical Corporation would be formally incorporated only sixteen months in the future. Two months later, on August 25, 1947, the state's Agricultural and Industrial (A & I) Board assumed the responsibility of analyzing the economic feasibility of building and operating nitrogen fertilizer facilities in Mississippi. The board's chief staff engineer, Robert Hand, immediately directed his energies to this priority project.

On October 23, 1947, at one of the largest and most extensively publicized farm meetings in Mississippi history, eight hundred farmers from five states convened for three hours in the Bass High School auditorium in Greenville to hear a distinguished roster of speakers proclaim the need for and feasibility of farmers' building their own fertilizer plants. "This was not just a Delta meeting," one newspaper reported. "By a show of hands one-third of those present were from South Mississippi and one-fourth from east of Highway 51. And there were a significant number of out-of-state farmers in attendance." Not everyone was convinced, however. The powerful Speaker of the state's House of Representatives, Walter Sillers, was concerned the venture might be a cooperative; he shared the trepidations of some that such collectively owned enterprises were actually socialistic or communistic endeavors. Congressman Will Whittington considered it wiser to buy an old government plant than to build a new one. His proposal was not without merit, since farmer co-ops frequently were poorly capitalized and ill-managed and rarely earned a profit. Instead of voting to proceed with the nitrogen plant, as the meeting organizer Owen Cooper had expected, those present gave their support to

The July 1948 *Nitrogen News* reported on stock subscriptions to build a nitrogen fertilizer plant in Mississippi.

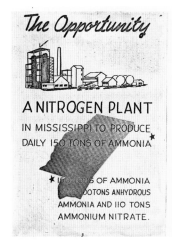

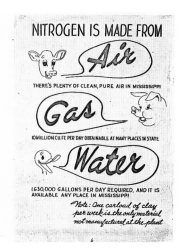

When the stock sales campaign was launched in March 1948 to fund Mississippi Chemical Corporation, thousands of Southern farmers were given the above brochure urging them to invest in the project.

a motion by Walter Sillers calling for a committee of twenty Mississippi farm leaders to study this matter further. It was soon named the Committee on Nitrogen Plant for Mississippi. Cooper was unflinching. "I am in no way discouraged," he said. "This is the greatest undertaking ever attempted by a group of American farmers and it's going to take some time."

In December 1947 two highly positive developments quickened the drive to build the farmer-owned nitrogen plant. First, in a nine-county survey conducted by the Farm Bureau, Mississippi farmers gave their overwhelming endorsement to the undertaking. Hundreds of them in the surveyed counties (four Delta—Bolivar, Humphreys, Leflore, and Sunflower; four hill—Pike, Pearl River, Noxubee, and Newton; and one half-Delta/half-hill county, Yazoo) were asked two questions: (1) Do you think we should build a nitrogen fertilizer plant? (2) If we build such a plant, will you invest your dollars in it? Nearly 100 percent answered "yes" to both. In Newton County rains were so torrential that the farmers' meeting was canceled. In spite of the weather, twenty-five of them showed up, and all of them pledged to buy stock.

The other significant encouragement

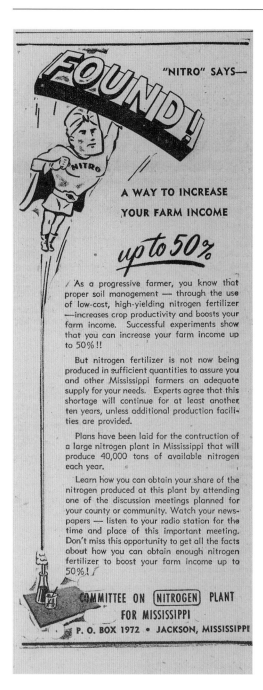

An advertisement run in Mississippi newspapers, urging farmers to invest in their own fertilizer plant. By mid-summer of 1948 five thousand farmers had invested $2.5 million to build Mississippi Chemical.

came from the release of the A & I Board's feasibility study. The board concluded that the construction and operation of a nitrogen plant to produce ammonia and ammonium nitrate was both feasible and economically sound, and that the total output of such a plant could probably be absorbed in Mississippi. (In its report to the Mississippi legislature the next year, the A & I Board boasted that this study, which would have cost more than seven thousand dollars by a commercial firm, cost the state only two hundred and fifty dollars.)

Responding to these positive developments, the Committee on Nitrogen Plant for Mississippi unanimously approved a motion by John Sharp Williams, son of the former U.S. senator from Yazoo County, to proceed with building the nitrogen plant, which they expected to cost $13 million. To promote the venture, the committee voted to request the legislature to appropriate fifty thousand dollars to buttress the campaign to build the plant. When legislators convened in Jackson in January 1948, it was obvious the farmers had done their homework during the Christmas holidays. On its first day in session, the Mississippi Senate suspended its rules and unanimously passed Senate Bill 1 to appropriate fifty thousand dollars for an educational campaign related to building a farmer-owned nitrogen plant for Mississippi. The House quickly concurred with only one negative vote.

In the late 1940s agriculture totally dominated not only the economy of the state but the legislature of the state as well: 90 percent of the senators and representatives had close ties to powerful farm interests back home. Oscar Wolfe of Duncan, the president pro tempore of the senate, was a member of the state nitrogen committee and a powerful ally of the movement to form Mississippi Chemical. Not everyone, however, agreed with the state support. "Here and now is the time to call a halt on that sort of boondoggling and till-tapping of our state treasury," newspaperman Fred Sullins wrote in an editorial in the *Jackson Daily News.* "If the Farm Bureau wants to build a $13 million fertilizer plant, fine, but let them use their own money to do so."

On March 8, 1948, the Committee on Nitrogen Plant for Mississippi formally initiated the then largest stock sales drive in Mississippi history to build Mississippi Chemical. Not surprisingly, this campaign was orchestrated by Owen Cooper. Five district meetings were held across the state, and soon a twenty-page operating manual was ready for county campaign committees. On May 11 the Mississippi Bankers Association and its president Frank Allen of Canton went on record endorsing the stock sales, and 139 local banks agreed to escrow stock sales proceeds. Allen, who was later to be an MCC board member, urged his fellow bankers to "invest in this important enterprise."

Stock sales drives were conducted in forty-two counties, the first commencing in Sunflower County on March 26, 1948. In each county local farmers were chosen to call personally on every farmer in that county to urge him to buy stock in this new plant. Farmers were required to purchase fifty dollars worth of stock to be entitled to buy one

On September 10, 1948, Mississippi's secretary of state Heber Ladner (second from left) issued Mississippi Chemical Corporation's charter of incorporation to Owen Cooper, who would serve as the corporation's executive vice president, and John Satterfield, left, who would serve as its first general counsel. Attorney T. Harvey Hedgepeth, right, also provided legal counsel to the company.

ton of ammonium nitrate and seventy-five dollars worth of stock to buy one ton of ammonia. So the amount of stock each purchased was determined by the amount of fertilizer needed. MCC hoped to sell $5 million in stock and planned to borrow the rest of the estimated $13 million. By May stock sales had surpassed the $1 million mark, but projections suggested that only $3.5 million would be sold statewide. To make up the difference, the state committee authorized sales of $1 million worth of stock in Arkansas and half a million in Louisiana.

Charles Jackson, Bob Fisackerly, Ward Seat, and Shelby Shows tenaciously led the stock sales efforts. Each was paid two hundred dollars per month, plus five dollars per day for meals and lodging by the state nitrogen committee from the $50,000 in state funds.

"These small farmers had never bought stock in anything, and convincing them to buy Mississippi Chemical stock was very difficult, even for me, and I'm a doggone good salesman," Charles Jackson, who sold more Mississippi Chemical stock than any other single individual, would recall. Jackson found it necessary to call on twenty to twenty-five farmers to find one willing to invest. At times he would grab a cotton sack, fall in with a farmer, and pick a row of cotton with him, all the while telling him about MCC and about how every farmer would own his own source of nitrogen. "On one occasion," Jackson remembers, "we got to the end of the row and the farmer said, 'Come on, young man.' He walked me up to his house, called his wife, and asked her to bring me a drink of water and bring out the money jar. She brought out an old tin syrup can, and that man counted out six hundred dollars to buy stock in MCC. I was so happy you'd thought I had a check for a million bucks. Honestly, most of the farmers who bought stock never thought MCC would get off the ground. But they were so desperate to get nitrogen fertilizer they figured they had to take the chance. Thank goodness they did."

"I'll never forget moving back to Greenville about that time and having my farm manager tell me he'd committed us to invest twenty-five thousand dollars in this new scheme," said farmer LeRoy Percy, adopted son of Greenville poet and author William Alexander Percy. "'You've done what?' I exclaimed. I couldn't see investing twenty-five thousand dollars in what sounded like a harebrained idea to me. My manager said that lots of folks were investing so they could get ammonia, but maybe it wasn't too late to back out of the deal. And there were some smart businessmen who thought the idea would never work. I remember Mr. Garret and Mr. Bledsoe, who founded Staple Cotton, saying that plant

On October 27, 1948, six hundred Southern agribusiness investors gathered at the Heidelberg Hotel in Jackson, Mississippi, to formally organize Mississippi Chemical Corporation and to elect its initial board of directors, above. Seated, left to right: Owen Cooper of Yazoo City, George Crawford of Madison, J. B. Cunningham of Brooksville, R. C. Malone of Pace, John Sharp Williams of Yazoo City, Ransom Aldrich of Michigan City, George D. Perry of Maud, M. T. Reed of Belzoni, R. E. Chapman of Lambert, and Fred A. Anderson of Gloster. Standing, left to right: honorary director L. A. Olsen of the Tennessee Valley Authority, C. D. Maddox of West, H. R. McIntosh of Picayune, Charles S. Whittington of Greenwood, Billy Duncan of Inverness, C. E. Denton of Shelby, Jasper Blount of Hickory, John W. Taylor of Sunflower, C. L. McNeil of Jackson, Hudson Kyle of Clarksdale, H. P. Sullivan of Walls, and LeRoy P. Percy of Greenville. Not pictured: director C. G. Cortright of Rolling Fork and honorary directors Oscar Wolfe of Duncan, state senator; Boswell Stevens of Macon, chair of the State Marketing Commission; Frank Allen of Canton, president of the Mississippi Bankers Association; and Dr. W. B. Andrews of Mississippi State College.

would never produce a pound of fertilizer."

Several factors contributed to the success of the stock sales drive:

• Farmers' trust in their Mississippi Farm Bureau, which took the lead in organization.

• Farmers' trust in their local county agent and vocational agriculture teachers, who played important roles in arranging and endorsing the project. Because of their trust in the Farm Bureau and their county agents, farmers ultimately invested their scarce capital in this bold idea of a farmer-owned fertilizer plant. "Without the endorsement of the Farm Bureau, the local county agents and vo-ag-teachers," Sue Tatum would remember years later, "those farmers would not have given Owen Cooper or anyone else with such a wild idea the time of day."

• Farmers' trust in their local bankers, who strongly supported the crusade to form Mississippi Chemical and agreed to hold in escrow at their banks all pledges to buy stock. Hence, the farmers' money never "left home" until the project got enough dollars to proceed.

• The unusual economic circumstances that could make additional quantities of nitrogen fertilizers highly profitable to farmers through increased yields, while their production and sale could be equally profitable to Mississippi Chemical.

• The resourceful leadership of Owen Cooper. "Owen is the greatest promoter I have ever met," Tom Parry, who succeeded Cooper as company president in 1973, later said. "It's a good thing he's the most honest man on earth, because he could talk you into investing in just about anything."

• The support of the state legislature in appropriating fifty thousand dollars to underwrite the drive.

By midsummer of 1948 more than five thousand Southern farmers had decided the risk was worth taking and had invested a total of $2.5 million in Mississippi Chemical stock. With that much in escrow, on August 19 the committee signed the legal papers to form Mississippi Chemical Corporation. Secretary of State Heber Ladner issued the charter on September 7, 1948. Six hundred farmers and farm leaders from six Southern states congregated at the Heidelberg Hotel in downtown Jackson for Mississippi Chemical Corporation's organizational meeting on October 27, 1948. Although the company, like a cooperative, would be owned by the farmers who would purchase the fertilizer, the founders had concluded after extensive study that Mississippi Chemical should be organized as a regular corporation, rather than as a cooperative. Some Southerners were still prejudiced against cooperatives, believing that they were socialist in nature, and the founders desperately wanted to avoid this ill-will. Also, Mississippi Chemical

Mississippi Chemical's initial officers: seated: John Sharp Williams, Jr., president; Mamie F. Marshall, acting secretary-treasurer. Standing, from left: Owen Cooper, executive vice president; Charlie L. McNeil, second vice president; and Charles Whittington, first vice president.

wanted to use the corporate concept of making the size of one's investment proportionate to the quantity of fertilizer desired.

Twenty-two notable agricultural leaders were elected as board members. One of them, LeRoy Percy, said, "Honestly, in the days leading up to meeting, I was thinking that maybe I should ask for my investment back. But when we got there, Owen Cooper was such an incredible and dynamic guy that he convinced me to serve on the board and even the executive committee. I ended up serving for forty years [the last twenty-nine as board chair], and working with Owen for those four decades is probably the greatest thing that ever happened to me."

To Be or Not to Be a Cooperative?

Mississippi Chemical was the first American business enterprise to organize itself as a "corporation doing business as a cooperative." This novel method of operating partly as a corporation and partly as a cooperative was the brainchild of the company's first general counsel, John Satterfield, later president of the American Bar Association while still serving as MCC's general counsel. A creative legal strategist, Satterfield wanted Mississippi Chemical to enjoy the benefits of both a corporation and a cooperative.

Businesses organized as cooperatives are owned by their customers, i.e., their shareholders and customers are the same, identical persons. Such co-ops do not seek to earn and retain a profit, but rather have the purpose of supplying product to shareholder-customers at exactly the cost of acquisition or manufacture. At the conclusion of the business year, a cooperative's expenses are deducted from all its income, and any remaining funds (what would be "profits" to a regular corporation) are distributed to the shareholder-customers in the form of patronage refunds. Because there is a pre-existing legal obligation for the cooperative to return its "profits" to customers, the cooperative is exempt from paying federal income tax.

On the other hand, corporations were required to pay corporate income tax at rates in the 1940s of up to 50 percent of profits before they could disperse the remaining earnings to shareholders in the form of dividends, which were then subject to a second federal income tax to the shareholder. John Satterfield wanted the company to take advantage of the cooperative federal income tax exemption and thus benefit its shareholders by subjecting company profits to only one level of federal taxation.

There was, however, a significant disadvantage to cooperative law in the late 1940s: it did not correlate purchases and patronage rights directly to the amount of stock a customer owned. Under then-existing co-op law, a farmer who owned only one share of stock in a cooperative could still buy huge amounts of product, and he would be entitled to patronage refunds on all his purchases. The effect was that a cooperative could not require farmers to buy stock in proportion to the amount of fertilizer they wanted to purchase. A corporation, however, can and does pay earnings to its shareholders in direct proportion to the amount of their investment. For Mississippi Chemical, tying fertilizer purchase rights and patronage refunds to a farmer's stock ownership level was absolutely crucial to the company's ability to raise the millions of dollars in capital needed to launch the company.

To gain the advantages of both a corporation and a cooperative, Satterfield created the organizational concept of "corporation operating as a cooperative" and fashioned Mississippi Chemical as such an entity. While the Internal Revenue Code of the time did not prohibit Satterfield's innovative configuration, neither did it expressly allow it. The Internal Revenue Service soon sought to levy enormous federal income tax claims against the new company. The crafty Satterfield and his legal associate Dudley Buford skillfully defended Mississippi Chemical's right to pay patronage refunds to its shareholders-customers and its right to an exemption from the payment of federal income tax. In so doing, they established modern cooperative tax law, still followed today, through precedents set in "the Mississippi Chemical cases," landmarks of cooperative tax law. The Satterfield cooperative concepts, later generally codified in the Internal Revenue Code, have been imitated by a huge number of businesses, large and small, which qualify as "corporations doing business as cooperatives."

"Throughout 1948 and '49 we mounted the most massive stock sales drive in the history of Mississippi," Owen Cooper later remembered. "Raising $4 million in those days was about like raising $400 million today. No one in Mississippi or any American farmers had ever done so. It was a huge hurdle. That was ten times the amount we had to raise to launch the Southern Farm Bureau Insurance Company and there were already four Farm Bureau insurance companies operating successfully in the Midwest. Farmers could see that had worked. But no group of farmers in America had ever built a synthetic nitrogen plant and most folks doubted we could make it work. We must've written a thousand news releases and held a thousand local meetings with farmers to explain the huge opportunity that Mississippi Chemical represented." By March 1949 seven thousand Southern farmers had invested $3.25 million in Mississippi Chemical stock. They would eventually invest another million.

Meeting in Greenwood on March 18, 1949, Mississippi Chemical's board selected Yazoo City as the site for their new plant, subject to voter approval of a bond issue and to negotiating an acceptable gas contract. The other finalists were Vicksburg, Jackson, and Greenville. Greenwood, Columbus, Canton, Pascagoula, Natchez, and Laurel had also been considered.

"Yazoo City had several pluses going for it," Cooper later explained. One was its plentiful water supply, vital for operating the plant. According to Cooper, "We needed 10 million gallons of cooling water a day. That was as much as the entire city of Jackson used at that time. Yazoo City has a stratum of water 60 to 120 feet deep that is cool—65 or 68 degrees—almost perfect. Then about 400 feet down you hit another layer of very high quality water that we could use for our boilers." Another reason, Cooper noted, was that Yazoo City was well located to serve farmers in the Mississippi Delta, where the new company expected to sell most of its fertilizer. Mississippi Highway 49 divides at Yazoo City into 49 East and 49 West, both roads going through the heart of the Delta. In addition, there were two natural gas suppliers to Yazoo City and a good railroad there.

The other essential element Yazoo City had in its favor was the enthusiastic support and influence of John Sharp Williams, II, who was president of MCC's board of directors. "From day one Mr. Williams had lobbied to have us located in Yazoo. And because of him the local leaders wanted us to come. That was not the case everywhere," Cooper observed.

"Greenville was one of the towns they considered for the plant site," LeRoy Percy recalled. "I was not there to speak for the idea, and several local fertilizer companies bad-mouthed MCC so much that the local folks weren't too interested in having Mississippi Chemical come to Greenville. Knowing what we know now, fifty years later, we would probably build the plant in Greenville, so we could use the river to ship fertilizer around the world. But back in 1948 we were thinking about sales to Belzoni [Mississippi], not sales to Beijing."

At the March 18, 1949, meeting the Mississippi Chemical board received superlative news from the Girdler Corporation of Louisville, Kentucky, a firm that specialized in the design and construction of chemical and petrochemical plants. It reported that the proposed plants could be built for $8 to $10 million instead of the $13 million originally estimated. A month later, on April 19, 1949, the infant company got another positive report. Yazoo County voters had approved a $750,000 Balance Agriculture with Industry (BAWI) bond issue for Mississippi Chemical by a margin of 3,843 for to 16 against and had set four records in the process: (1) the size of the bond issue approved was three times the previous highest in state history; (2) the 92 percent voter turnout was the highest in state history; (3) the 240 to 1 ratio was the largest margin of approval for any state bond issue; (4) and the $8 million plant was the most expensive Mississippi industry partly financed with a BAWI bond issue.

This overwhelming voter endorsement was a personal tribute to the faith Yazoo County voters had in their native son and Mississippi Chemical board president John Sharp Williams, II. Williams had worked tirelessly to convince the voters to approve this critical funding. According to Miller Holmes, who had just returned from World War II, the endorsements of Norwood Nichols, president of the board of supervisors, and of the two bank presidents, Phil Williams of the Bank of Yazoo City and Herbert Holmes of Delta National Bank, were also critical. "A lot of folks felt that the county's borrowing $750,000 on Mississippi Chemical's behalf was risky, and the board of directors of both banks went out on a limb and urged public support of the bond issues," Holmes recalls. Because of all these efforts to inspire the voters of Yazoo County, the novice corporation had a place to call home—Yazoo City, Mississippi.

Mississippi Chemical Corporation now faced multiple challenges: opening the company's first offices; assembling its management staff; hiring employees; completing designs for the first plant; and obtaining the remaining $3.4 million loan needed to build the plants. In the months to follow, Owen Cooper would work tirelessly to keep faith with the farmers who had so overwhelmingly given him their trust.

CHAPTER TWO

Early Struggles
and Successes

Yazoo County's emphatic approval of the $750,000 bond issue to assist Mississippi Chemical Corporation had given the embryo company a large step forward and a place to call home. Quickly opening temporary offices in a house on Yazoo City's North Main Street, Mississippi Chemical intensified its efforts on three fronts: selecting the best processes to use in its long-awaited synthetic nitrogen production facilities and the contractors to construct them; working to secure a critical $3.4 million loan from the Reconstruction Finance Corporation; and assembling and training managers and employees to build and operate the new facilities.

The company's first two appointments

Davis Allgood, who worked in Mississippi Chemical's initial ammonium nitrate fertilizer plant, won Yazoo County's 1955 corn yield contest for the bumper crop he harvested after generous applications of MCC ammonium nitrate fertilizer to his corn field.

were momentous ones. Owen Cooper was hired as executive vice president and chief operating officer on November 1, 1948, and H. Leroy Thompson was obtained as general operations manager ten days later. Both had important skills. Cooper possessed grassroots organizing talents and political contacts honed during a decade of leading the Mississippi Farm Bureau's founding of the major farmer-owned businesses. Thompson was an inventive engineer who brought his own unique ideas for building a new, less costly ammonia plant, which he had devised while helping the Tennessee Valley Authority produce nitrogen fertilizers during World War II in the government plants in Muscle Shoals, Alabama.

Owen Cooper's decision to direct Mississippi Chemical was not a foregone conclusion, LeRoy Percy says. At the time Cooper had a stable, exciting, and gratifying job as executive director of the Mississippi Farm

Bureau; transferring to this uncertain new venture represented a substantial personal risk. Cooper had persuaded Percy to embrace the cause of Mississippi Chemical, and now Percy would turn to Cooper with a similar plea. "Few people thought we would ever succeed," Percy recollects. "If we were to stand any chance, we had to have Owen. I went to him and told him how urgent it was to have him direct the effort to get a loan from the federal government. Without that loan, we could never build the plant, and I didn't think anyone but Owen could handle that. My memory is that he thought for a minute or two and then said, 'Well, somebody's got to see this thing through, and I guess I'm the logical one to take it on.'"

Throughout its history, Mississippi Chemical would utilize the latest technology and expertise in its fertilizer plants to reduce costs and increase efficiency. Its very first plant was no exception. As Owen Cooper later explained it, "We had to have some brand-new technology for making ammonia. The old processes used in Europe were way too expensive. Fortunately for us, Leroy Thompson figured out a better design, and it worked."

One of Cooper's old college classmates who worked for Spencer Chemical had given him an estimate, using conventional calculations, of $13 million to build the MCC plants, a huge cost for the new company. The projected design would have covered a sprawling forty acres. "They'd put the synthesis section over here," Cooper would recall, "and the electric generation over here, and the gas processing still at a third site, all the while venting millions of BTUs of heat while using more gas to generate electricity."

A more efficient design was devised by the technical wizardry of Leroy Thompson. While working at TVA, he had discovered a new method of building ammonia plants that would require one-tenth as much space and half as much money. Thompson conceived an ingenious method of linking together the three principal components of the plant so they used far less heat and electricity.

"Thompson's plan included using a French ammonia conversion design that utilized three times the highest pressure ever used in an American ammonia plant," Marion Brown, an engineer who implemented numerous technical advances at Mississippi Chemical over the next three decades, recalled. "Most American plants of that day used pressures no greater than five thousand pounds per square inch. France's Grande

Operations manager H. Leroy Thompson addresses visitors to Mississippi Chemical's partially completed Yazoo City plants on August 2, 1950. Thompson's innovative and efficient design concepts cut the capital cost of the company's initial ammonia complex to nearly half that of conventional plants.

Paroisse process operated at fifteen thousand pounds per square inch and offered improved economy over previous plants."

Convincing Thompson to come to work for Mississippi Chemical was no simple task. "There were these two Finklea brothers," Cooper later said, "both shade-tree mechanical geniuses up in Leland, Mississippi, who could build almost anything with bailing wire and a blowtorch. They saw all the farmers begging for ammonia, so they had somehow persuaded Leroy Thompson to move to Leland and help them build one of his

unique new ammonia plants. Well, the Finkleas didn't have a prayer of raising the money needed to build an ammonia plant, and we needed Thompson to help us. So I asked LeRoy Percy to drive over to Leland and try to lure Leroy Thompson away from the Finkleas and to come to work for us."

LeRoy Percy reflects on that fateful day, fifty years ago:

You know, when Owen called you, it was impossible to say no. So, I drove over to Leland and literally bought Thompson away from Jimmy and Aubrey Finklea. Those two guys had never graduated from high school, but man they could build anything—airplanes, farm machinery, and their own rigs to put ammonia in the soil. Well, when I drove up, old Aubrey was chewing tobacco and there were spittoons everywhere, and I said, "Aubrey, we got to have Leroy." Aubrey said, "You can have him for a million dollars." I said, "Ain't no way you're ever going to get a million bucks, but we'll be fair with you. We need this boy. We're going to build a plant like you're talking about, only much bigger, and the farmers in the Delta need it bad. What will it take for you to let us have him?" Finklea hesitated for a long while and then told me if we would pay him six thousand dollars, he would release Thompson to us. I didn't haggle around. I met it. On the spot. And it's a doggone good thing we got Leroy Thompson. We were way, way out on a limb trying to build an ammonia plant with very little money. We were betting Leroy could do it cheaper than anyone else in the world.

Leroy Thompson was the reason Mississippi Chemical had to pay Owen Cooper

On September 23, 1949, officials of Yazoo County and Mississippi Chemical opened bids for the construction of water wells, electric power facilities, ammonia storage spheres, a warehouse, and an office building to be built from the $750,000 bond issue. Standing, left to right: Dave Shackelford, chancery clerk; Leroy Thompson, MCC operations manager; Norwood Nichols, president of the Yazoo County board of supervisors; Charles Whittington, Mississippi Chemical board president; and Owen Cooper, MCC executive vice president. Seated, left to right: Vernon Whitaker, county supervisor; W. B. Dunwoody, MCC project engineer; H. T. Barrier, county supervisor; and Grady Davis, county supervisor.

such a "high" salary as the first chief operating officer. Leroy Thompson wanted a top salary and big bonus if his plans worked. MCC finally agreed to pay Thompson $1,000 a month, to be raised to $1,250 a month when the plant was under construction. The board decided that it could not pay Thompson more than its chief operating officer, so Cooper's salary was set at $1,000 a month, too. The minutes of Mississippi Chemical's first board and executive

committee meetings contain numerous lengthy entries about hiring Thompson, including a long legal release by the Finkleas and a board resolution promising to consider a bonus for Thompson if the plant worked as he promised; they contain only one line about hiring Owen Cooper.

The Mississippi Chemical board, composed almost entirely of farmers, relied on Thompson's knowledge to select the best contractor to design and build its initial

plants. After interminable meetings with four prominent contractors, in April 1949 the board accepted Thompson's recommendation that the Girdler Corporation of Louisville, Kentucky, be employed to design and construct its original nitrogen fertilizer plants. Its bid brought the total amount needed to finance the project to $8.4 million. "You might say we bet the farm on Leroy and won," Percy muses. "Turns out Thompson really did know how to build a cheaper, better plant, and he was a key player in getting Mississippi Chemical off and running."

The optimism in Mississippi over Thompson's pioneering ideas and his selection of the Girdler Corporation was tempered by a much less enthusiastic response from the Reconstruction Finance Corporation, an arm of the federal government set up by Herbert Hoover in 1932 to help businesses reorganize after the stock market crash of 1929. In 1948 Mississippi Chemical had applied to the RFC for the requisite $3.4 million loan to complete the $8.4 million it had to raise to build and start its first plants. Farmers had invested $4.25 million, and Yazoo County had lent $750,000. MCC was $3.4 million short. Small-town banks had agreed to lend farmers the money to buy MCC stock because they could offer farmland as collateral, but Mississippi Chemical had no such collateral. Those same banks and other commercial banks universally declined to lend the company the millions needed to proceed on the grounds that the project was too risky. The Reconstruction Finance Corporation was the only serious hope the fledgling company had for securing such a sizeable line of credit.

Throughout the spring and fall of 1949, while MCC was recruiting its core staff and contracting with the Girdler Corporation, RFC was conducting its investigation into MCC's loan request and the proposed plants. When the scathing five-page analysis prepared by the RFC staff was released in the fall of 1949, approval of the loan, so essential to construction of the plants, appeared extremely doubtful. The hesitations voiced in the RFC report by unnamed staff and consultants show just how visionary and risky the new venture was:

• We doubt the loan can be justified because of the inexperience of all associated with this project and the unproven technical changes they propose to use.

• The Girdler Corporation has never built an ammonia plant and were apparently chosen because of their willingness to cut corners and lower cost estimates. They propose to license patented French technology, and we doubt the plant will be as good as available from other American companies.

• This is a doubtful, marginal plant because of its small size, unnecessarily high synthesis gas pressure, and natural gas costs nearly twice that available to plants in Louisiana.

• We think it will be impossible for Mississippi Chemical to produce ammonia nearly as cheaply as the $23.19 per ton Girdler predicts.

• The project on the whole seems to have a desperate, pressurized tact. Every factor has been squeezed down or loaded up to get a favorable verdict.

• Because there is already 430 tons per day of

Mississippi Chemical's first sales staff and comptroller John Bergman, left to right: Ward F. Seat, Bergman, Shelby S. Shows, Charles J. Jackson, R. H. Fisackerly, and W. K. McWilliams.

The company's management staff, November 1949, seated, left to right: Charles Jackson, Leroy Thompson, Owen Cooper, Ernest Stewart and W. B. Dunwoody. Standing, left to right, John Bergman, Ward Seat, John Satterfield, and Doug Wilson of the Girdler Corporation, the contractor employed to build the original fertilizer facilities.

In the fall of 1949 Mississippi Chemical hired its first employees, shown above on the steps of the temporary offices at 220 North Main Street in Yazoo City. First row, from left: Ward Seat, John Bergman, unidentified woman, Marguerile Daniels, unidentified woman, and Carolyn Thompson. Middle row, from left: Vanie Burns, Esma Hawks, unidentified woman, Doris Wiggins, and Helen Coker. Back row, from left: Ernest Stewart, Charles Jackson, W. B. Dunwoody, Owen Cooper, Leroy Thompson, and John Satterfield.

new ammonia capacity being built in their region, we think the company would be better off to simply buy ammonia and try to convert that into other fertilizers.

Senators and congressmen from across the South began a long, arduous effort of vigorous lobbying throughout 1949 and into 1950, trying to convince the RFC to reverse its searing conclusions and approve the loan.

As the politicians in Washington considered the RFC loan, in Yazoo City the company aggressively continued assembling a solid group of employees. Although only half of the required $8.4 million was in hand, the company team set about to finish selling its stock, organize its offices, and design and build its plants. Many of these original employees played essential roles until their retirement decades later. In January 1949 R. H. Fisackerly, Charles Jackson, Ward Seat,

Courier in a Cadillac

When Mississippi Chemical opened its offices in downtown Yazoo City in 1950, the company's first local employee was the flamboyant Roscoe Fox, a Cadillac-driving courier who was a beloved figure among Yazoo's people and MCC's initial employees. "Roscoe was a charmer who had rapport with everyone who was anyone in Yazoo City," Sue Tatum would remember, "and we needed that in our early days." "I don't know where Mississippi Chemical placed Roscoe Fox on the organization chart, but Roscoe Fox placed himself as the number two man right below Owen Cooper," remembers banker Miller Holmes, who had offices across the street from Mississippi Chemical's quarters on Main Street.

Roscoe would drive around town in the new Cadillac with four-year-old Haley Barbour riding shotgun. Roscoe's wife, Hattie B. Fox, not only operated the famous Elite Cafe on Bridge Street but was also employed by the Barbour family and helped rear the three Barbour boys, Jeppie, Wiley, and Haley. Too young to be in school, the future chairman of the National Republican Party relished riding with Roscoe Fox on his courier route.

Sue Tatum recounts the day a salesman was impressed by two sights at the company's plant office. At 5:00 p.m. Fox parked his Cadillac and came in with the mail. Then Tatum and Esma Hawks slipped into the ladies' room and emerged in swimming suits for a dip at the company's recreation park Hilltop. The salesman turned to Tatum and exclaimed, "This is the place I have been looking for all my life. The courier drives a new Cadillac and the women wear bathing suits. Sign me up."

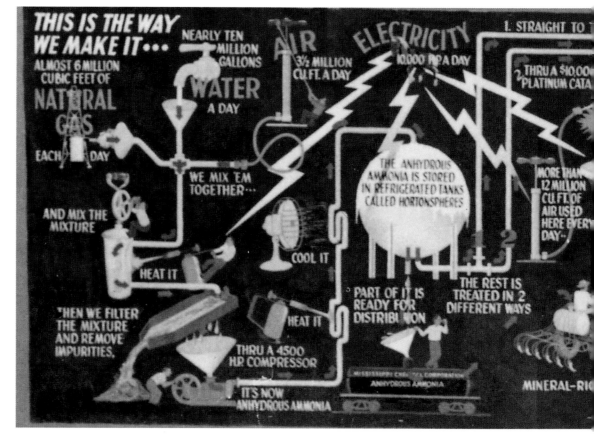

Shelby Shows, and W. K. McWilliams had been placed on the payroll to sell stock to farmers across the state. Seat, then Fisackerly, and later Jackson would each in turn lead the company's sales efforts. Doris Wiggins, Helen Coker, and Esma Adams Hawks became the first three women hired in the company's Yazoo City offices in August and September of 1949. Sue Tatum, who had been Owen Cooper's secretary at the Mississippi Farm Bureau, followed him to Yazoo City in November of that year. Tatum and Hawks served as Cooper's personal assistants and as secretary and treasurer of the company for nearly thirty years.

Attorney John C. Satterfield of Jackson

was elected general counsel of the company in the spring of 1949. To help oversee the construction and operation of the plants, Leroy Thompson hired Ernest Stewart as Yazoo City works manager in April, and in November he persuaded W. B. Dunwoody to leave the Universal Engineering Corporation in Kansas City to serve as project engineer for the new Yazoo City plant.

How did Yazoo City itself respond to the influx of new people brought in by Mississippi Chemical? "When we arrived in Yazoo City, we were 'those new people in town,'" Sue Tatum reminisced half a century after her arrival. "I believe most Yazooans were glad to have us; but their comments reflected

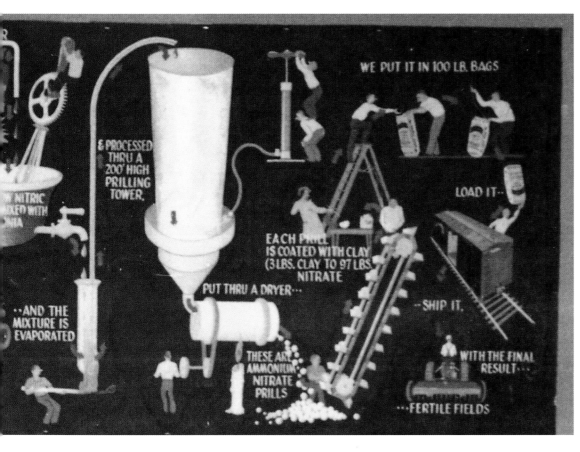

NITRIC
XED WITH
NIA

..AND THE
MIXTURE IS
EVAPORATED

& PROCESSED
THRU A
200' HIGH
PRILLING
TOWER.

PUT THRU A DRYER...

THESE ARE
AMMONIUM
NITRATE
PRILLS

EACH PRILL
IS COATED WITH CLAY
(3 LBS. CLAY TO 97 LBS.
NITRATE

WE PUT IT IN 100 LB. BAGS

LOAD IT...

— SHIP IT.

WITH THE FINAL
RESULT...

...FERTILE FIELDS

A schematic diagram illustrating how Mississippi Chemical's plants combine natural gas, air, and water to produce ammonia and ammonium nitrate fertilizers.

the fact that Yazoo hadn't had many new folks over the years, and change came slowly. Twenty-five years later they were still referring to us as the new folks in town." Yazoo City in 1949 had very little available housing, few apartments, and no public transportation. Tatum remembers that she walked from the room she had rented to MCC's offices on Main Street until she finally conceded that she needed to buy a car to get around town. The northern edge of town was about Fifteenth Street. There was no Country Club Drive, no Woodland Hills or Highland Drive or Clubview or Sunset Drive. All those developments would come later as the city and Mississippi Chemical grew.

When Mississippi Chemical hired Harold Keith from Chicago to help start the plant, his wife Shirley had to look in an atlas to find out where Yazoo City was. She later noted that moving to Yazoo City in 1950 was like "moving to a strange and wonderful foreign country." The Southern accents initially posed one of the greatest problems for the newcomers, especially the children. Keith

recalls that her son, an honor student in Illinois, came home with D's from Mrs. Gerrard, his fifth grade teacher in Yazoo City. "I went to her classroom to see what was wrong and sat down on the back row with my son. I soon saw, or rather heard, the problem. I couldn't understand a word the woman said. When I explained our language problem at the end of class, she volunteered to move my son to the front row. Pretty soon he was speaking Mississippi-ese and doing great." The Keiths never regretted their move to the South. "In Illinois no one ever spoke to me," Shirley Keith would remember. "From the first day I arrived in Yazoo all the clerks in stores would greet me, 'Hello, Mrs. Keith.' I guess they had so few outsiders they all knew us almost instantly."

As Norman Mott, Jr., the *Yazoo City Herald* newspaper editor, would observe in a Mississippi Chemical movie filmed twenty-five years after the new arrivals, "Even if you are a nobody, you're a somebody in a small town."

On July 24, 1949, just three months after Yazoo County voters heeded his appeal to approve a $750,000 bond issue for Mississippi Chemical, board president John Sharp Williams died unexpectedly of a heart attack. "Mr. Williams was so dedicated to seeing Mississippi Chemical become a reality and locate in his native Yazoo County that it has always saddened me he never got to see us succeed," Owen Cooper later said of this sudden loss. To succeed Williams, Charles Whittington of Greenwood was elevated from first vice president to president of the board of directors. (A few years later Cooper

Five members of MCC's board of directors visited the Yazoo City plant site on November 30, 1949, to inspect the construction of warehouses and initial offices. Left to right: W. M. Clingan, Charlie McNeil, F. A. Anderson, Sr., H. P. Sullivan, and Charles Whittington.

was named president of the company, and Whittington's title was changed to chairman of the board.)

In September 1949 Yazoo County sold its $750,000 in BAWI bonds at an interest rate of 2.323 percent. These county bonds were to fund five projects related to the new fertilizer company: water wells, electricity, storage spheres, warehouses, and initial offices for Mississippi Chemical's new plant. Two months later the county board of supervisors and Mississippi Chemical officials opened bids for the projects and discovered that the bids on all five were below the cost estimates. Within days, construction began on the plant site three miles north of Yazoo City.

The company and its contractor, the Girdler Corporation, purchased components and materials for the primary production units in the initial complex: a 120-ton-per-day high pressure ammonia plant, two units to convert ammonia to nitric acid, and the ammonium nitrate plant where nitric acid and ammonia would react together to produce solid ammonium nitrate fertilizer. The planned new ammonia plant would manufacture ammonia from air and natural gas. The resulting ammonia would be the principal ingredient necessary for solid ammonium nitrate fertilizer. In addition, some of the ammonia would be pressurized, stored, and sold to farmers for direct application using the methods introduced by W. B. Andrews. At the nitric acid plants, ammonia would be oxidized, or burned with oxygen, to produce the deep orange gas, nitrogen dioxide, which would be absorbed into water to form liquid nitric acid. The ammonium nitrate plant would combine nitric acid with more ammonia to make an aqueous ammonium nitrate solution. This solution would be concentrated in the evaporator, and then the hot molten ammonium nitrate would be pumped to the top of two-hundred-foot "prilling" towers and sprayed downward as enormous fans propelled cool air up toward the molten spray. The liquid ammonium nitrate would solidify as it cooled, and by the time it reached the bottom of the tower it would become white solid granules known as "prills," ready to be bagged and sold to farmers.

In November 1949 Mississippi Chemical announced that it would buy two used nitric acid units, operated for the U.S. government during the war, from Foster Hamilton, Inc. of Cincinnati and relocate them to Yazoo City. Leroy Thompson stressed that obtaining the used nitric acid plants instead of buying new ones would save MCC four hundred thousand dollars and that the plants could be disassembled and shipped to Yazoo City in a matter of months.

By late 1949 Mississippi Chemical found itself in a precarious position. Almost irreversibly committed to building its fertilizer plants, the tiny company had yet to convince the Reconstruction Finance Corporation of the feasibility of the project. Multimillion dollar orders for the components for the ammonia and ammonium nitrate plants had been placed by MCC in the hope, but without the certainty, that it would get the RFC

Celebrating the Reconstruction Finance Corporation's approval of a critical $3.4 million loan to Mississippi Chemical in 1950 are, from left, U.S. Representative John Bell Williams, U.S. Senator John C. Stennis, and Owen Cooper.

needed $3.4 million to pay for them. Every possible penny of stock had been sold. The RFC was the only remaining source of funds. "This was our last chance," Sue Tatum recalled. "If we couldn't get that RFC loan, Mississippi Chemical was a goner." The twenty-day drama in Washington seemed an interminable limbo to Cooper and others depending on the RFC approval. Cooper called the Yazoo office daily, mainly to recount the still serious objections by many on the RFC staff and many members of Congress: they did not want the RFC funds going for a new plant but instead were insisting that MCC buy and use an old war plant.

Cooper had visited old plants in Henderson, Kentucky; Morgantown, West Virginia; and Houston, Texas. His thorough research and well-reasoned report demonstrated to the RFC that it would cost more—up to twice as much more—to dismantle and move old government nitrogen plants than to build a new one. Because the old ammonia plants utilized out-of-date technology, were spread over many acres, and were built with thick brick walls, they would have been extremely expensive and impractical to move. The new plant Cooper proposed would be much more compact, more efficient, and less costly. On the other hand, the new company had acquired old nitric acid plants since their technology had not changed and they were more compact, lighter and thus much easier to move than an ammonia plant.

February 8, 1950, was the pivotal day. Cooper and a throng of southern congress-

loan necessary to pay for them. "We simply had to do a lot of things on faith. The whole venture was risky. No one, including those of us most involved, knew whether it would work or not," remembers Sue Tatum.

January 1950 began with a rigorous series of meetings in Washington involving Owen Cooper and numerous Southern congressmen. Mississippi's freshman senator John Stennis had kept in daily contact with RFC officials throughout the weeks of investigations and would prove to be integral to the final approval of the loan. "Mr. Cooper and Senator Stennis were friends," Sue Tatum,

who worked with Cooper for nearly four decades, remembered. "They were both Mississippi State men, and Mr. Cooper had helped Senator Stennis win his initial and very close special election in 1947 when Senator Bilbo died. Senator Stennis, Senator Eastland, Will Whittington, and our other congressmen went all out to get that loan for the state."

Owen Cooper did not dare leave Washington for three weeks. If he did not go back to Yazoo City with the RFC loan approval, there would be no fertilizer plant. MCC had already placed the order for the plants and

During 1950 Mississippi Chemical's original facilities rose rapidly from the rich earth of its Delta plant site. The bottom two photos show the arrival of two used nitric acid plants, purchased for $400,000 and relocated to the Yazoo City plant site in January 1950. At right, executive vice president Owen Cooper shows Mississippi Governor Hugh White construction progress in March. The company's initial offices were nearing completion in this photo taken July 27, 1950.

On August 2, 1950, thousands of visitors inspected construction progress at the world's first farmer-owned nitrogen fertilizer plants. An Illinois Central coach, above, ferried visitors to the ammonium nitrate plant some half-mile east of the other facilities. Among those completing the tour are, far left, Yazoo City attorneys Herman B. DeCell and Ed Cortright, Jr. Right, Mississippi's Miss Hospitality Betty Denton welcomes the visitors. Looking on, from left: Charles Whittington, board president; John Satterfield, general counsel; Si Corley, Mississippi's commissioner of agriculture; and Owen Cooper, executive vice president.

men from Mississippi, Alabama, and Louisiana, crowded into Senator John Stennis's Washington office for the decisive meeting with RFC director Hardley Hise. As the afternoon progressed, Cooper and the congressmen addressed every concern Hise and opponents of the loan had raised. Then the room fell silent. At last Hise took a deep breath and spoke the words Mississippi Chemical supporters had waited nearly a year to hear: "If you can comply with certain stipulations we must insist on, we can approve your loan." Celebratory cheers filled the senator's office in the U.S. capitol and soon thereafter eight hundred miles away in

the company's Yazoo City headquarters.

Still harboring doubts about the feasibility of MCC's plans, the RFC required that the company write to all the shareholders, giving them more information about the project and offering them the opportunity to request a refund of their money. The board gave the task of composing this letter to its shrewd legal counsel. "John Satterfield could write a letter not even a Philadelphia lawyer could understand," Charles Jackson later noted. "I'd sold much of that stock and was really worried that folks would decide to take back their investment. Well, when John Satterfield finished that letter, you had to be

a genius to know it was offering you the chance to get your stock investment back." Only about five out of the ten thousand stockholders requested their investment back. Jackson would speculate that they were the only ones who could understand Satterfield's letter.

Years later Sue Tatum would reflect on how narrowly disaster was averted: "That loan made the difference in our being able to build the first plant or not. We had no other sources of funds."

With the RFC loan finally approved, Girdler immediately urged suppliers to expedite shipments of the orders MCC had previously placed, and in February 1950 rail cars carrying the first components for the long-awaited nitrogen plants began arriving in Yazoo City. Soon other shipments appeared, and construction proceeded swiftly on both the ammonium nitrate and ammonia plants.

The company hired Charles Daniels, Lowell Mood, and Guy Gladden to oversee the construction of the nitric acid and ammonium nitrate plants and to train the new employees to run the plants. The three men came from Charleston, Indiana, where they had worked in the Du Pont ordnance plant making "smokeless gun powder" for World War II. Daniels, who would supervise the ammonium nitrate and nitric acid plants from their first day of operation until his retirement in 1982, would later remember the difficulty of their first task: assembling the nitric acid plants. "When I arrived in May of 1950, our plant was nothing but a cornfield with compressors and nitric acid plants laying in the mud. It was like a huge jigsaw puzzle. Pieces of the plant were lying all over everywhere, and not a single piece was labeled. We had to figure out what each piece was and how they fit together."

Daniels immediately began classes training new employees, many of whom had literally walked in straight off the farm. "When you'd see a guy come in wearing bib overalls," he would later recall, "you knew he was a farmer. Well, it was my job to help those farm boys learn how to make nitrate. It's sort of scary to know that all these farm boys' lives depend on how well you teach them how to make something as potentially

explosive as ammonium nitrate." Daniels, looking back fifty years later, is justifiably proud of the safety record the company set for operating those nitrate plants. Contrary to common belief, ammonium nitrate is not an explosive; it is an "oxidizer" (that is, it contains oxygen), and under normal situations poses no danger whatever. Ammonium nitrate, in fact, cannot explode unless three other factors are present simultaneously: a fuel source, a genuine explosive material (such as dynamite) that detonates, and confinement of all the materials in a relatively small space. Nonetheless, when MCC began producing ammonium nitrate in 1951, it took extreme caution to follow meticulously all safety procedures and to train its workers. One of the many precautions was to isolate the ammonium nitrate plant from the rest of the Yazoo City complex, locating it behind an eighty-foot hill. Another was to design and operate its ammonium nitrate and other plants so as to minimize the risk of contamination of the ammonium nitrate by metals and other extraneous materials. While over the decades the company has grown to be the largest producer of ammonium nitrate in America, its strict adherence to safety precautions has ensured that there has never been an explosion at any of the company's production or storage units.

The outbreak of the Korean War in June of 1950 and the union strikes against the steel industry delayed by four months the delivery of vital components, all made of steel. National Guard units from across Mississippi and the South were summoned to

active duty, taking with them the company's first personnel manager. "I applied for a job at MCC in the summer of 1950 at their offices on Main Street," Emery Gregory, who worked in MCC's ammonia plant for forty-three years, remembered. "Dan Jones, the personnel manager, looked at my papers and said, 'You're going to be called back in for the Korean War.' Well, in a couple of weeks I did get called back into the Army, and the first person I saw from home was Dan Jones. He'd been called back in, too."

In spite of these setbacks, on August 2, 1950, Mississippi Chemical hosted an enormous open house and tour to demonstrate the progress being made in building the world's first farmer-owned nitrogen fertilizer plants. Thousands of its 7,500 farmer-shareholders and their families and civic leaders from the state and across the South descended on Yazoo City to view first-hand the widely publicized plants then rapidly taking shape. Members of the Mississippi Highway Patrol and Boy Scouts were busy all day directing traffic. The first railroad passenger car to be used in years in Yazoo City shuttled visitors back to the ammonium nitrate plant built behind the hill. Charles Shuman, president of the American Farm Bureau, gave a speech, and the office building was dedicated to John Sharp Williams. "The directors attended a Rotary luncheon, while the wives were treated to a Coca Cola party by Mrs. P. C. Williams and then a tour of Mrs. Owen Cooper's new home on Grand Avenue," the *Yazoo City Herald* dutifully reported.

By New Year's Day, 1951, the nitric acid

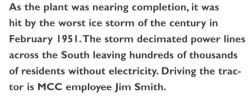

As the plant was nearing completion, it was hit by the worst ice storm of the century in February 1951. The storm decimated power lines across the South leaving hundreds of thousands of residents without electricity. Driving the tractor is MCC employee Jim Smith.

plants were reassembled. It soon became apparent that the ammonium nitrate plant would be finished long before the ammonia unit. MCC scoured the country for sufficient ammonia to allow it to start the acid and nitrate units without having to wait for its own ammonia plant to be in operation.

A month before operation was scheduled to begin, the heaviest snow and ice storm of the twentieth century deluged Mississippi on February 2, 1951, leaving few intact electrical lines in the entire state. "I will never forget that snow and ice," Harold Keith remembered of that night. "When I got ready to leave the warehouse at midnight, Charlie Daniels said, 'You'll never get home.' Well, being from Illinois, I had chains for my old Studebaker, and I hooked them up. I still almost didn't get home. When I finally got to the corner of Highway 49 and Fifteenth Street, you couldn't see hide nor hair of a street. I had to get out and get down on my knees and scrape off the snow to try to find the street to turn onto it. We didn't have electric power for days. I began to wonder what I had gotten into moving down to frozen Mississippi." Although the power was out in Yazoo City homes for over a week, that did not keep the work from going forward at the plant. In fact, Harold Keith and four others risked driving through the snow to the TVA plants in north Alabama to learn more about operating the plants that MCC was building.

The historic moment of initial production arrived on March 8, 1951. At 10:30 p.m. a small cluster of men huddled over a clear glass flask in the nitric acid plant and watched the amber liquid rise two-thirds the way up the flask before the outlet was shut off and the celebrating began. "It was great to see the nitric acid units crank off so smoothly," Charlie Daniels would recall. "I wish we could say the same thing about the ammonium nitrate and ammonia plants that were yet to come."

Mississippi Chemical next tried to combine the nitric acid and the purchased ammonia to initiate its ammonium nitrate plant and produce the much-needed solid nitrogen fertilizer. That first plant was very primitive and required many modifications when it started up in the spring of 1951. For example, several key parts were made of iron or regular steel instead of more durable stainless steel, and the acid ate through them. Then, the system for spraying the hot nitrate from the top of the prilling tower was nothing but a pipe with holes drilled in it. When the nitrate did prill, it stuck to the cone at the bottom of the tower. The towers were further plagued by such excess condensation that a trough had to be built to catch the water dripping down the inside walls. Girdler had failed to put up sidings to protect the outside dryers from the weather. "It would be raining cats and dogs," Harold Keith would remember, "and the plant was a total mess. Compared to the ultra-modern plants MCC has today, that first unit was almost like making soap in a black kettle."

One of Charlie Daniels's jobs was to light up the nitric acid plants, and he recalls one harrowing day when "the whole thing almost blew up." A tiny piece of metal had wedged the natural gas valve open, and the gas was sailing out until the metal piece was extracted. The pioneer employees of these early days frequently exhausted themselves trying to keep ahead of the continuing problems and ensure the safety of everyone. Daniels remembers one time working for thirty-eight straight hours. "I finally lay down on the concrete sidewalk by the guardhouse and asked them to call my wife to come get me. I was too tired to even drive home. That original gang had to fight and fight and fight and work and work and work to iron out all the bugs."

March 16, 1951, was a landmark day. MCC finally overcame its countless mechanical problems to turn out its

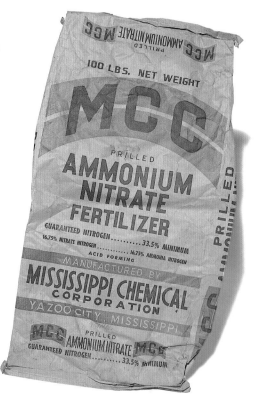

first tons of ammonium nitrate solid fertilizer. The following morning the first hundred-pound bags of ammonium nitrate ever made in Mississippi were prominently displayed in the offices of Mississippi Chemical, the *Yazoo City Herald,* and twelve other local businesses. "Finally we could see and touch those white fertilizer prills they had been talking about for years," editor Mott remembered. "It was a historic and exciting moment."

The company produced 1,550 tons of ammonium nitrate before exhausting its limited supply of the outside ammonia. To ensure that its momentous first shipments were allocated fairly to its thousands of customer-owners, MCC put the name of each fertilizer dealer in a capsule, placed all the capsules in a hopper, and then drew the lucky capsules to determine who got the scarce nitrate. In early April 1951 the first fifteen rail cars of nitrate moved across the state toward Starkville and the Oktibbeha County Farmers Cooperative, which had been selected to receive the first shipment.

Excited though they were by the commencement of their nitric acid and ammonium nitrate sections, the Mississippi Chemical people anxiously awaited the successful beginning of the anhydrous ammonia plant, because this was the heart of the entire complex. The ammonia plant was by far the most complicated, taxing, and costly assemblage of all, but it was also the fundamental first step in the entire fertilizer chain: it took nitrogen out of the air and turned it into ammonia. Ammonia was the key ingredient

In early April 1951 the company's first shipment of ammonium nitrate made its way from the Yazoo City plant to the Oktibbeha County Co-op in Starkville, Mississippi, where officials of the local cooperative gathered to receive it. Left to right: William White, co-op president; B. B. Ramsey, co-op director; Warren Oakley, Oktibbeha Farm Bureau president; and Gene Gatlin, co-op director.

in all the subsequent procedures and products. Without ammonia, no other fertilizers could be made. And for days and weeks there was no ammonia.

Starting up and achieving smooth operation of the ammonia plant proved to be a process hampered by mishaps. Bob Sherling, who was in the ammonia plant for the entire ordeal and would supervise it for the next thirty-five years, later described the challenge. "Half our problems were with the

design of the plant and the other half were with our green operators. We didn't have but four or five people who'd ever even seen an ammonia plant, much less run one. We did the whole thing on a shoestring and a prayer. A lot of other folks thought we'd never make it work. I remember that Monsanto [Chemical Corporation] came by and tried to buy our plant. They told us we'd never get it to run. Made me so darn mad, I wanted to throw them out of the plant. Well, in the long run we showed them who could run an ammonia plant." To learn more about how the plant should be run, Sherling and four other employees drove an old rundown station wagon to California to study a similar operation.

On June 6, 1951, the exhausted group finally coaxed a few tons of ammonia through the massive reactor, which was operating at fifteen thousand pounds of pressure per square inch and eight hundred degrees Fahrenheit. But there was little time for celebration: problems continued to beset the brave but inexperienced crew. "It was like an eighteen-month-long nightmare that we worked night and day and weekends to overcome," Bob Sherling recollected of that trying period. "An ordinary bunch of folks couldn't have gotten the job done. We had truly dedicated folks who did whatever it took to solve the long lists of problems we faced." First, whenever a cold snap hit, Southern Natural Gas would cut off fuel gas, and the plant would have to switch over to oil, a fuel source it was not designed to use. Then electrical power failures occurred with every storm, shutting down the whole process. Each time the power was out, the

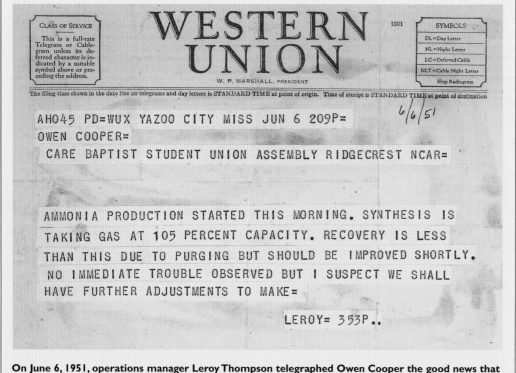

On June 6, 1951, operations manager Leroy Thompson telegraphed Owen Cooper the good news that the ammonia plant had produced its first tons. But for the next five months a string of operating problems in this new ammonia plant, shown above right, plagued MCC's inexperienced production team and almost bankrupted the fledgling enterprise.

water wells would fail. Bill Shipley, the plant's electrical engineer, eventually solved that problem by putting lightning arresters on all the lines.

Then came the catastrophe that almost destroyed Mississippi Chemical before it ever got started. Whenever the carbon monoxide was not perfectly scrubbed from the gas feed, the gas would ignite the catalyst and cause a major shutdown. In an effort to purify the gas and protect the catalyst, MCC supervisor Julian Rogers continually increased the temperature of the purification unit. This process would work for a few hours or a few days, but the extremely high temperatures caused a technical disaster, forever since referred to as "the stuck nut."

In late September and October, the unit was so hot that it finally melted the catalyst, warped the forty-ton catalyst carrier, and welded shut the huge nut on top of it. "That baby was stuck tighter than a turtle's jaws," Sherling would recall. "We tried everything on earth to turn that nut, which must have weighed two to three thousand pounds. It wouldn't budge." Finally, in desperation, MCC removed the entire forty-ton catalyst carrier, nut and all, and railed it to a machine shop in Pennsylvania. There the machinists cut the giant nut off and repaired the threads and the unit. But in the meantime, crucial production time was lost. MCC had no ammonia, no catalyst to make ammonia, and almost no money.

Recalling that fateful October 31 in 1951, Sue Tatum explained the crisis: "When we got that catalyst carrier back from Pennsylvania, Mr. Cooper called together all the employees and told us that the company had only enough money in the bank to meet payroll for thirty more hours. We'd borrowed every penny we could borrow. We were at the end of the line."

LeRoy Percy also remembers that portentous time: "We came perilously close to running out of money. Whether it was fate, providence, skill, determination, or some combination, I don't know, but that ammonia plant came back up and started to produce at a much steadier and more consistent rate." To get immediate cash, shareholders were sent telegrams asking them to bring their ammonia trucks and their cash payments and pick up ammonia. They brought enough cash, and MCC sold enough ammonia to meet the payroll and keep paying the bills.

The determination and dedication of the

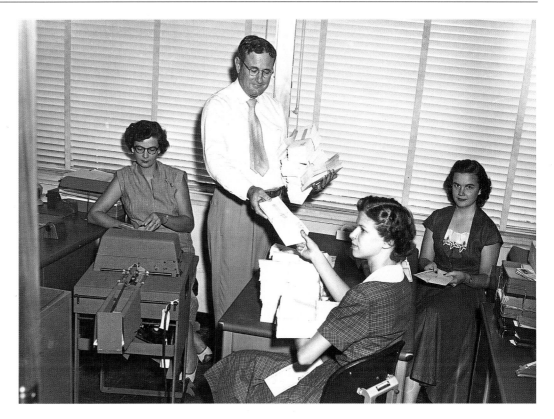

Mississippi Chemical returned its first patronage refunds of more than one million dollars to its shareholder customers in September 1953. Preparing the first refund checks for mailing are, left to right: Esma Hawks, R. H. Fisackerly, Mary Jean Wright, and an unidentified woman. From 1953 until it ceased operating as a cooperative in 1994, MCC would return patronage payments totaling $700 million.

original employees kept the plant running in those fateful days. "We simply refused to take no for an answer," Bob Sherling would recall. "I'd very much like future generations to remember and appreciate the guts of those first folks who kept on and kept on and kept on until they made those original plants run. Mississippi Chemical reminds me of a great baseball team. You can have the best ballplayers in the country, but without teamwork and dedication to winning, you ain't got nothing."

"In every person's and every corporation's life there are one or two critical, defining

moments," LeRoy Percy muses now. "Getting that original ammonia plant running was the critical moment that could make or break us. Thank goodness we turned the corner and we never looked back. Mississippi Chemical was soon to be a phenomenal success."

During its first production year, fiscal 1951–52,* Mississippi Chemical sold forty-one thousand tons of ammonium nitrate and ten thousand tons of ammonia to its

* The MCC fiscal year extends from July 1 of one calendar year through June 30 of the following year.

farmer-shareholders. "The plant showed a nice profit of $268,400 on sales of $3.9 million despite restricted production," the first annual report stated. The company's Yazoo City work force had grown to 229 employees, who took home average monthly wages of $396. MCC reported that its annual payroll would exceed one million dollars.

Three events in May and June 1952 exemplified attributes that would characterize the company for the future decades. The first came on May 5, when the company and its employees won national recognition for operating for its first 385 days and 526,406 man-hours of work without a lost-time accident, particularly noteworthy when one considers that the vast majority of its employees had never before worked in an industrial complex of any kind. (The company's commitment to safety has never wavered. Over the five ensuing decades, the company's employees at Carlsbad, New Mexico; Donaldsonville, Louisiana; and Pascagoula and Yazoo City, Mississippi, have been cited for numerous prestigious safety honors.)

From its inception Mississippi Chemical placed great emphasis on safe and accident-free operations, and its Yazoo City operating team earned national recognition for its outstanding safety record. Above left: To recognize outstanding safety suggestions, Owen Cooper presents savings bonds to (left to right) Sidney Henderson, R. L. Plunkett, Bill Burwell, and Davis Allgood in July 1955. In the picture below, W. W. Harpole, R. T. Huxtable, Jr., and G .W. Posey (second, third and fourth from left) received cash awards for outstanding 1953 safety suggestions from the safety committee composed of Harold Zumalt, far left, and, from far right to left, Bill Powell, Nat Walton, Mike Ellison, and Marvin Pearson.

Mississippi Chemical's fleet of transport trucks has always played a vital role in delivering fertilizer to customers. In January 1954 the company's team of transport truck drivers were, from left, C. O. Richards, Ralph Sanders, B. J. Ivers, T. E. Moore, L. C. McKennon, W. B. Holloway, and Omer Kettleman.

The second event defining MCC was its rejection of union organization on May 12, 1952, when the maintenance department voted against being represented by the International Association of Machinists. Throughout its first fifty years Mississippi Chemical would take immense pains to create a work environment, pay and benefits programs, and esprit de corps that would enable it to operate without unions in its facilities.

The third event came on June 17, 1952. Meeting in the same room at the Heidelberg Hotel in Jackson where the shareholders had organized Mississippi Chemical forty-four months earlier, stockholders voted to double the size of the company's nitrogen production facilities. When completed, this expansion would increase ammonia output from 120 to 240 tons a day and nearly triple ammonium nitrate output from 140 to 350 tons a day. To help finance this significant expansion, stockholders approved selling $3 million of stock in the seven Southern states of Arkansas, Alabama, Missouri, Louisiana, Tennessee, Georgia, and Mississippi. Exactly

five years after the Farm Bureau Board voted to study the idea of a farmer-owned nitrogen plant, Mississippi Chemical had far surpassed original expectations and was poised for significant growth.

To help the company finance the proposed expansion, Yazoo County voters again went to the polls and approved another $750,000 BAWI bond issue on August 19, 1952. It carried by 3,051, or nearly 80 percent, for, and 626 against. "We got a smaller majority this second time because many farmers were concerned that Mississippi Chemical was depleting the ground water resources they needed for irrigation," banker Miller Holmes, who led a Chamber of Commerce task force to pass the bond referendum, remembered. "We held meetings among MCC officials, state water management experts, and our local farmers to allay their concerns, but some folks still were afraid the expansion would hurt them."

That same summer the Mississippi Extension Service released a study comparing the economics of using small tractors versus mules on smaller Mississippi farms of thirty to fifty acres. It reported that Mississippi's 251,000 farms were using 52,923 tractors, one for every five farms, and 398,000 horses and mules to cultivate nearly ten million acres. The study indicated that smaller tractors were more economical in ideal circumstances, but mules were more economical in many others. Earlier that summer, a national magazine featured a photograph of dozens of cotton choppers hacking weeds from overgrown cotton fields in front of Mississippi Chemical's Yazoo City plants. While the

Mississippi Chemical's early success at producing nitrogen fertilizers inspired shareholders to double the size of the Yazoo City production facility during 1953–54. Above, the No. 2 ammonia plant is under construction in October 1953. MCC's creative employees came up with improved methods for making its nitrogen fertilizers. Above left, operations manager W. B. Dunwoody presents a $150 cash award to Earl Jones, center, for developing an improved spray header in the ammonium nitrate plant, held by Charlie Daniels, supervisor of the nitrate area. Below, Calvin O'Reilly (left) and Ford Harrington make patent applications for their inventions, a new pipe die and push button automotive jack.

1950s would bring dramatic shifts toward the employment of tractors and chemical herbicides, eventually displacing millions of Southern laborers, in 1952 the trend was just beginning.

Cottruel Generette, who has worked in Mississippi Chemical's labor services pool since 1951, remembered that hand labor played a substantial role in building and operating Mississippi Chemical's maiden complex. "They didn't have all the fancy machines we have today," he recalled. "There was dozens, maybe hundreds of folks, working with shovels and wheelbarrows and a few small tractors. And every pound of fertilizer made in those plants went into hundred-pound bags that we had to pick up and load. There was no such thing as a fifty-pound or eighty-pound bag back then."

In the mid-1950s, when many farmers wanted to receive their ammonium nitrate in bulk form rather than in bags, W. B. Dunwoody reported to Owen Cooper that it was impossible for the Yazoo plant to load out product in loose bulk form. "I can still remember hearing Mr. Cooper on the phone to Mr. Dunwoody," Sue Tatum would recall. "'Bill, do they still have shovels and wheelbarrows at Saxton's Hardware? Well, fix a way to load the nitrate out in bulk, or get enough shovels and wheelbarrows to do it by hand.' Mr. Cooper never did like to take no for an answer." Only weeks later Dunwoody and the Yazoo plant workers installed a conveyor system to load ammonium nitrate in bulk form directly into the farmers' trucks. Later, huge quantities in bulk form were shipped by rail and, even later, by barge.

During 1953–54 Mississippi Chemical sold nearly $4 million in stock to farmers across the South and in the Midwest to finance the doubling of its initial fertilizer production plants. Looking over a map of the eleven states where this stock was sold are field representatives, from left: W. K. McWilliams, Shelby Shows, Jerry Clower, H. D. Bland, and R. H. Fisackerly.

(Today more than 95 percent of the company's ammonium nitrate is sold in bulk form.)

In the fall of 1952 Leroy Thompson left Mississippi Chemical to build other ammonia plants, and W. B. Dunwoody was promoted to operations manager. Dunwoody's first priority was to establish an engineering department to solve the nagging technical obstacles that plagued the company's early plants and to design and construct its new expansion. By early 1953 the engineering department had fifteen employees busily finding ways to improve the existing plants and to build the most efficacious new ones. For the next forty-five years this robust engineering and technical adjunct would keep the company a world leader in fertilizer expertise. "Bill Dunwoody was a pioneer in recognizing the importance of a strong technical staff for our company and bringing that vision into reality," David Arnold, senior vice president of the technical group, observed in 1997. "All of us at MCC owe Bill Dunwoody

The company's Yazoo City nitrogen production complex had been doubled in size and capacity when this aerial photograph was taken in February 1955. The ammonium nitrate plant is in the top center, Hilltop recreation, top left, and Highway 49 East at the lower right.

In 1952 and 1954 union organizers waged intensive but unsuccessful campaigns to organize the company's Yazoo City plant work force. In the photo above, maintenance employees, from left, Andrew Davis, Meadow Perry, Earl Jones, an unidentified employee, and Victor Cochran take a snack break. At right, MCC's Yazoo City maintenance team heads home walking down a newly installed safety lane from the plant gate to the parking lot in 1956. Electrician Jack Vise is in the foreground; Earl Jones, Victor Cochran, Bill Burwell, Oscar McInnes, Bill Neely, and Pat Hearst walk behind Vise.

a huge debt of gratitude for his commitment to bringing the best technical minds and the best technical processes to our company."

With the plant expansion in progress, these new engineers immediately began to introduce improvements to the company,

applying numerous innovations to the design and construction of MCC's second ammonium nitrate plant. They would utilize in the nitric acid portion of that expansion a recovery turbine-compressor designed and built by Brown-Boveri of Switzerland.

Brown-Boveri had made many turbines for electric power plants, but this would be the first time that such a turbine had ever been built for use in a nitric acid plant. Replacing the old reciprocating compressors with a centrifugal compressor was a major innova-

"Let's Start Our Own Employee Bank!"

A spirit of innovation and positive thinking enabled MCC workers to solve countless obstacles and bring the world's first farmer-owned nitrogen fertilizer plants into successful operation. It likewise led them to form their own "in-plant bank"—the MCC Employee Federal Credit Union—which has been overseen by company employees and their families for forty-five years.

This all began with a famous Walter Winchell radio news radio show in 1953. MCC maintenance employee Otis Addison was a faithful listener to Winchell, and the advertisements from the National Credit Union Administration piqued Addison's interest. Addison solicited information on how to organize an employee credit union and subsequently shared it with his maintenance co-workers Vincent Vincent, Victor Cochran, Earl Jones, Jack Creel, and Claude Britton. After lengthy discussions these men decided to establish a credit union to benefit all MCC employees. Each of

Nineteen years after the MCC Employee Federal Credit Union was formed in 1953, deposits topped the one-million-dollar mark. Celebrating the 1972 landmark were, from left: Larry Lartigue of Coastal Chemical, Pascagoula; Brad Allgood of MCC's Yazoo City staff; Owen Cooper; and Harold Capello of Triad Chemical in Donaldsonville.

them invested $500, a princely sum at the time, to get the venture going. They then persuaded Nat Walton from the personnel office to handle their bookkeeping. Shortly thereafter, the MCC Employees Federal Credit Union was chartered by those six visionary employees, who served as its first board of directors and officers. As more employees joined the Credit Union, the company advanced the fledgling group an additional $1,500 to help it move ahead and later provided housing for the credit union offices.

Forty-five years later, in 1998, the MCC Employees Credit Union had 2,700 members—employees, former employees, and family members with $9.2 million in deposits—and provided a full range of savings and consumer loan services to company workers in Yazoo City, Carlsbad, Donaldsonville, and Pascagoula, and at Newsprint South in Grenada.

tion that radically cut energy costs by recapturing and using far more energy from exhaust gas than the conventional pumps ever had. The success with this new compressor would eventually give MCC the confidence in 1965 to revolutionize the industry by building the world's first Kellogg ammonia plant using similar technology.

The company also undertook its first research program in 1953, when Marion Brown began to experiment with methods of removing the traces of carbon monoxide from the synthesis gas in the new ammonia plant, the problem that in 1951 had led to the "stuck nut" and the company's most catastrophic financial crisis. "Because it took Albert Green and me longer than we planned to solve the problem, our findings

were too late for the ammonia plant expansion, but Mississippi Chemical eventually won a patent on our work to use a new oxide agent to clean this gas and smooth ammonia production," revealed Brown, who would spearhead the company's research for thirty-four years. The company recognized the benefits in investing in applied research to improve fertilizer processes and would continue to fund research and find solutions for the next four decades. Brown and Green would work with the production staff over the next several years to improve the quality of Mississippi Chemical's ammonium nitrate product at Yazoo City and its mixed fertilizers eventually to be produced in Pascagoula, Mississippi.

For the burgeoning company 1953 was an auspicious year, beginning with the groundbreaking ceremonies for the enlargement of its Yazoo City plants and ending with an encouraging 110-day stock sales campaign. During that campaign $3.7 million in stock was sold to farmers in Florida, Georgia, Tennessee and Kentucky, all of them anxious to buy products from the expanded plants. In September the company reported earnings of $1.3 million in its second fiscal year and returned its initial patronage refund checks, totaling more than a million dollars, to stockholder patrons. In December the company's board of directors presented fifty thousand dollars in company stock to Mississippi State College out of gratitude to the state of Mississippi for the fifty thousand dollars provided in 1949 to assist in Mississippi Chemical's organization.

In 1953 there was still an onerous shortage of nitrogen fertilizers. Farmers were not the only ones eager to get their hands on the scarce nitrogen. The Army Ordnance Corps ordered Mississippi Chemical to ship it six thousand tons of ammonia to make ammunition for the Korean War. Hoping to find a sensible way to serve both the nation and its farmer-owners, MCC persuaded another ammonia maker to sell the six thousand tons

to the government at a premium price so that MCC's product could go to its farmer-owners as promised.

The company more than doubled its capacity to produce ammonia and ammonium nitrate with the expansions completed from February 1954 through March 1955. The annual report at the end of that 1954 fiscal year noted that "274 efficient, loyal and cooperative employees are a major company asset." In a far-sighted action, the company founded a fully-paid employee retirement program in the spring of 1954. (Forty-four years later, in 1998, the assets in that retirement fund would have grown to over $100 million dollars.) "That was a red-letter day in the history of this company for all its employees," Charlie Daniels recalled. "From the very start Mr. Cooper was committed to getting excellent pay and benefit programs for our entire employee team."

Daniels and many others are convinced that Cooper's concern for the employees was the main reason the unions could never succeed in organizing the plant. Organizers from the United Gas, Coke, and Chemical Workers waged an intensive fifteen-month campaign in 1953 and 1954 to unionize the employees. On March 25, 1954, the union told the company it had sufficient support to demand a plant-wide election conducted by the National Labor Relations Board (NLRB) and promptly requested one. In a seven-hour hearing before the National Labor Relations staff on April 22, the company argued that it was exempt from NLRB jurisdiction because it operated as a cooperative. Six months later, in November, the NLRB rejected the

company's appeal and ordered a December election among hourly wage earners in the plant.

Emotions in the town and the plant ran high as the union vote approached. "I didn't come to work until 1955, but I heard that fist-fights broke out in the plant several times right before that vote," Emery Gregory recalled. The *Herald* ran emotional editorials urging Yazooans to reject the union, including one on December 2, 1954, the day of the election, containing an overt appeal to racism: "And what about the race question? Will the workers at the chemical plant be willing to give Negro employees equal voice in union matters. CIO unions elsewhere do so. Will there be a different policy here? We don't think so. Do workers here want to contribute to funds set up to break down segregation? We don't think so, as the Southern way of life has been too long ingrained in every being. Think these things over, employees of Mississippi Chemical Corporation." For whatever reasons, the company's employees voted 150 to 44 against the union. This ended the first and only significant union attempt to organize the Yazoo City facility.

The *Herald's* emotional words during the union campaign were not the last but rather among the first of a decade-long effort by the white power structure to preserve what it called "the Southern way of life" and postpone the end of segregation. The U.S. Supreme Court had shaken white Southerners and segregationists to their very core on May 17 of that year, when it issued its historic Brown v. Board of Education decision, in which the court rejected the old "separate but equal" dictum used to defend segregation since 1890. Governor William Winter has described the milieu of those times: from World War II until 1954, Mississippi's political leadership focused its concerns on economic development, on getting more and better jobs for its people; but, according to Winter, from the Supreme Court ruling in 1954 until 1964, the state's leaders and much of the populace were consumed with the question of race.

Neither Yazoo City nor Mississippi Chemical would be immune from the racial conflicts and social confusion that would grip the state and the nation during the next decade. In 1954 the prospect of social change, while frightening to many whites (and a few blacks), hardly seemed inevitable. Instead, the general approach of the all-white state government would be resistance and delay.

In its 1954 annual report, Mississippi Chemical enumerated its basic values and expectations:

(1) The world population will continue to grow rapidly, and only with increased agricultural production and use of fertilizers can we feed the world's populace.

(2) The company is proud of its continuing efforts to improve its manufacturing facilities and develop techniques to increase production, reduce costs, and increase the quality of our products.

(3) The company's greatest asset is its efficient, loyal, and cooperative employees. It

recognizes that employee cooperation, goodwill, and trust are essential to its success. It will continue to strive for mutual respect, understanding, and watchful concern for employee well-being.

(4) MCC is justly proud of the high standards of safety maintained in its operations.

(5) The company seeks to provide security for its employees through its new retirement program, its group life insurance, and its group hospitalization and surgery plan.

(6) The company looks with pride on the good citizenship of its employees. Two hundred and three employees gave $3,019 to the community chest and provide leadership to church, school, and civic activities in its community.

Even today the bedrock principles that defined the company's character in its earliest days have remained cornerstones throughout the five decades of Mississippi Chemical's corporate culture and have sustained its success. Even now the company's expressly stated objectives encompass the efficient, low-cost production of fertilizer by means of advanced technology; careful attention to safety and accident-free operation; deliberate consideration of employee welfare, compensation, and benefits; appreciation of employee loyalty and goodwill; and an emphasis on individual and corporate citizenship.

Mississippi Chemical and its Yazoo City plants and workers established records for production and profits in fiscal years 1955 and 1956. The company's fiscal 1956 annual report recapped the impressive return its

shareholder customers had received on their initial investments: "Through five years, stockholders who invested $100 in company stock and took all fertilizer allocated to them would have received back $130 in cash, $25 in stock, or a total of $155 in just four years of refunds." The company and its leaders, employees, and investors seemed both eager and optimistic about facing the arduous new challenges that lay ahead in the next chapter of its history.

For the company's first decade, its female employees celebrated Christmas with a gala Christmas dinner. Attending in 1954 were the following: First row, from left: Julia Russum, Gladys Wilson, Sara Sue Rush, Sue Tatum, and Ann Lacy. Second row, from left: Aline Ross (Remington Rand representative), Esma Hawks, Opal Terrell, Hannah Kelly, Merrick Hamley, and Dottie Lee. Third row, from left: Margaret Jenne, Lois Loftin, Rita Eady, Shirley Netherland, and Mamie Passons. Standing, from left: Yolanda Hearst, Winnie McMaster, Helen Coker, Jimmie Cothran, Ann Cuthbertson, Blanche Hester, Dot Harris, Opal Jean Alderman, Mary Gene Wright, and Georgie Jones.

From its earliest days Mississippi Chemical and its employees have given of their time and resources to build a better community. At left, Randy McCormack, Ann Lacy, and Mamie Passons prepare to deliver Christmas boxes for a dozen families adopted at Christmas 1955. Also playing key roles in that Christmas project were in-plant coordinators John Carley and Sim Dixon. For nearly fifty years Mississippi Chemical's float, like the 1954 version shown above, has carried Santa Claus as the grand finale of the Yazoo City Christmas parade.

Mississippi Chemical's Yazoo City office staff gathered on December 3, 1956, to prepare boxes of Christmas gifts and food for delivery to dozens of families adopted by the entire employee work force. Seated, left to right: Mary Jean Wright, Esma Hawks, Marjorie Smith, Sue Tatum, and Alta Shannon. Standing, left to right: Jerry Clower, Sabin Rush, William Allgood, Emma Jean Willis, Jack Hawks, Lurlene Lewis, Jimmie Cothran, Blanche Hester, Charles Jackson, Martha Martin, Fred Sullivan, Jerry Lewis, and Sara Sue Rush.

During its early years Mississippi Chemical began the annual picnic for all employees and their families. Photos on this page show the 1955 and 1956 company picnics for white employees held at the Hilltop recreation area located just east of the production plants.

September 15, 1956, the company picnic for black employees and their families was held at the Lamar Street Kindergarten. Employee children who won the 1955 fishing contest were, below left to right, Tommy Browning, Phyllis Reeves, Deborah Deaton, Nancy Willis, Wilkie Nile Harrington, Walter Fisher, Jane Carley, Leo Kirk Thomas, Manley Washington, and Bob Leister.

PART TWO

Expanding Horizons

"In the high summer of 1956," William Manchester wrote in his The Glory and the Dream, "the corn stood tall from Mount Rushmore to the Panhandle. America seemed to have returned, momentarily at least, to the frivolous 1920s, to wonderful trivia, hot music, placid politics, glamorous athletes, and automobile worship." This was the Eisenhower era. Over the next eighteen years the nation, the state, Mississippi Chemical Corporation, and I, too, would find horizons expanding in ways never before imagined.

The comfortable lethargy was shattered in 1957 when, to the nation's chagrin, the Soviets launched their earth satellite Sputnik, and a month later a more elaborate one with a little dog aboard. The space race was on. American schools introduced new science courses and even elementary students dedicated themselves to "keeping up with the Russians." The youthful new president John F. Kennedy, soon after his election in 1960, pledged that the United States would put a man on the moon within ten years. Right on schedule, in 1969 the whole world witnessed on television American astronaut Neil Armstrong fulfill Kennedy's prediction and make "one giant step for mankind" onto the moon's rocky landscape. Americans would become accustomed to the presence of guided missiles armed with nuclear warheads on both sides of the perilous Cold War chasm.

In Mississippi in the early 1960s industrial employment at last equaled agricultural, largely because of the monumental decrease in farm workers since World War II. To nurture industrial development in the state, Owen Cooper, with the support of Mississippi Chemical's shareholders, founded the state's original venture capital enterprise, First Mississippi Corporation. Farmers meanwhile would increasingly rely on the new herbicides and pesticides introduced in the 1960s to control weeds and insects plaguing their crops. Treflan, the weed and grass herbicide, was first used in 1960; sprayed on cotton fields before planting, it prevented weeds and grasses from growing in the cotton.

Against this expansive backdrop Mississippi Chemical's engineers and scientists were implementing technological advances in making fertilizer, and the company was extending its facilities beyond Yazoo City. In 1957 in a remote wilderness outside Pascagoula, Mississippi, wild and temperamental Brahma cows were chasing the MCC people around trucks and trees as they began to construct the new Coastal Chemical facility. A decade later MCC quietly began producing ammonia and urea in a huge complex in Donaldsonville, Louisiana.

In Yazoo City in the late 1950s and throughout the 1960s, as elsewhere in Mississippi, all life did not center on the state's industrial development and new scientific approaches to making fertilizer and farming. Instead, much of it seemed to revolve around the single issue of race. In neighboring Arkansas President Eisenhower had sent federal troops to Little Rock to ensure the integration of nine black children into Central High. Who knew what might happen in Mississippi? To fortify itself, between 1954 and 1964 the state legislature passed more than forty laws, resolutions, and amendments in a massive crusade to preserve segregation. The State Sovereignty Commission, a kind of boondocks KGB, was established to gather information on everyone considered "different." These were strident times for Mississippi, among its worst and most bottomless, and these days would be exceedingly difficult to live down in the state's more civilizing future.

I myself did not live in the state during these troubled years, but observed it from afar—from Oxford, England, where I was a student in the late 1950s; from Texas in the early years of the 1960s; and then from New York and the perspective of Harper's Magazine, which I edited until 1971. Even now as I recount the disruptive events, I see them, much as I did then, as a newsreel montage: lunch counter sit-ins; Freedom Riders arrested and sent to Parchman; riots at the University of Mississippi over the admission of James Meredith (the Last Battle of the Civil War, I have always called this); Mississippi NAACP field director Medgar Evers shot in the back by a powerful deer rifle in front of his wife and three small children; Freedom Summer of 1964, with young civil rights activists from all over America descending on the state, provoking three murders in Neshoba County and thirty-five black church burnings. Were these things actually happening? If I stop the tape, will they go away? But I cannot.

As saddening as the events were, they also served to call into action "the better angels of our nature" from courageous Mississippians like Mississippi Chemical's Owen Cooper, who began to speak out forcefully against the violence and the day-to-day injustices and to work quietly toward racial harmony. I was proud to hear and read about Owen Cooper's work and about the increasing prominence of what Mississippi historian David Sansing has called "the other Mississippi" of charity, wisdom, and nobility.

I got my first close-up view of national politics and life during this period. As a young reporter in the 1960 presidential campaign between Kennedy and Richard Nixon, I had been with others in a flatbed truck with one Secret Service vehicle between us and Kennedy's limousine as the caravan passed by the Texas Book Depository in Dallas, harbinger of an ominous and tragic day to come. I sat among the Baptist ministers in the Rice Hotel in Houston when Kennedy addressed himself pointedly to "the Catholic issue." Later I was with Lyndon and Lady Bird Johnson and two or three friends in Austin on that interminable election night as they prepared in a studio to go on national television after JFK's acceptance speech from Hyannis. Mississippi in that election refused to support the Democrat, but rather voted for unpledged electors. Eisenhower's farewell address had warned against the mounting influence of "the military-industrial complex." At the apex of its strength, a new generation of Americans felt that they had reached power with JFK, acknowledging with the words of his inaugural that they had been born in this century, tempered by a brutal war and uncertain peace, and eager to resume world leadership.

The great liberal course of the 1960s was just beginning with the emphases on racism, pollution, technology, bureaucracy. In the nation's capital glamorous Camelot briefly reigned, and feminine styles were being fashioned by Jacqueline Kennedy. The Beatles arrived on the scene. John Glenn orbited the earth. Martin Luther King, Jr., gave his "I Have a Dream" speech before a quarter of a million people in front of the Lincoln Memorial in Washington. But angrier and more aggressive young blacks were fighting their way to national attention. And international issues threatened to explode. In October 1962, during the Cuban missile crisis, mankind was poised before possible extinction until JFK called Khrushchev's bluff and the Soviet weaponry was withdrawn from Castro's island. The Soviets soon erected the Berlin Wall.

Most of us alive then remember where we were on that fateful day of November 22, 1963. America was profoundly torn by the death of its young president. I myself vividly remember walking through Greenwich Village in New York, hearing from every dwelling the doleful beat of the drums on the televisions during the funeral procession down Pennsylvania Avenue; the streets of the Village were utterly deserted on this day. Two days later Jack Ruby shot Lee Harvey Oswald in the Dallas jail. The disruptive, nearly hallucinatory national mood of the late 1960s was being set.

In the 1964 election President Johnson defeated the GOP's Barry Goldwater by the largest margin of popular votes in history—61 percent—but Goldwater carried Mississippi by 87 percent. LBJ's Voting Rights Act was passed by Congress in 1963, and this was to have significant effects on Mississippi. In the wake of this legislation the Mississippi legislature repealed discriminatory voting laws; in four years the registration of black voters increased from 26,000 to 260,000, and would burgeon even more in the immediate future. In 1967 Robert Clark of Ebenezer became the first black elected to the Mississippi legislature since Reconstruction. (The first time he was ever allowed to vote, Clark would recall, "I voted for myself.") The Republican Party was forcefully on the rise in the state. Just before signing the Voting Rights Act, LBJ turned to his chief-of-staff Bill Moyers, my old and honored classmate and friend in college, and said, "This will turn the South over to the Republicans in your lifetime."

The following year the Civil Rights Act was passed, making racial discrimination illegal in restaurants, hotels, and businesses engaged in interstate commerce. That would recast the social landscape and transform the workplaces in the state. Mississippi Chemical's board of directors unanimously adopted a resolution supporting the Civil Rights Act of 1964 and pledging compliance, a noteworthy stance at the time, and MCC was among the most progressive state businesses in carrying out nondiscriminatory policies.

We were approaching the zenith of the 1960s, and the focus of attention was shifting away from the South. The events of 1965 and 1966 represent an intensifying disintegration and abandon throughout the nation. The war in Vietnam was deepening by the day and threatened to divide the country as nothing had since the Civil War. Cassius Clay, who had changed his name to Muhammad Ali, refused to serve in that war and spent two years in jail. With the escalation of fighting in Vietnam and the splintering of the fragile black-white alliance on civil rights, organized militancy grew apace, and bloody violence was the ordinary headline; disillusion and bitterness would be inevitable, and even more menacing, strident backlash, eventually to engender dangerous confrontations in the country not so widely experienced in a hundred years. At My Lai, a small Vietnamese hamlet that would come to be known as the American Lidice, 567 old men, women, and children were annihilated by an American platoon and thrown in a mass grave.

It was an era of catchwords, and in the ensuing months some of them were: Ho Chi Minh, Cambodia, Watts, Woodstock, Tet, Lincoln Park, hippy, acid-zap, don't trust anyone over thirty, freak out, mind-blowing, love-in, flower power, Black Panthers. The albatross would be Vietnam. By 1967 American involvement there had already lasted longer than the Korean War or World War II.

The year 1968 would be the annus mirabilis, surely among the most tragic and cataclysmic in our history, transfigured by war, assassination, mayhem. Lyndon Johnson abdicated. Martin Luther King, Jr., and Robert Kennedy were murdered. Violence disrupted the Democratic Convention in Chicago. It was at that convention that the Mississippi Freedom Democratic Party was seated, and the regular Democrats opted for Governor George Wallace's third-party candidacy. Richard Nixon defeated Hubert Humphrey in the popular vote by seven-tenths of 1 percent. Mississippi went for Wallace. (Only twice in the two decades between 1948 and 1968 did the state vote for a Democratic or Republican nominee: Adlai Stevenson in '52, Goldwater in '64. The others were to the Dixiecrats in '48, the unpledged electors in '56 and '60, and Wallace in '68.)

President Nixon made an official visit to what was still called Red China as a prelude to American recognition of that behemoth. From 1968 to 1972 he was stringently reducing the number of American troops in Vietnam, and casualty figures were steadily plummeting. In the 1972 elections the president resoundingly defeated the hapless Senator George McGovern, but Watergate was already boiling beneath the surface, a reckless time-bomb for the administration. Watergate eventually led in 1974 to the first presidential resignation in our history and the succession of Gerald Ford, the only person to have succeeded to the White House without having been elected vice president. The Vietnam War formally ended with negotiations in Paris. The cost of that war had been high for America: forty-six thousand battle deaths, three hundred thousand wounded, and the expenditure of $110 billion. Vietnam and Watergate left the nation with a grave spiritual malaise.

If the national scene had been a spectacle of chaos in the late sixties and early seventies, the news from home was much better then. The beloved Eudora Welty of Jackson, Mississippi, won the Pulitzer for her novel The Optimist's Daughter. Jerry Clower, who had arrived at MCC in 1954 to be a fertilizer salesman and later became director of its thirty-man sales force, had attracted much attention for his storytelling. In 1971 he became a full-time humorist, though he would maintain an office and provide promotional services for the company for twenty more years. He would earn several gold records and twelve times be named Music City News Country Comedian of the Year. The Yazoo High Indians had an exciting running back named Larry Kramer who led my old school to its first and only Big Eight championship in 1969.

My mother sent me the Herald with photographs of Mississippi Chemical's new marble-faced headquarters building when it opened in 1968 atop a formidable bluff overlooking the Delta. It would be a year or so before I would see for myself. It did, indeed, "lord over the Delta like the Parthenon," as a reporter from the Atlanta Constitution had written. I drove the steep, winding road to the front of the building, and its terraced hill provided the most majestic and intimate vista I had ever seen of the vast alluvial flat land below. It was wintertime, and the cypress trees in the swampland across the highway were gaunt and bare. In the years since, I have stopped at that site time and time again, often showing it to visitors unfamiliar with the Delta.

On that visit to the new building, I was in my hometown to write about school desegregation for the 120th anniversary issue of Harper's. Yazoo was approaching a momentous juncture. In December 1969, fifteen years after the Brown decision, federal courts had ordered twenty Mississippi school districts to fully integrate their schools the first day after the Christmas break. In the integration of Yazoo's schools, Owen Cooper and other MCC executives and their families helped set a successful example. Overnight the enrollment of Yazoo City schools changed from nearly 100 percent white to 40 percent white and 60 percent black. The anniversary cover of our magazine featured a color photograph of a yellow Yazoo City school bus. We received hundreds of friendly letters from around the nation on the piece. Researching that article and later expanding it into a book allowed me to make a number of visits home and to renew friendships with those I had grown up with, several of whom were now MCC employees, and to meet some of the recent newcomers. The longer I lived in New York, I was discovering of myself, the happier I was to return home.

Later that year a photograph in the Yazoo Herald of the first integrated high school football team symbolized the changes: twenty white players and twenty blacks, and they were still called the Yazoo Indians. The Yazoo co-captain, "Gentle Ben" Williams, would the following year be the first black football player in Ole Miss history and as a senior elected Colonel Rebel, the school's top honor. This early salubrious integration in the town's school was viewed with considerable optimism. By the spring of 1971 Mississippi's public schools were the most integrated in the nation.

In Mississippi, the new and increasingly profitable catfish "farms" were dotting the Delta, several of them across the highway from Mississippi Chemical. Belzoni, twenty air miles from the MCC plant,

would be called the "Catfish Capital of the World." Rice farming also came to the Delta. Farmers could utilize the heavier clay "buckshot" soils, which hold water required for growing rice and raising catfish but are not favorable for growing cotton because of poor drainage.

By 1970 the number of agricultural farms in the state had decreased by two-thirds over the previous forty years, but the value of their products had increased fivefold. The next year the Environmental Protection Agency outlawed the use of DDT in cotton fields. Throughout the early 1970s, the extensive grain sales to the Soviet Union caused prices, which for a long time had been flat, to gyrate so wildly that farmers had to get a new tool: an electronic price monitor, not unlike a stock market ticker, to keep them informed on the prices. Cotton harvesting itself incurred its second revolution—the mechanical picker having been the first—when farmers near Greenwood imported thirteen cotton "module-makers" from the Rio Grande Valley. This equipment allowed farmers to harvest their cotton as swiftly as possible and to leave it safely in the fields in compressed white loaves without weather damage. Before this sweeping change, harvesting had been wholly at the mercy of the schedule of the cotton gins.

On my visits home I always found pride in observing the rising successes of Owen Cooper's grand fertilizer experiment. In 1973 Owen Cooper retired as president of Mississippi Chemical. This brave and civilized man had left a remarkable legacy. One could scarcely envision what Mississippi Chemical Corporation or Yazoo City would have been without him.

W. M.

CHAPTER THREE

Going Coastal

Mississippi Chemical was an indigenous success story by 1956, widely discussed across the South and beyond. Dozens of national and international articles in a wide range of publications featured the Cinderella-like rise of the world's first farmer-owned nitrogen fertilizer plant; such coverage encouraged a stream of visitors to Yazoo City from around the nation and the globe to witness the economic miracle being wrought there by Southern farmers and small-town men and women running their own cooperative enterprise. This success served as an underpinning for even more imposing ventures during the years from 1956 to 1967. Capitalizing on the trust generated by its profitable production

To produce fertilizers containing phosphates and potash, as well as nitrogen, **Mississippi Chemical organized Coastal Chemical Corporation and built a new fertilizer complex to produce these mixed fertilizers at Pascagoula, Mississippi.**

of nitrogen fertilizers, MCC and its CEO Owen Cooper created a significant new subsidiary corporation, Coastal Chemical Corporation, and built an ambitious new production complex at Pascagoula, Mississippi.

The new plant would make "mixed fertilizers," so called because they contained a mixture of three elements—nitrogen (N), phosphates (P), and potassium (K)—and were frequently abbreviated NPK. (While all soils require annual applications of nitrogen fertilizers for maximum yields, most also need applications of phosphate and potassium.) In order to produce NPK, vast quantities of phosphate rock, potash (which contains potassium) and sulfur would have to be brought in. Since water delivery of these heavy raw materials was necessary for the company to be cost competitive, the proposed new facility had to be located on a site that could handle ocean-going vessels.

In February 1956 Mississippi Chemical's

board of directors voted to build a $7.5 million mixed fertilizer production complex on a proposed industrial site in Pascagoula on the Gulf of Mexico. Jackson County had passed a $2 million BAWI bond issue to create the Bayou Casotte Industrial Park and put in the thirty-foot deep-water channel essential for ocean-going vessels to dock at industries in the industrial park. Pat Brabston, a thirty-year veteran of MCC's technical group, was sixteen years old when he was hired to guide engineers through the mud and swamp to lay out plans for the Bayou Casotte channel. "Back then, Bayou Casotte was twenty feet wide: now, it's several hundred," recalls Brabston. Mississippi contractor M. T. Reed was instrumental in convincing MCC to choose Pascagoula. An MCC director, Reed had built the naval base in Gulfport during World War II and was a close friend of Cooper and many of the Mississippi Chemical board members. He recog-

Above left: Finalizing plans for Coastal's new Pascagoula complex were, from left, state legislator Hermes Gautier; Coastal president Owen Cooper; Coastal director LeRoy Percy; Coastal director C. L. McNeil; W. R. Guest, Sr., chair of the Jackson County Port Authority; C. S. Whittington, Coastal board chair; and Edward Khayat, Jackson County supervisor. Above right: Looking over plans for the new deep-water plant site are, from left: Owen Cooper; C. S. Whittington; A. F. Dantzler, secretary of the Jackson County Port Authority; and A. P. Moran, president of the Jackson County board of supervisors. Left: To provide rail service to Coastal Chemical's new Pascagoula plant, the L & N Railroad laid nearly five miles of connecting tracks.

nized the potential of the deep-water venue.

"We were elated that Owen and his board chose to make Coastal Chemical the first industry to locate in our brand new Bayou Casotte industrial area," Alf Dantzler, who led the drive to carve this industrial complex from an isolated wilderness and convert it into one of Mississippi's prime locations for heavy industry, would recall. "When Coastal decided to become our first industry, it gave us the impetus to build the roads, utilities, and railroads out to that site. Until that time there was nothing at Bayou Casotte but Brahma cattle and scrub pines—not a road or power line or anything out there. I remember talking to the president of the L & N Railroad at a party on Friday night and telling him they just had to build a line down to the site. Well, on Monday morning they got started."

Coastal Chemical was formally organized in March 1956. Like Mississippi Chemical, Coastal Chemical was a corporation, and like MCC it would operate as a cooperative and pay patronage refunds to its customers. Its officers and directors were virtually the same as Mississippi Chemical's. MCC invested $250,000 to buy controlling stock in Coastal and to provide start-up funds. It was also MCC that would provide management, sales, and operating expertise. Coastal filed with the Securities and Exchange Commission, and the SEC approval to sell stock was granted that May. The creation of Coastal Chemical was explained to Mississippi Chemical shareholders in a newsletter: "For years, many stockholders have asked 'when can we set up an organization to sup-

Making NPK and DAP

The Coastal Chemical complex actually required the operation of four distinct types of plants to process the primary ingredients—natural gas, potash, sulfur, and phosphate rock—into appropriate mixes of nitrogen (N), phosphate (P), and potassium (K) in its various grades of finished NPK fertilizer.

1. Ammonia plants: Hydrogen from natural gas is mixed with nitrogen from the air to form ammonia, the source for the N.

2. Sulfuric acid plants: Molten yellow sulfur is oxidized by heating it to 1,900 degrees F. This produces a gas, sulfur dioxide, which is reacted with water to form sulfuric acid.

3. Phosphoric acid plants: Phosphate rock is ground into a fine powder, which is then reacted with sulfuric acid and water to form the brown, liquid phosphoric acid, the source of P.

Coastal Chemical supervisor Charles Roberts inspects a handful of NPK granules.

4. Granulation plants: Nitrogen and the phosphoric acid are reacted in a vessel called the neutralizer to produce a hot brown liquid slurry of monoammonium phosphate (MAP) and diammonium phosphate (DAP), compounds that are one part nitrogen and four parts phosphate. The reaction of the strong acid and the strong base is a violent one that causes the whole brew to boil and give off much heat. In a large rotating granulator drum the hot DAP slurry is mixed with the red, sandlike potash, the source of K. The slurry coats the potash to make BB-sized granules of NPK fertilizer, which are then heated to evaporate the moisture and produce firm solid granules for storage and shipping. Finally, the fertilizer is cooled so it will store well and not attract moisture.

Today the Pascagoula complex no longer produces NPK fertilizers or ammonia. In 1988 the complex was sold to Nu-South Industries, Inc. a company which spent over $12 million modifying the plant for the production exclusively of large quantities of DAP. After Nu-South filed bankruptcy in 1990, the complex was returned to Mississippi Chemical as a secured creditor of Nu-South, and then transferred to MCC's newly formed subsidiary, Mississippi Phosphates Corporation. The DAP fertilizer made by Mississippi Phosphates is 18 percent nitrogen and 46 percent phosphates.

The production is still a four-step process, nearly identical to the four steps outlined above for making NPK fertilizers. First, the complex receives and stores ammonia, rather than manufacturing this essential source of nitrogen. Step two—producing sulfuric acid—and step three—producing phosphoric acid—occur just as they do in making NPK. Step four—the granulation process—is different primarily in that no potash is added to the granulation drum. Instead, dry DAP is placed into the granulator drum and coated with the hot DAP slurry. The slurry coats the dry DAP to form BB-sized granules of DAP fertilizer, which are then dried and cooled as described above.

On February 26, 1957, officials of Coastal Chemical, Jackson County, and Yazoo County ceremonially broke ground for Coastal's new fertilizer complex. Above: Owen Cooper explains the project's far-reaching possibilities. Present for the ceremony were, from left, Dr. M. L. Smith, pastor of the Moss Point Methodist Church; W. B. Dunwoody, Coastal's general operations manager; Cooper; Fred Moran, president of the Jackson County board of supervisors; Hugh McGraw, Yazoo City councilman; C. S. Whittington, Coastal board chair; W. R. Guest, director of Jackson County Port Authority; and Norwood Nichols, president of the Yazoo County board of supervisors. Right, Owen Cooper prepares for groundbreaking of Coastal's ammonia plant in March of 1958.

ply our mixed fertilizer on the same basis that MCC supplies our nitrogen?' We now have an answer: Coastal Chemical Corporation." Its charter, closely paralleling Mississippi Chemical's, provided for the sale of high analysis mixed fertilizers to stockholders on a patronage basis. As with MCC, at the end of the year, all expenses would be deducted from the company's sales revenues, and the remaining funds, if any, would be returned to the stockholders in proportion to their purchases from the plant.

A lengthy report to the board in 1956 predicted annual Coastal earnings of $1,679,040—about ten dollars a ton—on the production and sale of 157,000 tons a year. (These optimistic forecasts would not be reached until five years later, however.) The report cited six vital reasons that the proposed plants would be economical and propitious:

(1) Their location on deep water, navigable by both ocean-going vessels and barge lines, would allow cost-competitive purchases of the critical raw materials: phosphate rock, potash, and sulfur.

(2) The plant would manufacture its own sulfuric and phosphoric acid at substantial savings over purchase elsewhere.

(3) Outgoing freight costs would be reduced by producing high analysis fertilizers that contained up to twice as much plant food a ton as low analysis fertilizers and by employing low-cost barge transportation.

(4) Overhead expenses would be minimized because these would be shared with Mississippi Chemical, whose administrative staff would also manage the new enterprise.

(5) A dependable market would be provided by the farmers and dealers who bought stock in the corporation.

(6) The plants would be flexible, capable of producing both complete mixed fertilizers and/or straight nutrient fertilizers, those products with only one of the N, P, or K elements.

The 1,360-acre plant site was purchased at $86 an acre. (Forty years later, in 1997, Mississippi Phosphates Corporation, a later MCC subsidiary, would pay more than $14,000 an acre to expand the Pascagoula plant.) In 1957 the average salary for Mississippi Chemical's 299 employees was $380 a month, good wages in that day. Mississippi's annual per capita income, the lowest of all the states, had just exceeded $1,000 for the first time in history. In that year Pascagoula's total population was 10,805. Market Street was a one-lane road on the eastern fringe of the city, and rent for two- and three-bedroom houses ranged from sixty to eighty dollars a month. Pascagoula had seven white public schools with 2,765 students, two black public schools with 538 students, and two parochial schools with 402 students.

In November of 1956 the citizens of Jackson County gave overwhelming approval to a $750,000 BAWI bond issue on Coastal's behalf. After an intense stock sales campaign across the South, six thousand shareholders had purchased over $4 million in Coastal Chemical stock by August 1957. Six months earlier on February 26, 1957—less than a year after the board's approval of Coastal Chemical's creation—ground-breaking ceremonies were held at Bayou Casotte, still a wilderness accessible only by a dirt road. Recalling that day years later, Alf Dantzler said, "Governor Hugh White's car got stuck in the mud, and we had to pull him out with a bulldozer. The Mississippi banks hadn't wanted to take a risk on those BAWI bonds, so Governor White twisted some arms to get our state's banks to buy them. He spent most of his two terms in the office working to bring more industrial jobs to the state. In the mud that day White may have wondered whether progress was indeed being made."

In early 1957 Coastal Chemical contracted with the Fluor Corporation of Los Angeles to build its initial phosphate fertilizer plants. Fluor used French technology from the St.

Throughout 1957 construction crews worked to build Coastal Chemical Corporation's new fertilizer complex on the Bayou Casotte channel at Pascagoula. Left, pilings are sunk for Coastal's dock.

Gobain Company in both the phosphoric acid plant and the ammonium phosphate granulation plant, which would be the first of its kind in the United States making homogeneous, high analysis mixed fertilizers.

Later that year Coastal shareholders voted to add an ammonia plant to the complex, and Chemical Construction Company—or Chemico—of New York was selected to build it. Marion Brown and Albert Green were assigned the task of evaluating four different technologies for making ammonia submitted by four competing firms. They recommended the Chemico process to W. B. Dunwoody, and later the board approved that plan. The ammonia plant was not the only sale made by the young Chemico sales engineer Jack Babbitt. He had first come to Mississippi with the Girdler Corporation to build Mississippi Chemical's initial Yazoo City ammonia plant. When he came back

south to sell the company its Pascagoula ammonia plant, Babbitt so impressed Owen Cooper that three years later Cooper would lure him from New York to head First Mississippi Corporation.

To oversee construction, MCC transferred engineer Sid Ferguson to Pascagoula. He was the first of nearly forty Yazooans who would move there to help operate and manage the Coastal facility. Second to move was John Lyles, who would work at Coastal in warehouse and purchasing jobs for the next twenty-eight years. He would recall those days in 1957: "Our plant site was the boondocks. The road into it was so muddy we had to use bulldozers to pull cars and trucks out of it. Mr. Delmas's Brahma cattle roamed at will through the plant site, and they were wild and mean." Once, one of the cows got stuck in a bog, and Sid Ferguson caught it by the tail and pulled it free. The

Coastal's plant site was isolated scrub pine pasture land, and construction workers and plant operators had to contend with a herd of Brahma cattle that roamed freely through the site from adjacent rangeland. Top left, a construction worker at Pascagoula enjoys the shade of his home-made hard-hat sombrero.

unappreciative Brahma chased Ferguson around his truck three or four times.

The Brahmas roamed through the Coastal Chemical plant for several years. At that time Mississippi had an open stock law, and property owners were not required to fence their cattle. Even when Coastal later built a fence around its complex, the Brahmas would come down the railroad line looking for something to eat. Charlie O'Brien, an instrument mechanic who transferred from Yazoo City to Pascagoula, also remembered those Brahmas: "Our tiny little plant was the only civilization in miles, and we had only a few small lights. One night I was walking through the pine trees between our guardhouse and the fertilizer plant in the pitch black dark, and I must have scared the Brahmas. Next thing I knew they stampeded toward me. I got behind a big pine tree and held on for dear life. Pretty soon they had all run off and I went on about my business."

The first plant to begin production was the sulfuric acid plant in December 1957,

and starting it up took some manipulating. "Our natural gas line wasn't yet complete," John Lyles recalled, "so they asked me to buy enough propane to fire up the sulfur furnace. About that time an unusual cold snap hit the coast, and everyone wanted all the propane available to heat homes. Finally I located five rail cars of propane, and we got enough in here to ignite our sulfur."

Production at the Pascagoula complex during 1958 and 1959 involved a long parade

of trials and errors, with more errors than successes for many months. At Yazoo City employees had to learn how to make one product and make it right. That was hard enough with the primitive instruments and controls at their disposal. But at Pascagoula's NPK granulation plants they had to learn how to make fifteen or twenty different grades of fertilizer, each with a different ratio of ammonia to phosphoric acid, a different granule size, and varying conditions of moisture, temperature, drying, acidity, and other factors. Charles O'Brien would recall the start-up headaches at Pascagoula. "Our operators had to use a slide rule and their best gut feel to try to get our grades to come out right. For months they almost never did. When it opened, that No. 1 NPK granulation plant was probably the prettiest plant in the world, but it was one of the worst designed and built. In two months it was the dirtiest plant in the world. The control panels weren't enclosed, and rain shorted them out. The electrical stations were poorly located and shorted out continually. I got so discouraged I almost quit."

The June 30, 1958, Coastal annual report explained that the No. 1 NPK granulation plant had encountered significant problems in adjusting mechanical equipment and developing techniques to provide optimum manufacturing conditions to produce ammonium phosphate fertilizers. By that time a deficit of $917,606 had accumulated. O'Brien recalled that the company still gave its employees a raise. "That made a big impression on all of us. Mr. Cooper was committed to treating us fairly and paying us good wages, even if it took us months to earn a profit."

While employees at the original NPK granulation plant continued to wrestle with multifold production problems, the Pascagoula ammonia operators prepared to bring up their plant with near record smoothness. Charles O'Brien, the chief instrument mechanic, was stunned by how smoothly the ammonia plant began operation in December 1958. "I was prepared to

Paul Lacy, right, and Jim Gambrell provided strong leadership to the Pascagoula production team for nearly three decades. Lacy came to Pascagoula in October 1958 as superintendent of the Coastal Chemical ammonia plant. Lacy succeeded Frank Bless as Coastal general manager in 1966 and chose Gambrell as his production manager. When Lacy moved to the corporate headquarters in 1975, Gambrell became general manager.

miss Christmas with my family," he recalled, "when, lo and behold, they had that plant running like a top and meeting design specs in less than three days." Paul Lacy, who was transferred from Yazoo City to Pascagoula in October of 1958 as ammonia plant superintendent, was not surprised, however. "A lot of the credit goes to the smart decision Mississippi Chemical management made to transfer a strong team of twenty folks from Yazoo City to Pascagoula in October to start up and run that new plant." This core group included six veterans from the Yazoo City ammonia plant (Paul Lacy, Ken Batton,

Elmo Barber, Bobby Neely, Jack Manning, and Billy Jay Overton) and fourteen from Southland's Yazoo County oil refinery, which was shut down by that time (Jack Brown, A. J. Adams, Thomas C. Adams, Jerry Martin, Henry Smith, Wesley Smith, Fred Shurley, Quinton Gammill, Wilson Perry, Warren Russum, James Roy Cline, Barney Lovette, Henry Harris, and Clyde Strickland).

In the meantime the first NPK unit continued to plague Pascagoula. "That No. 1 plant would go haywire and fertilizer would go all over everywhere," John Lyles remem-

Aerial view of Coastal Chemical Corporation, Pascagoula, 1959

bered. "It would come out the dryer too fast and run off the belt conveyor." Every night Lyles would have to shovel up the scattered fertilizer which covered the whole second floor.

John Rednour, who rose through the ranks from an entry-level operator in early 1958 to become production manager, would recall: "Mastering that No. 1 NPK plant was extremely challenging, like having a tiger by the tail. We had a new French process, new people, and very primitive instruments and control valves. Eventually—much later—we got better automatic control valves, but in those first years you had to fool with those valves every minute. In those first months you could go from making cannon balls to making dust in a matter of seconds. We made a lot of fertilizer that set up so hard, I had to use dynamite to bust it loose. We had to learn to react fast."

Start-up problems resulted in a loss of nearly half a million dollars for the fiscal year ending June 1959. At that time, the Pascagoula complex had five plants: an ammonia plant, a sulfuric acid plant, a phosphoric acid plant, the No. 1 NPK granulation plant, and the No. 2 NPK unit. The phosphoric acid and No. 1 NPK granulation plants were not operating well enough to be officially accepted from the contractor until November 1958. The No. 2 NPK plant, featuring an ammoniator-granulator designed by TVA, was not ready until the next June. There were difficulties with inexperienced personnel, an abnormal number of process and mechanical problems, poor quality control, and limited marketable fertilizer materials.

By mid-1959 the continuing production headaches in making NPK were taking a toll on all involved in the new complex. Management personnel had begun to lose patience, Coastal employees were concerned about the future of their jobs, and the Bank for Cooperatives* was beginning to doubt that it would ever see its loan repaid. A frustrated Owen Cooper flew to Pascagoula to warn the staff that they had only ninety more days to take care of their difficulties. "Owen Cooper was meeting with all the employees under an oak tree," John Lyles recalls that day. "We didn't have a meeting room. We met outdoors. It looked bleak. So bleak, in fact, that I started looking for another job." Charles O'Brien remembers seeing a well-dressed man who frequently toured the

Coastal Chemical's early production workers struggled to make a quality NPK product with primitive plant control systems. Frequently the fertilizer produced was so hard, it had to be broken loose with a sledgehammer.

* The Bank for Cooperatives was established by the federal government to provide a source of capital for U.S. agricultural cooperative businesses. It was the company's principal lender and, until Mississippi Chemical ceased operating as a cooperative in 1994, provided virtually all the bank loans to MCC.

troubled plant. One day he overhead the man say, "What's wrong now? If we ever get our dollars out of this, they won't get any more!" The man, O'Brien would later discover, was an official from the Bank for Cooperatives.

To find solutions and help turn around the failing company, a technical group composed of Marion Brown, Albert Green, Albert Alberede (a French engineer employed by MCC), Carl Osterthaler, and Al Soday was sent from Yazoo City to Pascagoula to work around the clock with the maintenance and production staff. Each Friday for six

months they met with the Bank for Cooperatives to outline plans and measure progress. The group finally published a textbook on the production of ammonium phosphates to assist the Pascagoula operators in dealing with the complicated chemistry. "Normal chemical equations did not work in our plant," Soday, who helped figure out what would work, recalled years later. "The chemistry required was quite novel to our own plants. If you followed it precisely, you could make either monophosphate fertilizer or di-ammonium phosphate (DAP), either of which is okay. But if you didn't follow the

Management According to John Rednour

"I am not a chemical engineer, but I know people, and I know how they like to be treated: fairly, justly, honestly and with respect and appreciation. In the Army I saw men being treated unfairly and I will never, ever forget that. I made a life-long commitment to treat every man I ever worked with fairly and justly, and that's what I demanded from my supervisors, as well. The secret to a successful organization is very simple: the guys at the bottom of the line bake your bread. They either make you a hero or break you. If you treat them fairly, squarely, with respect and dignity, they will make you a hero.

"Management is pretty simple. It involves reigning in the bad guys and affirming the good guys. That way, your good guys always carry the day for you. Any time one of my supervisors failed to

John Rednour

treat someone fairly, I took him on a long walk on the gyp pile and told him exactly how the cow ate the cabbage and exactly how I expected him to treat people in the future. The guys called me 'Black John' because I refused to compromise my core values like fairness and decency.

"Sometimes we have to make hard decisions. I hated those employee layoffs, but it had to be done. The greatest sin any company can commit is failing to make a profit. Without a profit, no one has a job. It's a fact of life.

"Mississippi Chemical is the finest company I have ever encountered, and it all started at the top with Owen Cooper. Every single man in our plant knew and respected Mr. Cooper and what he stood for. I equate him to the 'just king' in the book of Proverbs. The fourth and fourteenth verses of the twenty-ninth chapter state, 'A just king gives stability to his nation. But one who demands bribes destroys it. . . . A king who is fair to the poor shall have a long reign.' Owen Cooper was the just king who set up Mississippi Chemical and gave us a moral code of conduct that has carried this company forward for fifty years. When I look back on my life, I am most proud to have spent my life working for a company with a man like Owen Cooper at the top."

chemistry closely, you would get a mixture halfway in between that was virtually unusable. It would set up hard as concrete, and the farmers would ship it back to us."

These men later helped the Pascagoula operation's team devise a unique process for making DAP fertilizer that the Tennessee Valley Authority, not Coastal Chemical, later patented and sold around the world. "At our No. 2 NPK plant we were the first in the world to use preneutralizers and a rotary ammoniator-granulator," Brown would remember. "It was a major breakthrough. But we were all so busy trying to make satisfactory fertilizer that no one took time to realize that we had a process that could and should have been patented." For later inventions Brown and other company researchers would receive two John C. Vaaler awards, given annually for the best fertilizer process development in the nation.

Donald Valverde, the assistant plant manager, played a large role in confronting Coastal's failures and getting both the No. 1 and No. 2 NPK plants running satisfactorily. Valverde excelled at formulations and rigging up innovative mechanical solutions. He recognized that MCC had to either buy or invent better equipment to solve its problems. The original instruments were so faulty that Valverde and Frank Bless, the general manager, gave O'Brien almost a blank check to acquire better instruments. The original mechanical feeders were constantly breaking down. Subsequently, O'Brien and his crew designed and built pneumatic feeders—feeders that worked on air pressure—that were an enormous improvement.

The unflagging efforts of many people eventually enabled Coastal to realize its initial promise. John Rednour, who helped develop and record granulation formulas, held classes to teach less experienced operators all that the first crew had learned from its mistakes. "I was determined not to let that plant lick me or my men," he would later recall. "I don't believe in the word 'can't.' I'm an old infantry officer who believes that determination, drive, and improvising can do almost anything. And that's the way I attacked those problems. I lived, slept, and breathed those fertilizer plants. Things slowly got better."

Finally, in early 1960 Coastal began to show a monthly profit. By June 30 of that year it had earned its first-ever annual profits of $1,299,000, enough nearly to offset the losses of 1958 and 1959. During the 1960s Coastal's annual production, sales, and income were to grow rapidly, eventually surpassing those of its parent, Mississippi Chemical.

When Coastal began operating in 1957, Jackson County was strong union country. The largest industry in the area—and in the state—Ingalls Shipbuilding, was highly unionized, as was the nearby papermill, International Paper. Coastal was the first major non-union employer in the vicinity, and the unions tried diligently to organize it. Between 1957 and 1964 three campaigns to unionize Coastal would result in three elec-

Shirley Speights, Coastal's first female employee and telephone switchboard operator, was affectionately known as "the voice of Coastal."

tions, but as the employees at Mississippi Chemical had earlier done in Yazoo City, the Pascagoula employees each time voted against the union.

Emotions ran high during the union campaigns and elections. The National Labor Relations Board guidelines permitted representatives from the union to go into employees' homes and talk to them but forbade company management from doing so. To have an opportunity to present its side of the case, Coastal held several banquets for employees and their spouses. "I composed an anti-union song and sang it at each of those banquets," Shirley Speights, who served as a monitor during the three elections, would remember. "Some of the men in

maintenance got upset with me and went to my husband and asked him to shut me up. Durwood, my husband, looked at those guys and said, 'Number one, you don't know Shirley, and number two, you don't know me. No one is going to tell me or Shirley what we can do. This is a free country and I would appreciate you respecting our freedom.'"

From their inception, Coastal Chemical and its parent Mississippi Chemical had taken painstaking efforts to ensure that their employment practices, pay levels, and fringe benefit programs were fair and competitive. For three decades, labor lawyer Leslie Inman of New Orleans was a trusted advisor on these matters. Inman assisted the company in responding to the union organizing efforts at the Pascagoula plant as he had earlier in Yazoo City and would later at the company's facility in Carlsbad, New Mexico. "Faster than anyone I have ever seen, he could spot the problems and tell you what needed to be done to remove irritants and keep our rank and file workers feeling good about the company," plant manager John Rednour would explain.

Paul Lacy, who was Pascagoula plant manager during the final union vote, would recall: "We won each vote with a bigger majority each time. That last time, the union representatives were so angry with the vote that they humiliated our men who had worked for them. They told our men they were fed up with their not being able to deliver the votes and they were packing up, leaving town, and never coming back unless the men could do a better job of delivering votes."

During her twenty-nine-year tenure at Pascagoula, Shirley Speights would be affectionately known by several nicknames: "the Voice of Coastal" for her service as the central telephone switchboard operator who greeted every incoming caller for decades; "the poet laureate of Coastal" for the poems she prepared for retirement parties and other big events; and even "Miss Union Fighter" for her outspoken beliefs that the company and its employees did not need a union. But when she arrived on February 28, 1957, the Pascagoula *Press Register* headline read: "#98: Ninety-seven Men and One Woman! Cherchez La Femme" (Look for the Female).

Visiting fertilizer officials Paul Pothen, left, and V. S. Pillai, right, of the government of India, inspect bags of Coastal Chemical fertilizer ready for shipment to their nation; Pascagoula plant manager Paul Lacy looks on.

Shirley Speights broke the sex barrier at Coastal, and what had been a ninety-seven-member, all-male work force was never quite the same again.

"W. B. Dunwoody didn't believe that women had any place in a fertilizer plant and refused to let us hire a woman for months," John Lyles would remember. "We had to go along with Mr. Dunwoody because everyone at Pascagoula reported to him as operations vice president in the Yazoo City headquarters." Coastal hired men to be secretaries, clerks, and typists, but in the 1950s and early 1960s very few men had the appropriate background, training, or disposition for jobs then considered by many to be the province of women. Finally Lyles told Dunwoody the men were not working out, and Dunwoody reluctantly gave his permission to hire a few women.

When Speights broke the sex barrier in 1957, Coastal still had some practices that would be unacceptable, even illegal, today. "It was a sad sign of the times that in the late 1950s and early 1960s our company didn't treat blacks or women equally," she would reflect. Black employees were segregated by "white" and "colored" waiting rooms, change rooms, and even drinking fountains, which did not disappear until the Civil Rights Act of 1964 outlawed them. Female employees were paid lower wages than men and not even allowed inside the plant—to work or to visit. Shirley Speights was hired at $52.40 per week, a salary less than that of male clerks doing the same work. When she questioned the difference, she was told that men were paid more because they had families to support. For many years women were not allowed into the plant proper. One day a woman truck driver ran right through that policy when she and her husband, each driving a truck, appeared at the gate to pick up two loads of fertilizer. "Well, this threw the whole plant and office into a tizzy," Speights recalled. "You'd have thought the woman was trying to rob us, not buy our product. They phoned all over the plant to warn the

President Owen Cooper and board officer C. L. McNeil stand on Coastal's dock as fertilizer is loaded for export delivery. Because of its location on the deep water, the Pascagoula complex has efficiently made export sales and shipments of phosphate fertilizers for four decades.

guys that a woman was about to enter the plant. As soon as she parked her truck at the storage area, they drove her back to 'safety' at the waiting room."

Looking back on her job interview in 1957, Shirley Speights mused, "I'll never forget nearly sliding off the muddy, icy road going out to Coastal for my interview. I said, 'Lord, if you get me home safe from this place, I'll never come back again.' Well, I kept coming back for twenty-nine years and loved every day of it. For three decades I told

literally thousands of people, because I talked to that many on the switchboard, that 'I'm with Coastal Chemical.' I never said, 'I work at Coastal Chemical.' It was more than work; it was something special."

John Rednour had problems of a different kind getting his job at Coastal. In 1958, while he was superintendent of Jackson Chemical Company, he had seen "the handwriting on the wall: Mississippi Chemical was so profitable they were going to run us out of business. I wanted a job at their new plant in

Pascagoula." That resolve turned into a difficult task, putting to the test his fundamental belief in perseverance. "First, Dr. R. J. Moorhead, the company physician in Yazoo City, turned me down for a hernia. So I had surgery. Then he turned me down because of a World War II injury. So I signed a waiver. Then he turned me down unless I could lose twenty pounds in two weeks. I lost those pounds by fasting the entire two weeks of my Guard duty at Camp Shelby."

"We were very informal and friendly in our Pascagoula offices," Shirley Speights observed. "When Jack Phillips was vice president of operations at corporate headquarters and would visit us on the Coast, everyone called him simply 'Jack.' I think he might have preferred us to greet him a bit more formally, with 'Mr. Phillips.' But that's just not the Coast. Here things are much more informal and laid back. We respect each other, but we use first names. We might fight and fuss among ourselves on occasion, but don't ever let an outsider attack Coastal Chemical or one of our own. Whenever anybody had a personal problem, people would pitch in like family."

∽

Only 250 miles distant, Pascagoula and Yazoo City, Mississippi, are really worlds apart. Yazoo's milieu is defined by the rich, flat Delta dirt—king cotton, catfish, soul food, and the blues. Pascagoula's is shaped by the deep rolling waters, the winds and waves of the Gulf of Mexico—sea gulls, shrimp boats, submarines, and shipyards. Nothing rules the gulf and vexes its coast as much as the menacing winds and waters of its legendary hurricanes. Pascagoulans mark their history by major hurricanes, just as the Delta used to mark its by the disastrous floods it endured.

Because a major concern about locating Coastal Chemical on Bayou Casotte was the threat of hurricanes, construction was designed to withstand high velocity wind. Over the next four decades three major hurricanes— Camille in 1969, Frederick in 1979, and Elena in 1985— would test the plants' structures and find them sound. While Hurricane Frederick was the most direct hit on the Pascagoula plant, Camille by far did the most damage with the largest waves ever recorded on the Gulf Coast. Two hundred and fifty-eight people, most of them on the Gulf Coast, were killed. The winds were frightening enough, but the rising surge of water had the power to destroy anything in its path. Even though Pascagoula was fifty miles east of Camille's eye, the storm drove a huge wall of water at the Coastal plant, slamming into buildings, ruining motors, and damaging mechanical devices. The Coastal Chemical plants were inoperative for five weeks, but it would have been months had it not been for the determined efforts of the employees just before Camille hit and immediately after the waters receded. In the last twenty-four hours before Camille arrived, they worked frantically to shut down every plant, elevating all the supplies and equipment three feet off the ground, securing all moveable equipment, and taking every emergency precaution feasible on such short notice.

After Camille hit, the road to the plant was totally under water, and oil from Chevron's nearby refinery covered everything. "We immediately went to work jerking out every motor we could and rushing them to repair shops all along the Gulf Coast," Paul Lacy, who was general manager at that time, recalls. "That got us to the front of the line at those shops and saved us weeks and perhaps months of lost time." Camille damaged so much equipment on the Coast it took months to repair the damage. Coastal, however, was back in production in five weeks.

John Rednour was the first employee back in the plant after Camille hit, and he took hundreds of pages of notes on what to do before and after a hurricane. These notes would become the substance of Coastal's,

Don Tiblier, synthesis operator, left, takes a lunch break with reform board operator Tom Thames in the Coastal Chemical ammonia plant. Above: Red Hamilton, plant operator, right, and A. J. Adams, chief relief operator, at Coastal's ammonia plant in 1966.

and later Mississippi Chemical's, hurricane preparedness procedures that were ready by the time Frederick came along. He would later describe what the company learned from the experience of Camille. "After Camille, we developed a very specialized and elite hurricane task force," he would remember, "composed of every key skill we needed to shut down the plants before an impending hurricane and restore the plants to operation as soon as the hurricane had passed." When a big hurricane like Frederick was approaching, the hurricane task force was housed at the LaFont Inn in Pascagoula, and the company evacuated its families inland to Meridian, Mississippi. There was constant

radio contact between the plant and the hurricane control center at the LaFont Inn. The entire plan worked beautifully in 1979. Although Frederick destroyed five important conveyors and other equipment in the plant, Coastal was back to production in record time. Six years later when Elena hit Pascagoula especially hard and damaged many houses, Mississippi Chemical provided interest-free emergency loans to help employees repair their homes.

In the four decades since its founding in 1957, Mississippi Chemical's Pascagoula employees have battled Brahma bulls to carve their facility from the wilderness, overcome

tough organizational problems, survived the Gulf's fiercest hurricanes, dealt with union organizing campaigns, and as detailed in later chapters, overcome a severe financial struggle with the ominous fertilizer depression of the 1980s. Today the company's deepwater docks at Bayou Casotte are a gateway to the increasingly global phosphate markets, serving countries like China and India and providing farmers with quality phosphate fertilizers.

CHAPTER FOUR

New Vistas, New Ventures

From 1956 until its twenty-fifth anniversary in 1973, Mississippi Chemical and its expansionist CEO Owen Cooper created a series of new and far-reaching ventures, forming new corporations, constructing advanced new fertilizer production complexes and plants, and adding delivery terminals across the South. Not satisfied with the success of Mississippi Chemical and later Coastal in supplying Southern farmers with the indispensable fertilizers they needed, Owen Cooper and MCC board officer LeRoy Percy also wanted to create a new corporation that could bring a wide range of industries and lucrative jobs to the state. The South at that time was try-

The steam drum and flare stack of MCC's Kellogg ammonia plant in Yazoo City, completed in 1966. The first Kellogg 1,000-ton-per-day ammonia plant ever built, MCC's revolutionary new plant cut the cost of making ammonia in half and was soon replicated by dozens of ammonia-makers around the world.

ing to convince northern industrialists to bring their plants and investment dollars to the South. Cooper's concept for a home-owned investment company was radically different.

In a 1982 interview Cooper explained the idea: "Mississippi Chemical was making money hand over fist. We had proven that Mississippi farmers could build and operate a nitrogen fertilizer plant; now it was time for Mississippians to prove they could accumulate capital, create their own businesses, and pull the poorest state in the union up by its own bootstraps." Cooper named the new investment company First Mississippi Corporation because it would be the first time in state history that Mississippians had organized a statewide venture capital effort.

"Owen thought First Mississippi could serve both a civic purpose and a profit purpose, and he was absolutely right," said FMC director Dwain Luce. For Cooper it

was just as important, or more important, to prove that Mississippians could finance, start and manage their own industries and provide jobs for their own people, as it was to make money.

Years later LeRoy Percy would reflect that he, like everyone else, became caught up in Cooper's enthusiasm. "Owen generated an idea a minute. He was always cranking out new ways to help people and help our state. First Mississippi Corporation was one of Owen's greatest dreams. While it turned out to be a wonderful winner, there was many a day and night along the way when I wondered what on earth Owen had gotten me roped into!"

From its inception in the spring of 1957, and for the next forty years until it sold its fertilizer business to MCC in 1996, First Mississippi Corporation was closely linked with Mississippi Chemical. It was hatched in Mississippi Chemical's board room and hall-

Mississippi Governor J. P. Coleman, center, presents Owen Cooper, right, and Jackson banker Nat Rogers with the charter of incorporation for First Mississippi Corporation, which Cooper founded to develop home-owned businesses in the state.

rities and Exchange Commission ever approved it," Gordon Meador, the original treasurer, would later reflect. "It just goes to show you that you can't legislate trust, you have to earn it, and it's a very precious commodity" current MCC president Charles O. "Chuck" Dunn suggests. "Today the SEC would require a hundred-page document which virtually no one would read. The people trusted Owen Cooper and sent him $5 million on that trust, not on what some prospectus said."

MCC and First Mississippi were very tightly linked in the late 1950s and early 1960s. The two companies had common directors, officers, and shareholders. The MCC field sales staff canvassed the state urging Mississippi Chemical shareholders to invest in the new venture, and the personnel offices at Yazoo City and Pascagoula offered employees the opportunity to buy stock in the new company. While First Mississippi would eventually develop its own distinct staff, goals, and investments, during its formative years Owen Cooper, John Satterfield, and LeRoy Percy—key officers in both firms—frequently saw First Mississippi as an appropriate vehicle to conduct profit-making sales or handle projects that might be inappropriate for MCC or Coastal because they operated as cooperatives.

To shepherd the investment capital and get First Mississippi off the ground, Owen Cooper served as the unpaid chief executive officer for the first three years and as board chair until 1967, when he passed those reins to his close friend and MCC board chair, LeRoy Percy. Although First Mississippi was

ways, financed by MCC patronage refunds and shareholders, a partner with MCC in numerous plants and projects, and finally sold to Mississippi Chemical by its successor corporation, ChemFirst, on December 24, 1996.

On February 25, 1957, a month before Governor J. P. Coleman signed First Mississippi's charter of incorporation, Mississippi Chemical's Board gave the embryonic venture a major lifeline by approving the idea of allowing MCC shareholders to use their patronage refunds to buy stock in the new cor-

poration. From 1957 to 1960, shareholders were invited to direct their refunds to the purchase of stock in First Mississippi Corporation at four dollars a share by returning "penny postcards." When the returned cards were counted, seven thousand shareholders and a number of MCC employees, who had come to trust Cooper's reputation for business acumen, had responded by buying almost $5 million in stock.

"Our First Mississippi prospectus didn't even specify what we would invest the company's money in. It's amazing that the Secua legal entity separate from Mississippi Chemical, five of its first six investments were in projects at Mississippi Chemical or its subsidiary Coastal Chemical: First Mississippi purchased five hundred thousand dollars in Coastal Chemical stock and two hundred thousand dollars in Mississippi Chemical stock, financed an oleum plant to concentrate sulfuric acid and a superphosphate fertilizer plant (both located inside the Pascagoula complex and leased back to Coastal Chemical), and purchased ten aluminum rail cars to transport nitrogen solutions, leasing them to Mississippi Chemical. These proved to be wise and profitable investments. To oversee these and their many other investments, they hired as general manager Jack Babbitt, who as an engineer, first for the Girdler Corporation and then for Chemico, had so impressed Owen Cooper.

But the dream of building ten new plants a year for Mississippi soon led to a hodgepodge of unrelated and unprofitable ventures that almost sank First Mississippi before it ever earned a nickel. With little focus or staff, the company invested in a wide range of ventures that Babbitt described as "wild, weird, wonderful projects." These included a Gulf Coast cat food company, a New Albany metal extrusion plant, a paper bag plant in Yazoo City, a swimming pool manufacturer, a new insurance company, an egg carton plant, a model city south of Memphis, an ammonia plant in Arizona, and a Gulfport piping company that alone lost more than a million dollars over a two to three year period. It also considered fertilizer plants for

Cuba, Peru, and Panama and a paper mill for north Mississippi.

Several times during the first seven years money was so tight that Jackson bankers and First Mississippi board members Bob Hearin and Nat Rogers had to intervene with loans to meet the payroll. "It was a near disaster," recalls LeRoy Percy. "We owned so many cats and dogs that the board had to meet every Saturday to try to figure out what to do next. Always on the agenda was figuring out how to come up with next week's or next month's payroll."

Finally, in 1964 the troubled staff, led by general manager Jack Babbitt, decided that the only possible salvation lay in taking First Mississippi back to the basics, those businesses that First Mississippi and its board and staff knew best. Dumping most of the company's investments, they focused all their energy and assets into fertilizers and chemicals. Babbitt and Cooper, two master promoters, soon turned its fortune around. They built and sold an ammonia plant called First Nitrogen and then connected with MCC on a joint venture called Triad, both in Donaldsonville, Louisiana. More troubles followed until a new CEO, Kelley Williams, expanded its operation and profits and in 1975 made FMC the first Mississippi corporation ever to be listed on the New York Stock Exchange.

When the decade of the 1980s closed, First Mississippi Corporation, whose directors were ready to give up in 1971, had not only shown Mississippians they could successfully raise venture capital and successfully invest in their own companies; it had

shown the entire world. As Kelley Williams said at a 1982 banquet celebrating First Mississippi's first quarter-century, "The grand experiment of Owen Cooper, LeRoy Percy . . . and the other founders of First Mississippi has worked. They wanted to show that Mississippians could influence their own destinies. They could raise some capital, invest it productively and do some good with it. They proved that, along with everyone who sent back one of Owen Cooper's penny postcards."

On December 24, 1996, First Mississippi consummated a comprehensive restructuring with the biggest maneuver in its history and in MCC's. On that day, FMC transferred its specialty chemical businesses to a new corporation, ChemFirst, and sold First Mississippi and all its fertilizer operations to MCC for $314 million. After operating on its own for thirty-nine years, First Mississippi Corporation came home to the company that birthed it.

Meanwhile, in 1959, as First Mississippi was still gathering the penny postcards that would eventually bring in its initial $5 million in capital, Mississippi Chemical continued its growth in Yazoo City with the addition of a two-hundred-ton a day urea plant at a cost of $2 million. At that time there were fewer than a dozen urea plants in the world and only five in the United States. MCC selected a urea synthesis process perfected in Switzerland by the Holzverzuckerrung company and licensed by Inventa A.G., and a prilling process from Germany's Hoechst-Uhde firm. Vulcan-Cincinnati was

Loyal, long-service employees are a key to Mississippi Chemical's success. Blanche Hester, left, who has worked in payroll and special projects for forty-seven and a half years, is the company's longest service employee. She is shown preparing payroll data for MCC's Univac computer, the latest technology in the 1960s. Above, Marion Brown, a research and engineering staff member for three decades, and Hannah Kelly, longtime switchboard operator, receive service awards from Owen Cooper.

selected to build the new plant for MCC. Because this was Mississippi Chemical's first experience with making urea, a product that is 46 percent nitrogen and very popular with rice growers, it sent Marion Brown, Albert Green, Albert Alberede, and Bob Beisel to Switzerland and Germany for a month to learn how to operate the new plant.

One problem that neither the Germans nor Mississippi Chemical foresaw eventually caused the concrete urea prill tower to collapse with a giant crash that sent shock waves through the plant and the city. During processing, large quantities of urea would adhere to the concrete walls in the prill tower. On the evening of the collapse, September 30, 1960, the plant had shut down so that workers could wash away the accumula-

tion in the top of the structure. Without warning, a large chunk of urea broke away and fell with such force that it smashed the concrete wall at the tower's base, setting up a chain reaction that caused the entire tower to collapse.

"I can still remember that Friday night in 1960," Yazoo City banker Miller Holmes, Jr., then a high school senior, would recall. "We were at a Yazoo City Indian high school football game at old Crump Field, when the loudspeaker came on and announced that one of the chemical plant's towers had collapsed and that several employees had been rushed to King's Daughters Hospital for examination. Nearly half the spectators fled from the stands to go check on family members and neighbors."

"Fortunately and almost miraculously no one was seriously hurt," Harold Keith, who was working at the plant that night, would remember. "The concrete tower started to simply slide straight down, with Theopialis Kirk and Johnny Freeman trapped at the top of the tower riding it toward the earth, holding on for dear life. Thank goodness neither they nor anyone else was seriously hurt, but it gave all of us a scare." Mississippi Chemical brought charges in federal court against the companies that built the tower, and designed safeguards into the replacement tower to ensure that such a problem never happened again. Engineer Marion Brown, who helped plan the corrective steps, recalls, "First, we designed a wider tower, so the urea spray would not touch and collect on the

Victor M. Cochran, shown punching his time card for the final time March 29, 1957, at the Yazoo City plant, was the first company employee to retire.

wall. Then, we built the new tower out of steel and aluminum, which was much stronger than the original concrete block tower."

In 1960 Mississippi Chemical board president Charles Whittington of Greenwood reluctantly gave up his seat on the board upon reaching the company's mandatory retirement age of sixty-five for officers. Whittington had become board president after John Sharp Williams's unexpected death in 1949 and had provided years of strong and faithful leadership. "Mr. Charlie didn't bow out meekly," Tom Parry, who would later become company president, recalls. "He absolutely loved MCC, and for years he continued to attend every board meeting as director emeritus and frequently made important motions. That bothered John Satterfield, our general counsel, who was a stickler for legal details. Finally, John graciously but directly informed Mr. Charlie that he was no longer legally entitled to make or vote on board motions. This infuriated Mr. Charlie. For the rest of that day he made every single motion—something like forty-two motions—beginning each one with these words: 'John Satterfield be damned. I move that so and so.'" Whittington was succeeded as board chair by LeRoy Percy.

When First Mississippi was a three-year-old venture capital firm growing more independent of its corporate sponsor and Coastal Chemical, a five-year-old corporation recording its second profitable year of operation at Pascagoula, Mississippi Chemical celebrated ten years of production and

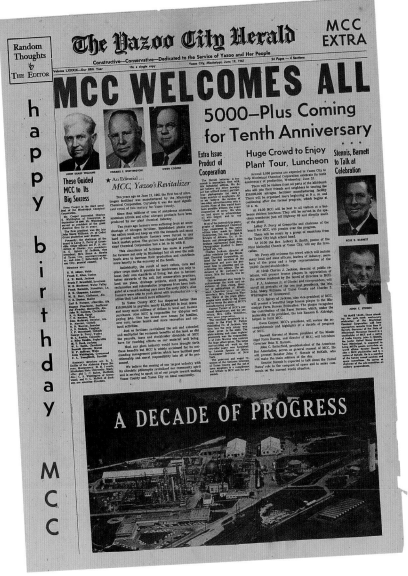

A twenty-six-page special edition of the *Yazoo City Herald* on June 19, 1961, commemorated the company's tenth anniversary open house.

Mississippi Chemical celebrated ten years of production at its Yazoo City plants with a gala open house on June 19, 1961. Top: Elizabeth Cooper serves her husband punch from a new silver punch bowl presented to the Coopers that day. Among the dignitaries on hand were, above left to right, Mississippi Farm Bureau president Boswell Stevens, Mississippi Governor Ross Barnett, MCC president Owen Cooper, U.S. Senator John C. Stennis, and MCC general counsel John Satterfield.

The Father of Anhydrous Ammonia

W. Baker Andrews, left, with MCC field salesman Howard Weir

Dr. W. Baker Andrews's pioneering work at Mississippi State College from 1943 to 1947 in perfecting the use of ammonia as fertilizer earned him the title "the father of anhydrous ammonia" and created a huge demand for ammonia that led to the founding of Mississippi Chemical. When six hundred Southern farmers met on October 26, 1948, to formally organize Mississippi Chemical, they chose the visionary Andrews as an honorary member of the company's initial board of directors. Andrews worked closely with Mississippi Chemical's sales staff and customers on the use of ammonia, and in 1957 left Mississippi State to become Mississippi Chemical's first full-time agronomist, a position he held until his retirement in 1971.

Andrews perfectly personified the absent-minded genius stereotype. Day after day he would closet himself in his tiny Mississippi Chemical office stacked from floor to ceiling with research reports, thick clouds of smoke billowing from his ever-burning corncob pipe, as he pondered radically new agronomic possibilities. Sometimes he emerged with profound breakthroughs like adding boron and zinc additives to mixed fertilizers, which cured problems plaguing Southern cotton and corn growers. Other times, he simply emerged to escape the plumes of smoke produced when the ashes from his corncob pipe ignited his overflowing trash basket. Although Andrews never labeled one of the thousands of files and research reports that cluttered his office and filled sixteen file drawers, he could always find the report he needed in a matter of seconds. On the other hand, it might take him a month to find his misplaced company paycheck. A modest, gracious, and extremely courteous man, Andrews lived the adage, "if you can't say something nice, don't say anything at all." A brilliant thinker who continually searched for unique ways to boost farm profits, Andrews often had difficulty communicating his radical new ideas in a fashion others could grasp and appreciate. If seldom understood, he was always respected by co-workers who affectionately addressed him as "Doc."

profitability. On June 19, 1961, more than four thousand people from across the South and other parts of the nation converged on its Yazoo City headquarters to tour the $20 million nitrogen complex that had produced twenty-six million bags of ammonium nitrate (enough to reach around the earth's equator) and generated $30 million dollars in patronage refunds for its shareholder-customers.

After hearing from a lineup of speakers that included Mississippi Governor Ross R. Barnett, Senator John Stennis, and Mississippi Chemical's own LeRoy Percy, Charles Jackson, Owen Cooper, John Satterfield, and company directors Fred Anderson and E. G. Spivey, the crowd was treated to a barbecue chicken dinner prepared and served in the ammonium nitrate warehouses. A twenty-six-page special edition of the *Yazoo Herald* displayed photographs of the company's 450 employees (with pictures of the white and black employees segregated on separate pages) and offered this summation: "Mississippi Chemical Corporation has not only helped southern farmers revitalize their soils and make them more profitable, it has brought $10 million in payrolls, $2 million in taxes, and a commitment to good citizenship and moral responsibility to our county. We believe the coming of our largest industry has revitalized the spirit of Yazoo County and Yazoo City." An advertisement taken out by the city of Yazoo proudly listed the benefits accrued to the city during Mississippi Chemical's tenure: population had increased from 9,746 to 11,236, new subdivisions had more than doubled the city's geographic size, better schools had been built, modern streets illuminated with mercury vapor lights had been laid, and a new fire truck had been bought.

To store and distribute fertilizers to its farmer-customers, the company acquired or built a network of distribution terminals across the South. The North Little Rock, Arkansas, distribution facility, below, was purchased in 1962, and a Decatur, Alabama, unit, right, was purchased from Alabama Farmers Co-op in 1967.

In 1961 and 1962 Coastal Chemical Corporation had good news for Southern farmers. With the help of company agronomist, W. B. Andrews, who had joined the company full time in 1957, Coastal perfected and introduced special grades of mixed fertilizers containing micro-amounts of boron and zinc, elements needed to overcome serious deficiencies plaguing Southern cotton and corn growers. While cotton and corn needed only minuscule amounts of boron and zinc, many soils contained none, and their absence crippled yields of king cotton and corn. Coastal's special grades were soon a popular addition to its product line.

To maximize output and minimize costs, MCC's and Coastal's plants ran twenty-four hours a day, 365 days a year, producing nearly equal amounts of fertilizers each month. Yet the company also had to meet the fertilizer manufacturer's central challenge: to accommodate customers with the desired type of fertilizers when they need it and where they need it, a difficult task since nearly two-thirds of all fertilizer was purchased and applied to the soil in the spring. To store the fertilizer produced in the fall and winter months, Mississippi Chemical purchased or built major storage units across the South. Some of these were located on navigable rivers so they could receive economical water shipments. In 1962 MCC acquired old fertilizer mixing and storage units in Canton, Hattiesburg, Meridian, and New Albany from the Mississippi Federated Cooperatives, and a similar plant in North

Reviewing construction progress on the world's first Kellogg 1,000-ton-per-day ammonia plant are, from left: Joe Regan, ammonia superintendent; Bob Sherling, Yazoo City plant general manager; and Buddy Lewis, ammonia plant operator.

Little Rock, Arkansas, from Southern Farmers Association. With the Arkansas plant came a cadre of skilled employees who served on MCC's field sales and administrative staff for the next two decades. These five outlying units actually produced some grades of NPK fertilizer, to supplement Coastal's output, as well as providing storage for the products made at Pascagoula and Yazoo City.

On September 14, 1964, the company's Yazoo River port facilities were opened five miles southwest of its headquarters complex, both to ship out nitrogen products and to receive barges of mixed fertilizers made in Pascagoula. In 1967 the company acquired two additional small NPK mixing and storage units at Decatur and Dothan, Alabama,

and opened a major distribution terminal at Liberty, Texas, on the Trinity River. (The latter would prove to be less than satisfactory because low water levels on the Trinity River would limit barge access to this terminal.)

In the late 1960s Mississippi Chemical built two important facilities in Yazoo City: one would dominate the Yazoo City landscape, while the second would dominate the world fertilizer landscape. These were Mississippi Chemical Corporation's new marble headquarters building set atop a majestic, 120-foot bluff overlooking the Delta and the world's first 1,000-ton-per-day Kellogg ammonia plant that would bring reporters and visitors to the plant at the base of that bluff.

First came the Kellogg ammonia plant, a

bold advance that was to revolutionize the world's nitrogen fertilizer industry and underscore Mississippi Chemical's role as a technological leader in that industry. Mississippi Chemical and the M. W. Kellogg Company stunned the industry in 1965 by successfully completing and bringing into production the largest and most efficient ammonia plant the world had ever seen. This single-train Kellogg plant in Yazoo City was capable of producing 1,000 tons of ammonia a day, or 350,000 tons of ammonia a year, a quantity equal to one-fourth the ammonia output of all North America in 1948 and ten times the ammonia Mississippi Chemical could produce in its original Yazoo City plants. And it did so at costs 50 percent lower than any other design or plant in history.

"Mississippi Chemical took a calculated gamble when we contracted with Kellogg to construct the largest plant ever built in the world, using radical new processes," Marion Brown recalls. "It combined three major new processes all together." The synthesis gas section, which produces the nitrogen and hydrogen later combined to make ammonia, operated at higher pressures than had ever before been used. Secondly, the ammonia conversion area, where the nitrogen and hydrogen are chemically combined, operated at much lower pressures than earlier ammonia plants. Third, highly efficient centrifugal compressors, innovatively designed and constructed, compressed the synthesis gas. "Mississippi Chemical had led the world in incorporating centrifugal compressors in our nitric acid plants, so we thought it was a

Spring Busy Season: An Avalanche of Urgent Orders

Until recently, spring meant one thing at Mississippi Chemical: the critical "busy season," when 60 percent of the year's sales were squeezed into ninety frantic and taxing days. For MCC's sales and delivery staff, the telephones constantly rang from mid-February until mid-May with urgent calls from farmers and dealers across the South anxious for their spring fertilizer shipments. Trucks formed long lines at plants and storage units; the demands were to load out right here, right now. The company worked round-the-clock to get millions of bags and thousands of truckloads of plant food to customers desperate for fertilizers so critical to their spring plantings. DeWitt Dixon and Barbara Standley, deans of the Mississippi Chemical sales staff who have survived more than forty of those tumultuous seasons, today describe the most memorable aspects of those springtimes.

"Those busy seasons of old were enough to try your soul," Dixon recalls. "Every single person in sales, including temporary employees, worked from early to late, six days a week—and we still couldn't keep up with orders, shipments, and patronage refund records when things were really ginning. That was before we had computers to do our paperwork. We didn't even have dial phones when I was hired," Dixon remembers. Standley recalls, "We'd take orders by hand, type up a worksheet for shipping, then go to the huge stockholder Rolodex file that covered an entire wall and match every single ton to

Salesman Royal Harrelson, left, discusses a fertilizer shipment with an Alabama shareholder-customer.

a stockholder. No truck or rail car could be shipped out until every single ton was tied to a stockholder's allocation."

Today the company's sales and deliveries are distributed much more evenly throughout the entire year, and likewise with export and industrial sales of urea and potash. MCC now ships most of its products in barges and rail cars to regional storage terminals well in advance of the spring rush rather than encouraging truckers to collect at the plant, which was so common in previous springs. "Today it's a rare occurrence to have a truck pick up a load of N-Sol at our Yazoo plant," Dixon says, "but twenty years ago, they'd line up down Highway 49 waiting to get a load."

"When I arrived in 1956, no one had ever dreamed of barge shipment," recalls Standley, who today manages barge deliveries of nearly nine hundred thousand tons of fertilizer a year.

Among the colorful personages who helped the company survive those hectic springs, Fred Sullivan heads the list. The hulking field salesman covered the Mississippi Delta for more than three decades, frequently striding into the home offices in Yazoo City to plead the case of his large customers with passion and occasional abrasiveness. "Fred was the most honest, direct man on earth," Dixon muses. "If everyone was as honest as Fred, there wouldn't be any policemen. And if everyone was as blunt, we might need more counselors." In the 1960s when ammonia was in scarce supply, Kit Butler, who managed ammonia sales, closed his door and warned everyone not to interrupt him. Sullivan rushed into town to confront Butler about delays in ammonia shipments. DeWitt Dixon admonished Sullivan that opening Butler's closed door was a sure way to encounter his wrathful temper. "Let me tell you one thing, DeWitt," Sullivan replied. "I looked the Germans eyeball to eyeball over the hedgerows in Normandy, and I ain't the least bit scared to go toe-to-toe with some ammonia peddler hiding behind an office desk." Another time, Sullivan, occupied with other matters, was called to sell a young Delta farmer some company stock; when he arrived the farmer kept cutting into Sullivan's sales pitch, talking about everything but stock. Sullivan interrupted the talkative customer. "I want to ask one damn thing," he said. "Did you call me up here to explain our stock program or to listen to you talk?" The young man replied that he indeed wanted to know about the stock. "Well, if you'll be quiet for a few minutes I'll tell you how Mississippi Chemical's stock program works," after which the man invested several thousand dollars in MCC and its all-business representative Sullivan.

Retired salesman Royal Harrelson of Oneonta, Alabama, is frequently cited as the all-time champion at rounding up early morning fertilizer orders. Harrelson, whose son Jim Harrelson followed in his father's footsteps as a company field salesman based in Union City, Tennessee, would be calling on farmers by 4:00 a.m. and by 7:30 would have telephoned in a dozen or more orders to Yazoo City. Charles Chambers, who first represented the company in Louisiana and later in south Georgia, was described by DeWitt Dixon as "the nicest guy I ever got to deal with. Charles was a real pro. Competent. Calm. Always a gentleman even in the storm of the spring season." Another field salesman, Leon McWilliams, brother of Mississippi State and Army's All-American running back Shorty McWilliams, is today complimented by many for quietly posting strong sales year after year.

During the hectic spring season all the salesmen were expected to work long hours. The Yazoo City office staff was surprised to receive a newspaper clipping in April 1965 from Dwight Hulgan, a salesman in Alabama, reporting that his fellow company salesman there, Doug Hall, had just won second place in the Atmore, Alabama, golf tournament on the previous Thursday. Dixon and Billy Byrd of the Yazoo headquarters sales staff prepared a forged "official" memo to Hall from sales vice president R. H. (Bob) Fisackerly and stapled it to a bag of "Golf Queen" fertilizer, a specialty fertilizer product made from ma-

nure. The memo read: "I noticed in the paper where you won the golf tournament last Thursday. So you can sell some fertilizer as you go to future golf tournaments, here is some Golf Queen to put in your satchel." The pranksters then persuaded their co-worker Judy Moore to forge "Mr. Bob," as Fisackerly was affectionately known, and sent the package to Hall, who took the memo for the real thing. Hall feared his job was in jeopardy. When Dixon called to see how Hall was doing, Hall read him the note, then added, "Well, since he signed the note 'Bob' I think I've got a fighting chance of staying with the company. If he'd have used his initials 'R.H.F.' I would've mailed in the keys to my company car."

Don McGraw, who later became the company's sales vice president, recalls his first busy season in 1957 and Fisackerly's kindness. A rookie in the personnel office, McGraw volunteered to supervise the night shift in the ammonium nitrate warehouse from 5:00 p.m to midnight each evening and help load shipments to farmers. At 7:30 every night Fisackerly and his wife would drive into the warehouse and deliver McGraw a plate of supper. Four years later Fisackerly gave Billy Byrd his first busy-season job keeping the same nitrate warehouse open all night to fill customers' trucks. Six years after that, in 1967, Byrd and Jim Pierce, the transportation manager, conceived a substantial innovation to alleviate the spring delivery problems. With Tri-County Co-op in Pickens, Mississippi, they pioneered the use of enormous pneumatic trucks to deliver fertilizer in bulk and blow it from the trucks into storage bins, hence bypassing the considerable expense of handling bags by hand. Prior to this development bulk shipments had required other, more expensive methods of offloading to storage bins. Billy Byrd designed a special pipe to transfer the fertilizer from truck to bin, strapped a supply of the pipes on top of his car, and traveled the South seeking to convince dealers to try this new bulk delivery system in order to save labor and money.

The humor of another retired sales worker, Meadow Perry, kept his colleagues smiling even when tempers were frayed in the demanding spring sales season. The telephone was particularly busy one day when Perry yelled, "Uh-Oh. Excuse me. I got my loosa's and my poosa's confused!" Everyone looked at Perry with puzzlement. "I said I got my loosa's and my poosa's mixed up. Hasn't that happened to you before? I meant to dial the Tuscaloosa, Alabama, Farmers Co-op, but instead I dialed the Tallapoosa, Alabama, County Co-op. I got the poosa's but I wanted the loosa's!"

Two natural performers. Sue Tatum, above, long-time corporate secretary, brought down the house with her song and dance routine at the 1961 employee picnic. Field salesman Jerry Clower was yet to get his model car or his entertainment career into high gear.

sound bet to go this radically new route in our ammonia plant," Brown would explain.

Mississippi Chemical's new Kellogg ammonia plant was a resounding success. In a matter of weeks, reporters and industry leaders were streaming to Yazoo City to see the operation that could produce one thousand tons of ammonia a day at costs so low that it was the envy of the fertilizer industry. News of the plant's profitability soon set off a massive chain reaction. In a virtual stampede to capitalize on this new technology, existing fertilizer companies as well as new entrants into the fertilizer business—oil companies and oil rich nations like Saudi Arabia and the USSR—began building dozens of Kel-

logg ammonia plants around the world. By 1980, 95 percent of the world's ammonia would be produced by this Kellogg process, pioneered in Yazoo City, Mississippi, by Mississippi Chemical in 1965.

The second effort to utilize this revolutionary technology was made by Jack Babbitt, then president of First Mississippi Corporation, and Owen Cooper, who was both president of MCC and board chair of First Mississippi. Before Mississippi Chemical's first Kellogg ammonia plant attracted world attention, these two visionaries plotted a maneuver that would turn First Mississippi and Mississippi Chemical into long-term and profitable partner-owners of a nitrogen fer-

tilizer complex and turn the tiny town of Donaldsonville, Louisiana, into the ammonia capital of the world.

Only months after Owen Cooper and Mississippi Chemical had negotiated in 1964 with the Kellogg company to build the plant in Yazoo City, he and Babbitt decided to buy an identical plant for First Mississippi. Their idea was for First Mississippi to construct and operate a Kellogg ammonia plant for Central Farmers, one of the nation's largest fertilizer cooperatives, headquartered in Chicago. Central Farmers, desperate to get more ammonia, trusted Cooper and Babbitt and eventually contracted to buy the plant's entire output. Central Farmers and the

Chase Manhattan Bank agreed to bankroll virtually the entire $15 million venture, but one critical ingredient remained missing: a plant site on deep water with a low-cost, long-term source of natural gas, the single largest ingredient in ammonia cost.

Texaco had just the answer in its Louisiana gas fields—the largest gas reserves in the U.S.—and an eagerness to pipe that gas across the state of Louisiana to the west bank of the Mississippi River. Donaldsonville, Louisiana, strategically located on the Mississippi's west bank, was the perfect site to locate that major gas pipeline and the huge new ammonia plant. But before the project could proceed, First Mississippi had to breach its founding principal of investing within the borders of Mississippi. Cooper was committed to building plants and creating jobs inside his home state, so he and Babbitt searched for a way to move the gas and plant site to Mississippi. Exhausting numerous possible options, they found no affordable way to get the essential, inexpensive gas across the Mississippi River to a deep water site. Donaldsonville would soon welcome First Mississippi's Kellogg ammonia complex, First Nitrogen. Production began in October 1966, and in January 1967, after only ninety days, Central Farmers was so pleased with production and costs that it exercised its option and bought the plant from First Mississippi for $17 million, producing $2 million of pure profit for the venture capital corporation.

Babbitt then proposed an even bolder project to Cooper and Mississippi Chemical. Babbitt's idea was to build a $34 million

Triad Chemical, a joint venture of Mississippi Chemical Corporation, Coastal Chemical, and First Mississippi, was built in the late 1960s on sugar cane lands purchased from A. J. Simoneaux at Donaldsonville, Louisiana. The Simoneaux's farmhouse, above, has housed Triad's administrative offices for three decades.

complex at Donaldsonville featuring not only another Kellogg plant but also the largest urea plant ever built anywhere in the world. Babbitt initially proposed that First Mississippi would build, finance, and own the entire complex and that MCC would help sell the output but make no equity investment. The Chase Manhattan Bank, on which Babbitt relied to lend most of the money for the project, refused to approve those terms. The bank wanted Mississippi Chemical, which had a far stronger financial position, committed to help fund and guarantee the project's success. Between April 1967 and April 1968, Babbitt and Cooper presented proposal after proposal, first to the Mississippi Chemical board, then to First Mississippi's board, and then to the Chase Manhattan Bank. Each time, Mississippi Chemical was asked to put up more money or guarantee to purchase a larger share of the plant's product.

In May 1967 MCC approved investing $3 million in debentures in the project and taking one-third the output. At that point, the proposed funding was $21 million from Chase, $6 million from First Mississippi, and $3 million from MisCoa, a partnership

Charlie McAuley, Triad's general manager from 1969 to 1975, stands on the Mississippi River levee as Triad urea is loaded into a river-going barge.

Aerial view of Triad Chemical's plants under construction in May 1968. The site, only yards from the Mississippi River, was selected to take advantage of inexpensive natural gas then available in Louisiana and the freight savings of shipping fertilizers on river-going barges. In the foreground are Triad Chemical's ammonia and urea plants. At left is the initial Donaldsonville ammonia plant built by First Mississippi Corporation for Central Farmers.

between MCC and Coastal. In June, MCC agreed to increase its investment to $4 million. In August it again upped its investment, this time to $5 million, and agreed to take 40 percent of the product. In April 1968 a special board meeting approved MCC's becoming a 50 percent joint venturer in the project. The two partners would jointly invest $9 million and would borrow $25.5 million. Because the project involved three companies—First Mississippi, Mississippi Chemical, and Coastal Chemical—it came to be known as Triad Chemical, a name it retained for three decades.

By mid-summer of 1968 Triad Chemical rose from the sugar cane fields of Donaldsonville. For the next twenty-eight years, its two partners had occasional disagreements about the nature of their relationship and management objectives at Triad, but the project was highly profitable and generally worked to the mutual benefit of the partners.

Optimism prevailed in Triad Chemical's early months. The Kellogg ammonia plant was completed in record time, started smoothly in June 1969, and produced a world-record 368,000 tons of ammonia in 1970. But the Triad complex, like its two predecessors in Yazoo City and Pascagoula, would encounter serious setbacks that threatened to sabotage the joint venture. The massive Dutch-designed urea plant, which had the capacity to make more urea than had been consumed in the entire United States the prior year, presented several challenges. Charlie McAuley, Triad's general manager at the time, recalls the grinding, two-year battle to get the urea plant running properly: "It ran well for a few months and

Donaldsonville, Louisiana: "Laissez le bon temps roulez!"

Triad's home, Donaldsonville, a tiny hamlet on the Mississippi River between Baton Rouge and New Orleans, had been the birthplace of Louisiana's Cajun culture two centuries earlier. In 1765 Donaldsonville had welcomed hundreds of fleeing French when the king of England demanded that the French leave the Acadia district of Canada. The settlers made the long and perilous sea journey from Canada to Louisiana, where they hoped to build a new Acadia.

Triad may have looked nearly as out of place when it appeared in Donaldsonville as had the first Frenchman. Sugar cane fields and antebellum mansions lined the west banks of the river. Oak Alley, Nottaway, and other fabled plantation houses only minutes from Triad drew thousands of tourists down River Road, a serpentine blacktop strip that slips between the plant and the Mississippi River levee a few yards away. Today, massive petrochemical plants rise throughout the area, but in 1968 Triad and its predecessor, First Nitrogen, were the only ammonia plants there.

Triad gathered its production crew from local recruits with French and other "foreign" names like Caillet, Marioneaux, Pizzolata, Hidalgo, Mistretta, LaBlanc, and Schexnayder from their hometowns of Napoleonville, LaPlace, Pierre Part, Terrebone, Plaquemine, Sorrento, Vacherie, and Thibodeaux, Louisiana. The culture they embodied was as different from Mississippi as were their names from Cooper and Jackson, Satterfield and Clower.

This is Cajun country, where *Laissez le bon temps roulez* (Let the good times roll!) is the cultural motto. "A wedding here is a three-day party," Buddy Ball, a Triad veteran explains. Music and repartee, hospitality and food abound. A Triad engineer who grew up nearby says, "We'd go into town on Saturday morning and listen to Cajun bands and dance all day and into the night."

Food is the essential ingredient of every social activity, even funerals, and a major factor in corporate life as well. Visitors who come to conduct business at Triad learn that one of the favorite items on the agenda is where to go to lunch and which Cajun dishes to sample. Gumbo and jambalaya—often cooked outdoors for festive occasions—red beans and rice, boudin (rice and pork stuffed in a casing), and spicy andouille sausage are staples blending French, Spanish, German, Anglo-American, Afro-Caribbean, and Native American influences. In Donaldsonville, which received an influx of Sicilian immigrants in the 1890s, Italian dishes are also common fare.

Ascension Catholic Church dominates tiny Donaldsonville's downtown as the Catholic religion does its everyday life. The yearly round of church feast days, fasting days, holy days, and festivals organizes family social activity and business holidays as well. Mardi Gras, the day before Lent begins, is the biggest of them all. The Triad offices and all the other businesses and schools shut down, and everyone who can goes to New Orleans for the parades or to one of the nearby Cajun communities where an even more raucous brand of singing, dancing, buffoonery, and inebriation prevails.

A cardinal rule of Cajun culture is that no one is left out. Babies are brought along to parties, and young children dance with elderly adults on the dance floors. "So strong is the gregariousness," Cajun authority Barry Jean Ancelet has written, "that the culture assimilates unwary outsiders with considerable ease, almost deliberation, into almost every field of social interaction." Little wonder that Buddy Ball, who grew up in Texas Baptist provinces and migrated to Triad's bayou country to help start the urea plant, says he intends to spend the rest of his life there. "These folks," he says, "are the most fun-loving, family-oriented people in the whole world." Dale Andrews, who arrived from Los Angeles to become engineering manager, agrees: "These are the greatest people on earth. These South Louisiana people work hard and they play hard. They love to banter and enjoy life. When work is done, they believe you're supposed to have fun. And they do."

The Cajun culture surrounding Triad is known for its fun-loving celebrations. Above, Lucille Cabellero, receptionist, passes her "swimming test" in preparation for the 1975 employee picnic.

Above: The company's expansions to Pascagoula and Donaldsonville, Louisiana, required its managers to travel there regularly. Company pilot Jack Hawks, center, prepares to take finance vice president Tom Parry, left, and Owen Cooper to Triad Chemical in Louisiana. Right: Throughout 1970 and 1971 the Triad complex struggled to solve critical corrosion problems in the new urea plant, then the world's largest. An emission control device, attached by cable to a helicopter, is hoisted into place atop the urea prill tower.

then failed completely. When we opened it up, we were shocked to see massive corrosion in a brand-new plant. This puzzling and very serious corrosion caused seven separate, extended shutdowns during 1971, and we could produce at only about 65 percent of capacity. There was an around-the-clock effort to solve these critical problems. The Dutch sent their best engineers and we [Mississippi Chemical, First Mississippi, and Triad] had our best people working on it. In the final analysis, Lee Dowdy, our maintenance superintendent at Triad, solved the problem."

The item that caused all the trouble sounded more like a French Quarter attraction than a piece of Dutch equipment: it was the stripper. Buddy Ball, an operator in that urea plant for three decades, would later explain: "This delicate machine is called 'a stripper' because it removes or strips the water, ammonia, and carbon dioxide out of the urea liquor to give you the concentrated urea you need. Mr. Dowdy, who was a mechanical whiz, finally invented a special Teflon seal that made that stripper perform the way we needed, and things got much better." When

McAuley left Donaldsonville in 1975 to work at First Mississippi's corporate office, Lee Dowdy succeeded him as complex manager.

In the mid-1970s, when oil and natural gas prices skyrocketed, Triad's long-term contract with Texaco, with a twenty-three-cent ceiling, made the complex among the world's lowest-cost and most profitable fertilizer operations. The Institutional Research Report from Raymond, James and Associates of April 28, 1975, called the Triad gas agreement "possibly the single most favorable gas service contract outstanding in the U.S.

fertilizer industry today." John Satterfield, who served as general counsel for both Mississippi Chemical and First Mississippi, is credited with negotiating the favorably priced contract at a time when Texaco had surplus gas stocks and was anxious to find customers. "I would like to claim credit for the gas contract, but the credit has to go to John Satterfield," Jack Babbitt recalls.

Today, the Louisiana nitrogen complex features not one, but two, modern ammonia plants. In a subsidiary called AMPRO, First Mississippi built the second plant, a 1,150-ton-a-day unit, immediately adjacent to the original plant at a cost of $82 million. On December 24, 1996, Mississippi Chemical would acquire full ownership of Triad, AMPRO, and the rest of the fertilizer facilities held either solely or jointly by First Mississippi.

∾

On October 17, 1968, an appropriately sunny autumn afternoon, MCC dedicated its handsome marble headquarters building in Yazoo City, with the Yazoo City High School Indian band performing march music and a thousand Yazooans there to tour the new building and try out its elevators for a quick ride up to the fourth floor. Dedication remarks were delivered by Dr. William Giles, president of Mississippi State University, and Norwood Nichols, longtime president of the Yazoo County Board of Supervisors. Echoing the sentiments expressed in the *Yazoo Herald* on the occasion of the tenth anniversary, Nichols's speech at the dedication also acknowledged a civic gratitude to MCC: "In the twenty years they have been

here, from 1948 to 1968, Mississippi Chemical has paid $50 million in wages in Yazoo County. Their six hundred employees and $5.2 million annual payroll represent one-third of the total non-agricultural payroll in our county. . . . We can never measure the profound, civic-minded, Christian influence this one organization has had on our county. . . . Mississippi Chemical and its visionary President Owen Cooper are known from New Albany to New Delhi, from Pascagoula to Panama, from Washington to Wichita. But we come here today to recognize them in Yazoo County. We should. Mississippi Chemical is the finest thing that ever happened to us. Thank you for coming."

The completion of the headquarters

building coincided with the first recession in the fertilizer market since MCC's beginnings. When dozens of competitors around the world followed Mississippi Chemical's lead and constructed new Kellogg ammonia plants, world output of ammonia soon surpassed demand and caused serious problems for the fertilizer industry from 1969 to 1971. Founded because of a severe world shortage of fertilizers, Mississippi Chemical now had to cope with an entirely new dilemma: the oversupply of fertilizers and the resultant falling prices, collapsing profits, and fierce competition. The construction of the $2 million marble headquarters building, followed so closely by the recession, led caustic shareholder Colonel James L. Watts of Pela-

The MCC administration building under construction in 1968

Ten thousand refugees from the 1927 flood waters camped on the hill that today houses the MCC headquarters building.

Camp Quakemeyer Stood on MCC Hill

Exactly forty years before ground was broken for the Mississippi Chemical Corporation's headquarters building in April 1967, on the slope of that imposing bluff, had stood the Quakemeyer Refugee Camp, housing Deltans forced to flee the rampaging waters of the Mississippi's flood of 1927. That flood, the greatest natural disaster in American history, left one of every 120 Americans homeless. Yazoo native Norman Mott, Jr., remembered: "My dad commandeered a naval vessel when the levee broke in 1927 and raced up and down the lower Delta, rescuing hundreds of folks from rooftops and trees to bring them to that site where Mississippi Chemical's headquarters sit today." The land was owned by the Regan family, whose son Joe Regan was four at the time of the famous flood. He would later serve as a supervisor in MCC's ammonia plant for thirty-eight years. "In 1927 the 'Yellow Dog' rail line connected to the Illinois Central at the bottom of the hill, and I can still see hundreds of Delta flood survivors arriving on the Yellow Dog railcars, unloading, trudging up that hill with the few life possessions they escaped with," Regan recalls.

In the 1920s and 1930s the American Legion operated a recreational swimming park and dance pavilion called Camp Wyoming at the base of the hill just south of the current headquarters building. "Thousands of Yazooans would gather out there for fourth of July political rallies, carnivals, and even professional boxing matches," Regan remembers. "Camp Wyoming was a popular swimming spot, and I spent many a hot summer afternoon out there," Sam Olden, president of the Yazoo Historical Society, recalls. "You could swim all day at Camp Wyoming for a nickel."

A thousand well-wishers watch the U.S. Navy color guard hoist the American flag in dedication ceremonies for MCC's new corporate headquarters building on October 17, 1968. Eighteen months earlier, retiring sales vice president R. H. Fisackerly gives corporate secretary Sue Tatum a warm hug at groundbreaking ceremonies for the new building. At their left is David Highbaugh, then president of the Yazoo County Chamber of Commerce.

Above left: Export sales director
Wyeth Ramsay inspects bags of urea
as they come off the plant conveyor
destined for the Republic of Korea.
Over its five decades, MCC has made
sales to nearly fifty foreign nations in
all corners of the globe. Above: Charles
J. Jackson, instrumental in selling the
stock to form Mississippi Chemical,
succeeded R. H. Fiskackerly as sales
vice president in October 1967. Left:
Searching for ways to cut costs are
members of MCC's accounting and
finance team, from left, Charles Davis,
Lea Black, and J. W. Wilkerson.

The fertilizer recession ended in 1971 and Mississippi Chemical set a new sales record of $100 million for its 1971–72 year. Celebrating that new record are, from left, finance vice president Tom Parry and sales managers Billy Byrd and Doug Hall. That year the company paid patronage refunds totaling $9,135,975 to customer-owners.

hatchie to criticize the company and Owen Cooper for extravagance, calling the new office complex "Cooper's Mausoleum" and "The Taj Mahal."

From the new headquarters, MCC initiated a series of cost-cutting measures to weather the recession. An employee suggestion system, titled Mr. CLUE (Cost Lowering Ups Earnings), prompted hundreds of employee ideas for improving efficiency. While not nearly so severe or long-lived as "the Great Fertilizer Depression" that would follow in the 1980s, the economic outlook in the early seventies did cause considerable dismay for nearly three years. For the first time in its twenty-one-year history, the company

had to reduce its work force to lower payroll costs. The company's original ammonia plant, which could no longer be operated efficiently, was shut down, and the employment of eighteen maintenance and production employees in the Yazoo City plant was terminated on April 30, 1969. The company also realigned and consolidated functions to economize further. The most significant consolidation occurred in 1972, when Coastal Chemical Corporation was merged into Mississippi Chemical, thereby eliminating the need to keep dual stockholder, sales, and financial records.

To reduce both inbound raw material costs and outbound freight costs, the com-

pany centralized all NPK production at Pascagoula, where the deep water port allowed phosphate rock to be brought from Florida in fourteen-thousand-ton ocean-going vessels, molten sulfur to be barged from South Louisiana, and potash to be either barged from Houston or delivered by ship from Canada. NPK production was phased out at the older, smaller plants acquired a decade earlier at Meridian, Hattiesburg, New Albany, and Canton, Mississippi; North Little Rock, Arkansas; and Decatur and Dothan, Alabama. These units, known throughout the company as "the outlying plants," continued to serve as warehouses and distribution points for prod-

In 1966 the company and county opened a Yazoo County port complex, in upper left of aerial photo, which allowed fertilizers produced at Yazoo City to be shipped out by barge and also enabled the company to receive barge shipments of NPK mixed fertilizers produced at Pascagoula. Left: Inspecting a barge delivery are Yazoo County Port Commissioners, from right, Walter Bridgforth, Joe Curran, and Charles Jackson. Above: A crowd of dignitaries watches a tugboat bring in the first barge shipment in May 1966.

uct made in Pascagoula and Yazoo City. During the three-year period from 1969 to 1971, while total NPK output was rising steadily, the company shifted from making only 56 percent of its NPK product at Pascagoula to producing 100 percent there.

Over this same time period, Mississippi Chemical further reduced costs by delivering a higher percentage of its fertilizers to its storage and sales network in bulk form and by utilizing less expensive water freight whenever possible. In 1971, for the first time in company history, bulk deliveries equaled bagged deliveries at six hundred thousand tons each. From 1972 until 1998 the percentage shipped to customers in bulk form increased annually.

To facilitate the shift to barge delivery, during the period 1969–72 MCC added new storage terminals capable of receiving barge shipments. These were located at Pine Bluff and Augusta, Arkansas; Corpus Christi and Rio Hondo, Texas; Hayti, Missouri; Montgomery, Alabama; Bainbridge, Georgia; and Friars Point, Mississippi. The company already had leased water-based storage terminals at Liberty and Harlingen, Texas; North Little Rock, Arkansas; Decatur, Alabama; and the Yazoo City port. (Economics and market conditions eventually dictated closing some of these terminals.) MCC also increased to three hundred the number of dealer fertilizer storage terminals designed and leased to handle product in loose bulk form rather than the previously traditional bag shipments. These dealer units, strategically located over eight Southern states—Mississippi, Louisiana, Arkansas, Texas, Tennessee, Alabama, Georgia, and Florida—were capable of storing 125,000 tons of bulk fertilizer product.

Continuing its strategy of using the most modern and efficient production technology, Mississippi Chemical converted all its ammonium nitrate production from a low-density product to a new high-density form in late 1968. This conversion was made possible by the development of a patented ammonium nitrate additive, Permaline, to stabilize the ammonium nitrate crystals. For developing Permaline, company researchers Marion Brown, Albert Green, and Ladell Blanton won the John C. Vaaler award given annually for the best new chemical process developed in the American fertilizer industry. The company was soon licensing this additive process and related know-how to fertilizer-makers around the globe. This, and other changes, enabled the Yazoo City complex to produce over four hundred thousand tons of nitrate in 1971 for the first time. And the company was building the world's largest sulfuric acid plant and a new superphosphate fertilizer plant in Pascagoula to gain savings through economies of scale there.

The three-year fertilizer recession ended in 1971, producing a sharp rebound in profits as the company neared completion of its first quarter-century. But the optimism following the recession was offset by two major cost challenges facing Mississippi Chemical and the fertilizer industry for the next decade: growing shortages of natural gas, phosphate rock, and other key raw materials, and new federal environmental standards that would require massive investments of capital and manpower.

"The natural gas crisis" began in 1971. That year, Southern Natural Gas Company sharply increased gas prices while drastically decreasing the quantities of natural gas Mississippi Chemical could buy for its Yazoo City ammonia plant. The gas shortage curtailed the plant's output by eighty thousand tons, nearly 20 percent of its capacity. Ammonia costs rose several dollars per ton, and the company began an intense search for a new and long-term gas supply. That same year, 1971, potash prices escalated by 75 percent because the Canadian government fixed prices and limited movements from its huge deposits. Phosphate rock prices also rose sharply as the world's developed phosphate balance swung from plenitude to shortage. By the close of this period, the cyclical American fertilizer industry was headed from a surplus of product and recession to a period of expensive and short supplies. Securing dependable, reasonably priced quantities of all these essential raw materials—natural gas, phosphate rock, and potash—would consume much of the company's attention and capital in the coming years.

The final challenge of this era was the massive effort and investment required to bring the nation's and Mississippi Chemical's fertilizer plants into full compliance with stringent new federal environmental standards, which set acceptable levels of air and water emissions permitted to leave any

For its first three decades Mississippi Chemical sponsored the "Dollars for Scholars" program offering all children of employees a $1,000 scholarship to the college of their choice. Among the 1973 recipients of these scholarships were, from left, Lawrence Long, son of Larry Long; Cindy Pierce, daughter of Jim Pierce; and Jimmy Whitaker, son of Vernon Whitaker. Right: Mardi Gras balls are major social events for company employees at both Pascagoula and Donaldsonville. Celebrating Mardi Gras 1972 in Pascagoula are general manager Paul Lacy and his wife Betty.

plant. In 1969 Mississippi Chemical began what would prove to be a monumental twenty-five-year effort to meet and, when possible, surpass every federal and state emission standard. In just three years the company's technical and professional staff had grown to include fifteen persons working full time to meet environmental guidelines. By 1972 the company had installed seventy-five advanced emission control systems at an initial cost of nearly $3.5 million. That same year Mississippi Chemical estimated that $10 million would be required to finish the job.

Over the next quarter-century, from 1972 to 1997, the company would spend nearly five times that sum to assure its neighbors, its employees, and the federal and state governments that the air and water leaving its plants was safe to people and the environment.

As difficult as they were, the fertilizer depression, raw material shortages, and far-reaching emission regulations did not threaten the company's heart and soul. But the pending retirement of president Owen Cooper would strike close to the company's

core. How would the company, its culture, its customers, and its management respond to the void sure to be left by the retirement of the visionary leader who had guided the company from a near-impossible dream in 1948 to an incredible success twenty-five years later? This question would be answered in the company's second quarter-century.

In November 1970 women employees celebrated the good news of a new dress code: the company permitted female employees to wear pants suits. Modeling their new, more comfortable attire are, above left to right, Joan Foster, Helen Coker, Blanche Hester, Pat Davis, Dot Hatchett, Lanelle Montgomery, Sue Tatum, and Polly Crum of the Yazoo City headquarters staff. That same day Pascagoula's female staff members, at left, Barbara O'Mary, Shirley Speights, and Jo Ann Head wore big smiles and the first-ever pants suits.

CHAPTER FIVE

The Legacy of Owen Cooper

The man who conceived Mississippi Chemical Corporation and directed it for its first quarter century was born Lawrence Owen Cooper on Easter Sunday, 1908, on a Warren County dairy farm eight miles north of Vicksburg, along the old road that meandered from Yazoo City through Phoenix and southwest to Vicksburg. His father, William Samuel Cooper, had come down the Mississippi River from Kentucky on a two-man skiff with a cousin, Daniel Boone, the great-nephew of the legend. Like most farm houses of that time, Cooper's was without indoor plumbing or electricity. His first schooling was in a one-room elementary school run by his mother, Malena Head Cooper, whose French-speaking family had migrated to Mississippi from Nova Scotia.

Owen Cooper stands in front of a plaque unveiled at retirement ceremonies, April 19, 1973, naming the company's headquarters building in his honor.

From early childhood young Owen was called "Governor" by his father, whom he admired and from whom he learned much, and this nickname must certainly have planted the seed for Owen Cooper's gubernatorial aspirations. "I guess I learned how to make public speeches from my dad, who was one of the greatest speakers I ever knew. He never got to finish school, but if he had, he'd have been governor," Cooper would recall. Owen Cooper excelled in public-speaking contests at Culkin Academy, one of the state's first consolidated public schools. "It was good training because I spent the rest of my life trying to persuade farmers and Baptists to take on important challenges."

At seventeen he enrolled at Mississippi A & M College, making a train journey with three changes from Warren County to the Starkville campus. He swept sidewalks and delivered the Memphis *Commercial Appeal* to pay his expenses. After graduation in 1929

he served as Mississippi State's alumni secretary for a year, the first step toward fulfilling his father's nickname for him. "I thought I'd run for governor someday and I was kind of laying the groundwork," he would confess. He would hold to that ambition for most of his life but in fact made only one attempt to win an elected office. While teaching high school in Leland, Mississippi, in 1935, he ran unsuccessfully for the state legislature.

After a short-lived career as a school teacher, Cooper received a master's degree in public planning from the University of Mississippi. His master's thesis expounded an elaborate scheme for better utilizing Mississippi's ten million acres of land and presaged the many solutions of large-scale problems to which he would devote his life. Concerned about the outbreak of war in Europe, he wrote *Reader's Digest* with his own bizarre strategy for ending armed conflicts among populated countries. He proposed establish-

John Satterfield: Pioneering General Counsel

John Satterfield

For three decades attorney John Satterfield was a key figure in successfully turning Owen Cooper's dreams for Mississippi Chemical, Coastal Chemical, and First Mississippi Corporation into legal realities, serving as general counsel for the three corporations and as a trusted advisor to their boards of directors and to Cooper. Satterfield drew up Mississippi Chemical's charter and bylaws in 1948, structuring Mississippi Chemical as a regular corporation, and establishing ways for the company to operate as a cooperative and return earnings to shareholders as patronage refunds, thereby minimizing federal income taxes. The skilled arguments of Satterfield and his partner Dudley Buford with federal tax agents and before the federal courts played a principal role in shaping the U.S. Internal Revenue Tax Code and determining precedence concerning the payment and deductibility of patronage refunds by regular corporations. "John used to say that Mississippi Chemical was a creature of the courts and not the law, because there were no laws covering our unique set-up," Tom Parry said. Satterfield also negotiated Triad Chemical's long-term gas contract with Texaco in 1967, which proved to be one of the company's most valuable resources long after he retired in 1973.

Satterfield was legendary for the long hours he worked and the lengthy legal documents he produced. "John Satterfield gave new meaning to the term workaholic," says Sue Tatum, who was corporate secretary during the quarter-century Satterfield served as Mississippi's general counsel. "His legal documents were so thorough and so long that we accused John of thinking he was being paid by the pound." Satterfield frequently worked all night and even on Christmas Eve and Christmas Day. Tom Parry recalls that John Satterfield called him at home one morning at two o'clock to review a pending federal tax issue. "After giving John my answers to the questions he posed, I said, 'Now, John. I've got a question for you. Do you have any idea what time it is?' He didn't. He was so consumed by his work that time meant nothing to him."

Though he was only five feet, five inches tall and weighed just 115 pounds, the brilliant Satterfield was a towering figure on the American legal horizon. He is the only Mississippian and only corporate general counsel ever to serve as president of the American Bar Association. Although he and Owen Cooper disagreed politically—Satterfield being a strong advocate of segregation— the two men remained close friends and trusted business partners throughout their lives. Their relationship is an example of how Mississippi Chemical employees and leaders put aside their personal differences to work together for the good of the company.

ing an International Council for Conducting War and holding all world conflicts within an isolated preserve in central Africa. (Cooper's letter was never published in the magazine.) It was neither the first nor the last of Cooper's ideas deemed wholly impractical.

To develop specific plans for his home state's problems, Cooper went to work as assistant director of the Mississippi State Planning Commission. In the evenings he earned a law degree from the Jackson School of Law, run by a young lawyer named John Satterfield. The two men became life-long friends, and Satterfield would eloquently serve as Cooper's right arm and Mississippi Chemical's general counsel from 1948 to 1973. In 1938 Cooper met and married Elizabeth Thompson, who would devote her next fifty years to managing their household and five children so efficiently that he was free to pursue his countless interests.

When Governor Paul Johnson, Sr., replaced him with a political ally in 1940, Cooper coordinated the state's first federal housing programs, then a controversial portion of President Roosevelt's New Deal agenda to pull the nation from the Great Depression. Later that year, he became executive director of the Mississippi Farm Bureau Federation and during the next eight years helped that organization and its thousands of farm families organize Blue Cross & Blue Shield of Mississippi, the Southern Farm Bureau Life Insurance Company, the Southern Farm Bureau Casualty Company, and finally Mississippi Chemical Corporation.

Cooper spent his entire adult life summoning his fellow Southerners and farmers to unite and encouraging them to take bold action to solve their own problems. The roster of enterprises and programs owing their genesis to Cooper is legion. In his thirties he spearheaded a nationally acclaimed program to improve health care in rural Mississippi. He helped convince the Mississippi legislature to create a state hospital commission, which he later chaired, and to build over one hundred rural hospitals. At age seventy-eight, from his hospital bed in the Mississippi Baptist Medical Center that he had helped to build, Cooper marshaled citizens to pass the AHEAD highway program, the most comprehensive highway construction enterprise the state had ever known.

In between, Cooper gave strong leadership to unprecedented networks such as Cooperative Fertilizers International and American Cooperative Development International. He also provided the spark to help organize not only Mississippi Chemical Corporation, but First Mississippi Corporation (now ChemFirst) and the Indian Farmers Fertilizer Cooperative. Even one of his "unsuccessful" projects—organizing northeast Mississippi tree farmers into cooperatives to supply timber to a newsprint mill to be financed, built, and owned by newspaper publishers (the publishers ultimately withdrew)—resulted, indirectly and years later, in the creation of Newsprint South, Inc., a Mississippi Chemical subsidiary that succeeded in constructing a newsprint mill in northeast Mississippi and subsequently

In 1954 Boswell Stevens, left, president of the Mississippi Farm Bureau, recognized Owen Cooper as Mississippi agriculture's "Man of the Year," saluting the noteworthy job Cooper had done in spearheading Mississippi Chemical's organization and early success.

bought millions of dollars worth of timber from those tree farmers so close to Owen Cooper's heart. In 1997 the total sales of these four widespread businesses, along with those of the three insurance operations he founded at the Farm Bureau, exceeded three billion dollars. The millions of families served by the firms Owen Cooper had brought into being spanned the globe.

"While he had many passions and loves, the thing nearest and dearest to Daddy's heart throughout his life was his Christian faith and his Southern Baptist denomination," his oldest daughter Nancy Cooper Gilbert would remember. From the time he

entered Mississippi A & M College in 1925 until his death sixty-one years later, he was an evocative and popular lay-preacher and organizer of Southern Baptist missions on five continents. He was elected president of the Southern Baptist Convention in 1972, and in 1985, a year before his death, the Mississippi Baptist Convention named Owen Cooper "The Southern Baptist Layman of the Century."

LeRoy Percy relishes recounting how he wired Cooper victory congratulations on his election to the Southern Baptist presidency in the midst of an unusually severe summer drought, with this postscript: "'Since you now have a hot-line to God, would you please order me a rain for my cotton crop?' The next morning my son Billy walked into the office and said 'Daddy, you ain't gonna believe what happened last night. We got a three-inch rain on Trail Lake, and it didn't rain a drop on our neighbor's land!'"

Cooper's many activities within the Baptist church and Mississippi Chemical's early hiring of a number of vocal Baptists led some of the non-Baptists inside and outside of the company to refer to Cooper and his MCC associates as the "Baptist Mafia." In his day a glass of wine at a company dinner was strictly taboo. His well-known personal morality left some employees feeling uncomfortable, even naughty. "I remember how very much we respected Mr. Cooper and the high moral standards he set," Shirley Speights recalls. "In fact, when he'd fly into Pascagoula with our company pilot Jack Hawks, we'd hide our cigarettes so Mr. Cooper wouldn't see them. At noon each day we'd eat sandwiches together and play a popular card game called, 'Oh Hell.' One day Mr. Cooper walked into our lunch game and asked what we were playing. We paused and all looked at each other and Mark Joachim, Jr., sheepishly replied, 'We're playing "Oh Heck," Mr. Cooper. It's a great game.'"

Cooper had his own weaknesses. He craved ice cream so much, his friend Dr. W. W. Walley recounted in *Diary of a Country Doctor,* he would sneak off from his wife and gorge himself. Walley and Cooper once went to Baskin & Robbins, and Cooper ordered one scoop of every flavor. The attendant put thirty-two scoops in a big

Evangelist Billy Graham congratulates Owen Cooper on his election as president of the Southern Baptist Convention in Philadelphia, Pennsylvania, in 1972.

aluminum pan and by Walley's account, "he ate every bite of it, keeping one eye cocked so [his wife] Beth wouldn't catch him."

Cooper was so focused on global projects that benefited thousands of people that he could be abrupt and curt with the individuals who reported to and worked for him. Co-workers jokingly suggested that Cooper loved humanity in general more than the humans at hand. While he was quick to tackle tough corporate and community issues, he avoided confronting performance problems in individuals he supervised. If Cooper lost faith in an assistant or manager, he would simply stop using that person.

Although line employees like Charles Daniels and Charles O'Brien credited

Cooper for generous pay policies, some who worked behind the scenes with Cooper on these matters reported that he hated to deal with pay increases and performance appraisals of his staff. Tom Parry, who was Cooper's vice president of finance, recalls, "While Owen was my boss for years, he only talked with me about a pay raise one time. The other times I learned about pay increases from Sue Tatum or Robert Perkins, when he delivered my new pay slip. In all our years together the only time Owen ever complimented my performance was the day he said I was the most underpaid man in the company."

According to Don McGraw, who managed company pay and benefit programs, the

If I Had My Life to Live Over

Owen Cooper wrote this in answer to Jerry Clower's question: If you had your life to live over again, what would you do?

If I had my life to live over, I would love more. I would especially love others more.

I would let this love express itself in a concern for my neighbors, my friends, and all with whom I come in contact. I would try to let love permeate me, overcome me, overwhelm me, and direct me.

I would love the unlovely, the unwanted, the unknown, and the unloved.

I would give more. I would learn early in life the joy of giving, the pleasure of sharing, and the happiness of helping.

I would give more than money. I would give some of life's treasured possessions, such as time, thoughts, and kind words.

If I had my life to live over, I would be much more unconventional; where society overlooks people, I would socialize with them.

Where custom acknowledges peers as best with whom to have fellowship, I would want some non-peer friends.

Where tradition stratifies people because of economics, education, race, or religion, I would want to fellowship with friends in all strata.

And I would choose to go where the crowd doesn't go, where the road is not paved, where the weather is bitter, where friends are few, where the need is great ... and where God is most likely to be found.

Popular radio broadcaster Paul Harvey visited Owen Cooper in 1969 while in Yazoo City to address the Yazoo County Chamber of Commerce banquet. Harvey saluted Cooper and Mississippi Chemical on one of his radio broadcasts.

company's labor lawyer Leslie Inman had to prod Cooper to make the company's pay, benefit, and personnel policies more competitive. "While we all loved Mr. Cooper, it was his nature to be conservative in these matters, and we can thank the influence of Leslie Inman for a lot of the progressive pay and personnel policies that Mississippi Chemical instituted," McGraw recalls. Cooper's interest in financial success was less than his interest in serving Mississippi and its farmers, and he felt that employees of a cooperative, i.e., a "non-profit" organization, should not have salaries as high as those of a company's commercial competitors.

Yet Cooper had a wry, self-deprecating sense of humor. Owen Cooper, Jr., remembers the two jokes his father always told at small rural Mississippi churches when he substituted for vacationing preachers:

After a glowing introduction of him, Dad would share how he'd been reading the paper about a great man the night before, at home with his wife, and wondered out loud how many great men there were in the world. Her reply, "One less than you think," always got a good laugh. His second story was that he got a bit lost trying to find the church and had stopped to ask directions. A helpful man gave him directions, then added, "I don't think I'd go to church today if I was you. We've got a wonderful preacher, but he's on vacation, and this Sunday some jackleg from Yazoo City is going to speak."

During the quarter-century he led Mississippi Chemical, Cooper regularly set aside nearly half his work day to give leadership to non-company programs, whether they were in India or downtown Yazoo City. "I love to work on several new projects at the same time," he once said. "If I had spent all my time on Mississippi Chemical business, I

Owen Cooper is seated immediately behind and to the right of President John Kennedy as the president addresses the National Association of Manufacturer's annual meeting in 1961. Cooper was a director of the group.

would've driven the rest of the staff crazy interfering with their work. I'd have been more a hindrance than a help."

What Cooper could accomplish in the half-days he devoted to civic matters amazed his own staff and others who called on him for counsel on various matters. Harriet De-Cell Kuykendall recalls his decisiveness.

I'll never forget the afternoon Mary Louise Williams, Jo G. Prichard, and I went for a thirty-minute meeting with Owen to get his advice about this wild idea that the Ricks Library board had. We wanted to build an addi-

tion to the Yazoo City library and at the same time purchase the historic Main Street School immediately next door to the library and convert it into a museum and civic center for our area. Most folks thought it was an impossible dream, and we hoped Owen would give us a boost, perhaps even ten thousand dollars. He outdid our fondest hopes. In thirty minutes he planned the six-hundred-thousand-dollar capital campaign on the back of a number ten envelope and pledged fifty thousand dollars from Mississippi Chemical to kick-off the drive.

Cooper, himself was a generous philanthropist and a master fundraiser for the many causes he embraced. One of Mississippi's wealthiest businessmen and most generous charitable donors recalls Cooper's approach. After being asked repeatedly by Cooper, the businessman complained that Cooper had asked him to give so much that it hurt. Cooper immediately responded, "Well, if it still hurts, you haven't given enough."

The heart of Cooper's creative genius lay in contriving an elegantly simple, direct solution to a complex problem and then disregarding the nay-sayers who insisted it would not work because it had never been done before. He was a dreamer who refused to be deterred by skeptics who said that Southern farmers or farmers of India could never band together to build and own their own nitrogen fertilizer plants. Since doing so was the most direct solution to their problems, Cooper determinedly led them down that road never-before-traveled to immense success. "I get more excited about starting a new venture than managing a proven one," he once declared.

Examples of his creative solutions were organizations called Universal Concern and Books for the World. When India would not admit foreign missionaries and his own Southern Baptist denomination refused to fund indigenous missionaries, he formed Universal Concern, which trained Christian Indian leaders to be missionaries in their own country and to start new congregations in India's sixty thousand villages. Similarly, when he discovered that millions of English-speaking children in Africa and other third-world nations had no English textbooks, he established Books for the World, an organization that collected thousands of discarded American textbooks and shipped them to needy students all over the world.

A master of arithmetic, Cooper frequently made complex calculations in his head or computed detailed production or investment figures on the back of an envelope. "When he was seventy, he could multiply two three-digit numbers in his head," Chuck Dunn, who worked closely with Cooper to start the Newsprint South newsprint mill, recalls. Cooper did not like waiting on lengthy engineering and financial studies. When he gathered associates to attack a problem, he wanted it solved that day, and he frequently computed expected outcomes on the spot. Banker Griffin Norquist, Jr., recalls, "I will never forget the time Mr. Cooper mentally calculated the return on a major investment and came within a decimal point of the number an accountant had spent days computing. The accountant was stunned that Cooper produced the same answer in seconds and with such apparent ease."

Cooper held a profound belief that human beings have the ability to solve their own problems, and he demanded that those he hired use that talent. Numerous Mississippi Chemical employees could recall how doggedly he challenged them to keep searching for answers until a workable one was found. "Mr. Cooper refused to take 'no' for an answer," Sue Tatum would say. "I bet I heard him tell other folks a thousand times 'don't tell me why we can't do this. Come

In 1975 some eighteen years after Mississippi Chemical and Owen Cooper were instrumental in launching First Mississippi Corporation, that firm became the first Mississippi-based corporation to be listed on the New York Stock Exchange. Celebrating the occasion were, from left, Owen Cooper; Kelley Williams, president of First Mississippi; and LeRoy Percy, board chair of both First Mississippi Corporation and Mississippi Chemical.

back and see me when you have figured out a way that we can.'" Owen Cook was one of those who would never forget the first time he told Cooper one of his ideas was not practical. "I can still hear his response. 'Now Owen, you're a very bright young man. I know you can figure out a way to do this, and I can't wait to see how you do.' By golly, I walked out of his office and worked and worked until finally I did come up with a way to do what Mr. Cooper thought we could in the first place."

Cooper frequently bypassed the chain of command to go straight to a pressing problem and demand action. This frustrated managers who felt systematic studies were crucial. Rex Brown vividly remembers Cooper gathering a room full of managers

from all levels to get to the bottom of delays in one of Cooper's pet projects. "There was no doubt who the boss was, who was making the decision, or what he was expecting. He wanted answers and action, not excuses or studies. Mr. Cooper was barking out commands, making assignments, and demanding action." Brown recalls.

Paul Lacy and Jim Gambrell, who were managing the Pascagoula complex in the 1960s, remember Cooper's command to eliminate the bottleneck in loading ammonia rail cars, which was restricting spring shipments of ammonia to three hundred tons a day, far less than customers wanted. Cooper insisted that a method of loading one thousand tons a day be devised within seventy-two hours. Lacy and Gambrell

Mr. Heart and Soul of MCC: Charles J. Jackson

If Owen Cooper is the most revered figure in Mississippi Chemical's history, his close friend and trusted associate, Charles Jackson, is perhaps its most memorable one.

Hired by Cooper in early 1948 to persuade farmers to invest in the venture soon to be known as Mississippi Chemical Corporation, the lanky and gregarious Jackson sold more stock in the company than any man before or since. For the next thirty-five years he inspired, entertained, and cajoled the company's shareholder-customers and employees with his unparalleled gift for gab. "I'd rather listen to Charles Jackson speak than eat," Robert Jones, a fellow employee also known for his stories, declared. Mississippi Governor William Winter, who persuaded Jackson to come out of retirement and direct three different state agencies during his administration, judged Charles Jackson "the most enthusiastic human being I ever met."

Banker Miller Holmes describes a Chicago audience's reaction to this enthusiasm. Holmes, Jackson, and two other Yazooans were in Chicago to convince an industry to relocate to Yazoo County. While waiting at O'Hare Airport for their return plane home, everyone but Jackson had ordered a beer; he settled for a Coke. Jackson was regaling everyone in the bar with stories. When the waitress appeared at an adjoining table and asked the onlookers what they wanted to drink, a Midwesterner said, "I don't know what that tall fellow's drinking, but whatever it is, bring us all one of them!"

A tireless community leader for three decades, Jackson recruited new industries for Yazoo City, served on the Yazoo County Port Authority, and was a long-time city alderman. Although his natural leadership gifts and job as company sales vice president put him in frequent contact with civic and business leaders, Jackson prided himself of being "a friend of the little man."

Throughout his career he was an advocate for the company's plant workers

Charles J. Jackson

and smaller customers, but he loved to poke good-natured fun. He relished recounting a story about his brother-in-law Truett Duncan, who worked in the company warehouse. While he and Duncan were watching an especially exciting NFL football game one Sunday afternoon, Owen Cooper called Jackson and invited him to come to his house next door and sing from the Stamps Brothers hymnal with a group of visiting Baptist ministers. Jackson immediately collected a stack of hymnals and walked toward the door. Duncan chastened him: "Charles, you've told me how much you dislike that hymnal and how much you want to see this game. Why did you say 'yes' to Mr. Cooper?" Jackson replied, "Truett, that's the very reason you're sitting out there in that hot, loud, dirty warehouse, and I'm sitting up in an air-conditioned front office with my feet propped up on the desk. When Owen Cooper says sing, I ask: 'What song and how loud?'"

Jackson was once escorting visiting dignitaries on a tour of the Yazoo City plant when one inquisitive guest asked why there were several giant U-shaped bends in the otherwise straight pipelines running back to the ammonium nitrate plant. "The truth of the matter," answered Jackson, "is that we bought too much pipe, and this is the only way we could figure out how to use it."

He was much more than merely funny, however. "No one will ever know," Jerry Clower said, "how many fellow employees—most of them single-parent mothers—Charles gave a monthly check to help buy groceries for their kids." In words echoed by many others, Owen Cook said of Jackson, his mentor, "He epitomized the heart and soul of what makes Mississippi Chemical great. He was generous to a fault. He never saw a family in need that he didn't personally do all in his power to help them. Mr. Cooper went around the world doing good, but Charles Jackson went to the other side of the tracks right here at home. He taught all of us how to care for others."

quickly developed a makeshift method to increase loading to six hundred tons a day and called Cooper expecting him to applaud their work. Instead, the stern Cooper said, "That's a good idea boys, but I want two of those new systems in place by Monday." By Monday both new devices were in place, and ammonia was loading out at a thousand tons a day.

Cooper's own ability as a problem solver impressed those who worked with him closely and knew him best. Jerry Clower remembers the time he and Charles Jackson were trying to help a friend round up his cows that had broken through a fence and were wandering on the road. "Charles said, 'I wish Owen was here.' I said, 'Why?' And he said, 'Well, he'd be over yonder in that shade, and in about fifteen minutes he'd figure out a way that them cows would run and jump through that hole in the fence.'"

If imaginative problem-solving was the heart of Cooper's talent as a leader, his ethical sense was its soul. In a 1982 interview Cooper spoke about organizational values. "A company has character just as much as an individual person does. And I think the character of our organization is one of its most important aspects. Character isn't something you DO. It's something you ARE."

The years leading to Mississippi Chemical's twenty-fifth anniversary in 1973 would significantly test Owen Cooper's principles of corporate character. In the 1960s and early 1970s the nation, the South, and the company dealt with a mosaic of challenges and

Mississippi Governor Hugh White, right, with Owen Cooper, after touring the company's production facilities during Mississippi Chemical's gala tenth anniversary celebration in June 1961.

changes as monumental as any since the Civil War, culminating in the sweeping transformation of Southern society, schools, and workplaces. Throughout these years, the company responded conscientiously and provided leadership for its employees, its home community, and its state. Owen Cooper personally set an example for tolerance and harmony and for helping those in need at home and all over the world. He inspired a corporate climate in which these values of tolerance and compassion could grow and flourish, and he motivated others at

Mississippi Chemical to work not just for the good of the company, but for the benefit of the larger society as well.

In 1962 there was not yet a single integrated classroom in the state of Mississippi, from the first grade through the highest post-graduate level. No black person could rent a room at a major hotel or motel or eat a meal at a restaurant not operated specifically by or for blacks. All public buildings and businesses, including Mississippi Chemical Corporation, had separate water fountains and restrooms for "white" and "colored." Few if any black people held white-collar jobs in any white-owned business in the state; Mississippi Chemical had approximately one hundred black employees, all males engaged in manual labor.

September 30, 1962, was a pivotal day that signaled the end of one era in Mississippi and the beginning of another. On that Sunday afternoon, after months of legal and propaganda battles aimed at blocking his admission, James Meredith became the first black person ever enrolled at the University of Mississippi; his entrance ignited a night of mob violence and anarchy that left two people dead and 375 injured, and caused President Kennedy to federalize two Mississippi National Guard units and twenty-eight thousand federal troops to restore order and protect Meredith.

Mississippi's governor, Ross Barnett, whose rhetoric had contributed to the climate that stimulated the riots, stood quietly by, but Mississippi Chemical's president reacted swiftly. The next day, Monday, October 1, Cooper worked from early until late with Lamar Life Insurance head Billy Mounger to persuade 130 of the state's most influential business leaders to draft and sign a public statement abhorring the violence and pleading with Mississippians to respect and obey the laws of the land. The prompt and widespread dissemination of that forceful statement helped bring many Mississippians to their senses. In 1964 thirty-five black churches were burned, and Cooper organized the Mississippi Religious Leadership Council, which spoke out intrepidly against the bombing and burning of

In 1967 Owen Cooper recruited Louise Dean, above, as the first African American member of the corporate headquarters staff.

churches and synagogues. "The burning of those black churches left him livid," Sue Tatum recalls. "It was one of the few times I ever saw him enraged."

President Lyndon Johnson and the Congress were also angered by reports of racially motivated violence in the South. Inspired in part by Martin Luther King's "I Have a Dream" speech during the march on Washington in 1963, Congress passed the Civil Rights Act of 1964, mandating desegregation of all public accommodations and businesses engaged in interstate commerce in the United States. This legislation brought the civil rights movement inside the hallways of Mississippi Chemical. Till then, Cooper's sweeping words of caution and moderation had been focused on the public at large rather than on Mississippi Chemical. As he later acknowledged, "We always had a large

number of black people employed in our operations and maintenance departments, and frankly, in the early days we didn't treat them right. By that I mean that many of them were just as competent as the white mechanic, but the black person was paid as only a helper. I don't know why I wasn't more conscious of that and of what we should have been doing, but for a long time I wasn't. And I'm sorry for it. After I began to catch on, there wasn't any problem making the transition." With the passage of the 1964 Civil Rights Act, Cooper would act decisively.

In May of 1965 Mississippi Chemical's board of directors passed a resolution in support of the goals of the Civil Rights Act and stating their intention to comply with it. On June 10–11, 1965, Owen Cooper held a special meeting with all Mississippi Chemical supervisors to explain the far-reaching implications of Title VII of that legislation, which made illegal any act of discrimination in hiring, promotion, or terms of employment. Preparing for these changes, the company had already eliminated its separate "white" and "black" change rooms and restrooms. Cooper directed the supervisors to join the company in fully complying with the Civil Rights Act and, if they could not, to resign. No one resigned.

Realizing the importance of his personal example, Cooper made sure the first black staff member in the corporate headquarters worked directly for him. On March 13, 1967, Louise Dean came to work in his office, supporting the corporate secretary, Sue Tatum. Dean's professionalism and diligent work

Owen Cooper, right foreground, welcomes his close friend U.S. President Jimmy Carter, center, to Yazoo City in July 1977. To President Carter's left is Yazoo City Mayor Floyd Johnson, a former MCC employee. U.S. Senator John C. Stennis is in background to Cooper's right. After conducting a televised town meeting, Carter spent the night with the Cooper family.

ethic quickly won the respect of her co-workers. "Louise Dean was a competent, considerate, committed employee who quickly became a valuable and respected member of our team," Sue Tatum remembers. "You must remember that those were the days when several cars had been bombed in Natchez, so crossing the color-barrier had its dangers. Every morning for months Louise would report for work by 7:30 a.m. and not clock in until 8 a.m. When I talked with her about this, she said she came early to get the parking place immediately adjacent to the front door of the office building.

She did this because she felt her car would be safer in plain view and less likely to be bombed. While I never thought for a moment that a Mississippi Chemical employee would commit such a sorry act, it shows you the courage that it took to integrate the work force in those days."

As Mississippi Chemical was proceeding to eliminate traces of segregation inside the company, Cooper and others in the company became involved in trying to broaden educational opportunities for disadvantaged black and white preschoolers on the local and state level. Owen Cooper perceived an

opportunity for responsible Mississippians to come together and use federal funds to help those most in need. In the spring of 1966 Cooper guided the formation of a biracial committee of Yazoo County leaders, who sought and secured one of the nation's initial grants from the Office of Economic Opportunity to serve disadvantaged preschool children. These funds made possible five summer Head Start programs for low-income Yazoo County preschoolers, black and white, in July and August 1966. The programs ran smoothly, and Vernon Jordan, who would later become head of the National Urban League, visited Yazoo to tour the program and meet Owen Cooper. The local group chartered itself as Yazoo Community Action, Inc., and over the next thirty-two years this organization would become a state and sometimes national model in administering millions of dollars in federal grants.

In early September Owen Cooper and LeRoy Percy received urgent telephone calls from U.S. Senator John Stennis, prompting them to take a stand for better race relations in the state. Mississippi was about to lose its "War on Poverty" dollars—some $10 to $15 million—unless responsible leadership stepped forward to administer the grant. The Childhood Development Group of Mississippi (CDGM), which oversaw a statewide Head Start grant, was accused of mismanaging federal monies and accordingly was opposed by both of the state's U.S. senators and by Governor Paul Johnson, Jr. Senator Stennis suggested that Cooper and Percy help provide that leadership.

"After hanging up from Senator Stennis,"

LeRoy Percy would recall, "Owen called me and said, 'LeRoy, the time has come for folks like you and me to take a stand for better race relations and do what's right for these poor children who need a head start. Let's show people that white leadership and black leadership can sit down and work together for the good and for the future of our state and our children.' And we did."

In September 1966 LeRoy Percy and Owen Cooper put their reputations on the line to form Mississippi Action for Progress, Inc. (MAP), a partnership of white and black Mississippi leaders working together on the same public board for the good of the state. A banner headline in the *Jackson Daily News* on September 30 carried the news: "12 Man Board Replaces CDGM. Made up of White and Negro Leaders." A new board, headed by Cooper and Aaron Henry, a Clarksdale pharmacist and president of the Mississippi NAACP, would take over federal programs formerly operated by the controversial Childhood Development Group of Mississippi and expand into sixty Mississippi counties. This unprecedented panel also included white farmers LeRoy Percy and Oscar Carr, newspaper editors Hodding Carter III and Oliver Emmerich, and black leaders Charles Young, George Owen, Rev. M. W. Lindsey, James Gilliam, and Rev. R. L. T. Smith.

The MAP board's first awkward meeting took place over lunch in Mississippi Chemical's board room on a September Sunday afternoon. "Now back in those days, blacks and whites were not supposed to be sitting down together, much less having lunch with

each other. Doing so could be bad news," LeRoy Percy would remember. As the brand-new biracial board tried to work through the burdensome issues on their agenda, it became obvious that the blacks had virtually no trust in the representations being made by the white leaders. Several times Hodding Carter III, editor of the Greenville *Delta Democrat Times* who had worked with many of these black leaders to form the Mississippi Freedom Democratic party, had to stop the debate and say: "These are not your usual white folks. When Owen Cooper and LeRoy Percy say they'll do something, you can trust them."

Cooper and Percy's creation, Mississippi Action for Progress, elicited sharp criticism from both liberals and conservatives. Southern segregationists lashed out at its biracial composition and opposed all integrated federal antipoverty programs, while national liberals demanded that federal "War on Poverty" funds in Mississippi remain in the hands of the CDGM group, because its political stance was more liberal. Cooper chaired MAP through many turbulent times. He was also the catalyst and chair of Mississippi Industrial and Special Services (MISS), which solicited federal funds to build and operate more than three thousand low-income housing units across the state.

Owen Cooper, whose long-cherished ambition was to be governor of Mississippi, knew that he was relinquishing that goal when he decided to work actively for racial equality and harmony in the state. LeRoy Percy recalled: "Owen knew that forming this biracial coalition [MAP] would get ma-

jor press attention and would doom his life-long dream of running for governor of the state. He told me: 'I know what a lot of folks in Mississippi will think, but it's time for somebody in Mississippi to do what's right and I'm ready to do it.'" Once he made this decision, there was no turning back, but Cooper had struggled for many years with the issue of race. He said he grew up with "all the prejudices rural country folks have toward blacks. As a kid, I refused to read *Up from Slavery* because it was written by Booker T. Washington."

Years later, in 1986, the black leader Aaron Henry led a memorial service for Owen Cooper, saying that his own life had been blessed and changed from having had the privilege of working with him. Mississippi's largest black newspaper, the *Jackson Advocate,* credited Cooper for his early outspoken demands to halt the anarchy at Ole Miss and for then going on to lead a radical transformation and new era of cooperation between the races.

∾

Owen Cooper's public stand for racial harmony created an environment at MCC's Yazoo City headquarters and set a tone in the community that fostered cooperation and calm reason and elicited the support and leadership of many inside and outside the company. When the public schools were to be desegregated, Cooper himself worked quietly behind the scene, but several MCC employees worked actively for a smooth transition. In October 1969 the U.S. Fifth Circuit Court of Appeals ordered thirty Mississippi school districts, including Yazoo

When federal courts mandated immediate integration of public schools across the South in January of 1970, Mississippi Chemical employees helped make the transition in Yazoo City a smooth one and played key roles in organizing Friends of the Public Schools, the state's first broad-based community organization to support the public schools. "Friends" volunteers included, from left, **Charlotte Harrison, Betty Raney Crout, and company executives Gene Triggs and Jo G. Prichard.**

City, to totally desegregate their public schools. On January 7, 1970, when the local public schools opened after the Christmas holidays, Yazoo City was crowded with national reporters and TV crews there to report on the first major test of massive school integration in a town with a black majority.

On that Monday morning, over three thousand students—1,362 whites and 2,077 blacks—peacefully entered the integrated schools and began classes together for the first time in Yazoo City's history. That day, Yazoo City demonstrated more support of its public schools than any other school district in Mississippi. Why did Yazooans choose to send their children to integrated public schools, when less than thirty miles away in Canton, Mississippi, whites totally abandoned their newly integrated schools? Owen Cooper and Mississippi Chemical were frequently cited in the state and national media as paramount reasons for the calm judgment that prevailed.

Throughout the 1970s Mississippi Chemical and its employees led attempts to maintain and strengthen the public schools in its headquarters' hometown of Yazoo City. "Good public schools were crucial to recruit-ing and keeping top people for our company, so it behooved us to do everything in our power to strengthen our schools," remembers Gene Triggs, who before coming to Mississippi Chemical had managed the gubernatorial campaigns of both Paul Johnson, Jr., and William Winter. The importance of the public schools to MCC employees and their families is evidenced by the fact that the vast majority of those employees with school-age children sent them to Yazoo City's public schools in the 1970s. The rancor and resistance of the 1950s and 1960s had given way in Yazoo City to cooperation and optimism for the future.

In 1970 Triggs, MCC general counsel Holly Raney, MCC researcher Gerald Tucker, and others were instrumental in organizing "Friends of Public Schools," the state's first broad-based, biracial support group of parents and community leaders. This group played an influential role in getting a $3 million bond issue passed in 1976 to build a new Yazoo City High School. This was the first school bond issue to win voter approval in Mississippi since school integration. "In a number of neighboring communities, white students and the white power structure had virtually abandoned the public schools," Holly Raney remembers. "But in Yazoo City, largely to the credit of Mississippi Chemical's presence, leadership, and hard work, whites and blacks worked together successfully to build a new high school to serve all students—black and white." Over the next quarter-century Mississippi Chemical would support public education in the communities where it had facilities and employees, as well as across the larger South. Mississippi Chemical provided the funding to bring two nationally respected consultants from Auburn University to Yazoo City to conduct a ten-day comprehensive study with the goal of improving the public schools. The company helped found and continues to provide leadership and funding for the Public Education Forum of Mississippi, an organization of business, legislative, and education leaders working to improve public education across the state of Mississippi. When Gene Triggs retired from MCC, the company funded a position at the Forum so he could continue to work for legislative reform of the state's school systems.

While Cooper and the company were playing constructive roles in the rapid changes that swept the South in the late 1960s, he and Mississippi Chemical were also engaged in an intense drama thirteen thousand miles away in India, exactly halfway around the world from Yazoo City.

In 1965 the U.S. Agency for International Development (AID) office asked Mississippi Chemical to host a team of Indian leaders and show them what the company had done to help Southern farmers help themselves. India was Mississippi Chemical's largest purchaser of exported fertilizers, and through the years the company had hosted and helped train a number of India's fertilizer production workers and managers. When the group arrived in Yazoo City, both the Indian visitors and the U.S. AID officials pleaded with Cooper to help them build their own fertilizer plants. Only with infu-

Owen Cooper signs an agreement to fund a Coastal Chemical promotional program in India with brothers Ahmed Rahimtula, left, and Ali Rahimtula. In the early 1960s this program planted thousands of demonstration plots across India to convince Indian farmers of the value of fertilization.

sions of fertilizer could India hope to grow sufficient rice and wheat for the people in the world's second most populous nation. Their stories and supplications captured Owen Cooper's heart and imagination.

Soon Cooper was approaching other American cooperative leaders to form a team to help the Indian farmers. He won a powerful convert, Ken Lundberg, president of Chicago's Central Farmers, one of the world's largest fertilizer cooperatives. In spring 1967 Cooper, Lundberg, and the head of AID flew to India, where they met with India's deputy prime minister and leaders of India's cooperative movement. They discussed how the Indian farmers should or-

ganize and what Mississippi Chemical and Central Farmers could do to assist them. When they returned to America, AID pledged the U.S. government to invest a substantial portion of the estimated $150 million the project would cost. That was enough for Cooper. Mississippi Chemical engineer Al Soday and Don Thomas from Central Farmers were sent to India to create detailed project plans and to choose the best site for the plant.

"I'll never forget the destitute and starving women and children I saw all over India. It made me do everything in my power to aid them," Al Soday remembers. "We like to complain that the South is the hottest place on earth. When we arrived in New Delhi in June of 1967, it was 118 degrees and humid and got up to 126 degrees in the desert near Kandla, the site we finally selected to build the first plants. I've never experienced such heat." For six weeks Soday and Thomas flew, railed, and sweated their way across the subcontinent seeking the ideal plant location and devising plans for nitrogen and phosphate fertilizer plants. "One day I had to ride on the running board of the train, outside the cabin, hanging on for dear life for two hundred miles" Soday reflects. At every stop on their tour, the American group confronted stout political pressure from vendors eager to sell their processes and equipment for the proposed plants, and then pressure from dignitaries in each locale, all hoping to be chosen as the venue for the new facility. One province set up a three-acre tent and giant carnival in an attempt to win the bidding, and Prime Minister Indira Gandhi was there to welcome them. "We were determined not to make a political decision," Soday says. "Instead, we wanted to make the best economic decision for the people of India."

Finally, the team picked the port city of Kandla on the west coast of India because of its dependable electricity, water, and work force and because the finished products could be distributed by both rail and ship. They recommended building a large-scale Kellogg ammonia plant, a sizeable urea plant, and a large NPK production plant.

In August 1967 Cooper went back to India to urge the plans forward. Don Thomas, who accompanied Cooper and was soon

named to head the India project, remembers: "Owen was the best promoter I've ever seen, although his accent was the slowest the Indians had ever heard. And not only was he a good promoter, he was honest, and his heart was in the right place. There's no doubt that Owen Cooper was the glue that held this massive India project together. Time and time again the folks in India would say 'Oh, that won't work.' And Owen would say, 'Why won't it work?'"

Cooper convinced the government and farmers of India to form the Indian Farmers Fertilizer Cooperative (IFFCO), an all-Indian farmer cooperative to own and even-

tually to assume management of the entire enterprise. For centuries Indian farmers had been fragmented politically among their innumerable local districts. They had never worked together on such an undertaking. As an incentive Cooper pledged that Mississippi Chemical and other U.S. cooperatives would donate a million dollars and furnish the expert leadership to build and start up the plant.

The Mississippi Chemical board gave the project an important boost when it voted to donate three hundred thousand dollars and assign engineer Al Soday to the enterprise. In two weeks, on September 13, 1967, Coopera-

Owen Cooper visits with President Richard Nixon in the White House, in June 1970, after Nixon named him to the Atomic Energy Commission. U.S. presidents appointed Cooper to serve also on the General Advisory Committee on Arms Control and Disarmament, the Federal Reserve Board, and U.S. Bank for Cooperatives Board.

Owen Cooper and Mississippi Chemical assisted the government and farmers of India in building modern fertilizer plants. When the huge new Indian fertilizer complex was completed in the early 1970s, Tom Parry (in shorts) represented MCC at the dedication ceremonies. Below: Indian officials welcome Cooper in celebration of the project's success.

tive Fertilizer International (CFI) was chartered to coordinate the efforts and funds of U.S. cooperatives. Days later, Cooper convinced Don Thomas to serve as president of CFI and see the plan to completion. Thomas remembered, "Ken Lundberg was never one to let Owen outdo him, so he said Central Farmers would put in four hundred thousand dollars. With a lot of help from Owen and Ken, we finally raised $1,040,000 from American cooperatives."

The million dollars raised and donated by the American cooperatives paid every penny of the salaries of those who built the plant and oversaw it into operation. "You try to explain to the folks there in India that you were just there to help them, and they'd look at you very puzzled," Soday remembers. "You could see the question in their faces, 'What's in it for you? You must have some other motive.' They found it hard to believe we simply wanted to help them succeed in feeding themselves."

The scheme succeeded beyond the most extravagant hopes of all involved. Shortly after the commencement of operations in 1973, the facility was so successful that Indian farmers built a second, third, and fourth Kellogg ammonia plant and four matching urea plants. "The U.S. Agency for International Development has been helping foreign countries for a quarter of a century, and this project is by far the most successful one they've ever been involved with anywhere in the world," Don Thomas would note. The Indian Farmers Fertilizer Cooperative would eventually grow to be the largest fertilizer producer in Asia with sales in 1990 of more than $800 million. (By comparison, Mississippi Chemical's fertilizer sales that year were only $200 million.) Today, delegations from developing nations travel to India to visit IFFCO, just as the delegation from India had come to Yazoo City in 1965 to seek assistance from Mississippi Chemical.

"The IFFCO project is one of the principal reasons the nation of India was able to reach self-sufficiency in feeding its own people," Don Thomas says. "In the 1960s no one thought that could be done. No one but Owen Cooper and a very few others. If Owen Cooper hadn't pushed so hard those first couple of years, this would never have happened. It was a high point in the life of everyone who was connected with it."

April 19, 1973, was a historic day for Mississippi Chemical. On a dazzling spring afternoon thousands of employees, stockholders, community leaders, and well-wishers assembled outside its marble-faced headquarters building high atop a majestic bluff overlooking the Delta to celebrate the completion of the company's first twenty-five years and to salute the man whose skills had been so central to the achievements of that remarkable quarter-century.

Facts and figures from Mississippi Chemical's first twenty-five years, spanning the period from its founding in 1948 to Owen Cooper's retirement in 1973, were indeed impressive. In 1973, for the first time in its history, its annual fertilizer sales totaled more than two million tons and exceeded $100 million in sales. In twenty-five years Mississippi Chemical had earned patronage

Owen Cooper and his wife, Elizabeth, visit with Sohan Singh, managing director of India's Punjab Markfed. Cooper made numerous trips to India between 1960 and 1985 to help its farmers build their own Indian fertilizer plants.

refunds of $184 million, all returned to its shareholder-customers, $174 million in cash. No other Southern cooperative had ever returned such an amount to its farmer-owners, nor had any American cooperative ever returned such a high portion of its patronage payments in cash.

By its twenty-fifth year Mississippi Chemical was owned by twenty-two thousand Southern farmers and farmer cooperatives who had invested $48 million to finance the company's plants and facilities. Its Yazoo City nitrogen facilities were now capable of

producing ten times the output of the plants opened there in 1951. The company's Pascagoula complex now produced four million pounds, or two thousand tons, of NPK fertilizers a day.

On its twenty-fifth anniversary, Mississippi Chemical's employee work force numbered 1,230 and its annual payroll exceeded $12 million. The average employee's earnings in 1973 was three times the average employee pay level in 1951 when production began. Mississippi Chemical could claim technological leadership in the fertilizer industry on

Cooper was surrounded by family and friends on his retirement day, April 19, 1973. Above: Owen Cooper and his wife Elizabeth are flanked by their four daughters, from left, Frances Cooper Miles, Carolyn Cooper, Nancy Cooper Gilbert, and Elizabeth Cooper, Jr. The three Cooper grandchildren present were, from left, Betsy Gilbert, David Ladner, and Edith Gilbert. Top left: Jerry Clower presented his long-time mentor Cooper with a "Knock 'em out John" cap, commemorating the tall tale that launched Clower's entertainment career. At left, Elizabeth and Owen Cooper enjoy a retirement banquet given in their honor by the Mississippi Chemical Board of Directors.

several fronts. Its patented process and related technology and know-how for manufacturing a higher quality ammonium nitrate fertilizer were being used by fourteen major firms in the U.S., Canada, and Europe. In 1972 the company had completed at Pascagoula the world's largest sulfuric acid plant, featuring an advanced process that sharply reduced emissions. In 1973 Mississippi Chemical's researchers patented a unique, award-winning ammonium nitrate neutralizer design, an integral part of the company's environmental protection program that greatly reduced emissions into the air. To assist the industry in meeting federal air emissions guidelines, the company decided to license its neutralizer design and related technology and expertise to any industry member that desired it; the company charged only a nominal one-time fee.

∽

At a celebration on the afternoon of April 19, 1973 the company unveiled a bronze plaque that read: "Owen Cooper Administration Building. Dedicated in grateful appreciation to the man, who as chief executive officer from 1948–73, was primarily responsible for the founding, growth, and success of Mississippi Chemical Corporation."

As Owen Cooper, a Warren County farmboy, was passing the president's reins to Tom C. Parry, he received accolades rarely accorded to anyone in the state's history. Commemorating the event, the state's largest newspaper, the Jackson *Clarion-Ledger,* issued a special twenty-four-page edition emphasizing the success of Mississippi Chemical's first quarter-century and the

Mississippi Senator Herman B. DeCell of Yazoo City presents Owen Cooper with a resolution from the Mississippi legislature commending his business, civic, and religious leadership to the state, South, and nation.

contributions its retiring president had made to business, church, civic, and community organizations across the South and around the world.

The imprint of Cooper's values on Mississippi Chemical is indelible. He set impeccable ethical standards of conduct and demanded that the company adhere to them. He believed passionately that Mississippi Chemical had a sacred trust with its small and large farmer-owners and a responsibility to be wise with their resources. He thought the company had an overriding pact with its employees and a responsibility to treat them fairly. He implanted in the company's cul-

ture the desire to be a civic-minded and accountable contributor to the broader community. In the twenty-five years since Owen Cooper's retirement, Mississippi Chemical has followed and nurtured these principles, just as it has Cooper's original vision for helping farmers. And that is perhaps his most enduring legacy.

∽

Rising to the Challenges

The optimism of the early 1960s in America began to descend into frustration and a lessening of confidence and trust in the decade of the 1970s following Vietnam, Watergate, Iran, and the exigencies in Southern school integration. The period 1973 to 1993 was characterized by a sharpening impact of far-reaching world events on MCC, on both its successes and its failures.

This was Tom Parry's era as president. The initial years of Parry's stewardship were luminous ones for the fertilizer industry. An emphatic rise in demand combined with a nationwide gas shortage led to sharp increases in nitrogen prices and exceptionally strong earnings. MCC acquired the nation's largest potash mine and reserves in Carlsbad, New Mexico, and the next year an extensive stock sales drive produced $30.6 million in equity for the company. But there were dire moments ahead.

I had left New York City to live in a village near the Atlantic on eastern Long Island to write books but continued to make frequent trips home. I observed considerable activity in Yazoo City, and I was acutely aware that much of it was connected to the Mississippi Chemical people. The Yazoo Arts Council was formed, and the imposing old Main Street Elementary School, where hundreds of the town's white children had been educated, became the Triangle Cultural Center, which would also eventually house the county historical museum. MCC's financial support of these new cultural institutions was large and invaluable. Artists came in and out of town to work with students and townspeople. The Yazoo Historical Society was established. An old high school chum, Jack DeCell, a graduate of the Yale School of Architecture, was enhancing the landscape with his restorations of historic buildings, including a new addition to Ricks Memorial Library, and stunning architectural designs of his own. The first black police officers were hired, and blacks were being elected to the city council. In 1972 Dr. Robert W. Harrison of Yazoo City, who lived only a brief distance from my family house, became the first black person appointed to the state board of trustees of the Institutions of Higher Learning and quickly rose to be its chairman.

Fellow Southerner Jimmy Carter defeated Gerald Ford for President, in no small measure as a backlash to Watergate. He was endorsed by Southern Baptist Convention president Owen Cooper. Carter carried Mississippi by a narrow margin, the first time the state had voted for a Democrat since FDR in 1944, and likely the last. In July of 1977 President Carter visited Yazoo City for a large town meeting in the new high school building. Time Magazine asked me to come down and write a column on how an official Presidential visit affects one's small hometown. I noted that practically every lawn in town was newly mowed, American flags were ubiquitous, even on the dwellings of the most Republican citizens, and White House communications and Secret Service and the national media en masse took over the Yazoo Motel and Stub's Restaurant.

Carter's lengthy and intimate friendship with Owen Cooper and the town's embrace, at least tentatively, of school integration made the presidential sojourn a logical choice for him. Carter spent the night in the Cooper house on Grand Avenue. The irrepressible Charles Jackson, MCC executive and Cooper's next-door neighbor, caused something of a stir by picking up the Red Phone installed in the Cooper's house for presidential emergencies only. After the town meeting I had to stay up all night writing the Time piece, in that period before FAX machines, to dictate it on the telephone the next morning. Norman Mott, Jr., installed me in a back room of the Herald with a typewriter and a Thermos of coffee. To my dismay, I learned at noontime that the President and Owen

Cooper had been calling all over town to ask me to drop by for a visit. Shortly after Carter's departure his hosts presented his breakfast plate and knife and fork to the local museum, although the remaining specks of scrambled eggs had been cleaned away.

By 1977 Delta farmers finally acknowledged they had to irrigate cotton to produce high yields, following three successive years of droughts and crop failures. Soon the giant irrigation machines resembling long steel dinosaurs hissing mists of water across the ravenous Delta soil became familiar fixtures on the alluvial landscapes. Agricultural methodology continued to improve in the 1980s. BASF, the German chemical giant, introduced the plant regulator chemical called PIX that inspires cotton to produce more cotton faster and on a shorter stalk: this development would allow farmers to plant later and harvest sooner, before the fickle autumnal rains that historically threatened crops.

The state's new catfish industry was flourishing. Three-quarters of the world's production of homegrown catfish, which would become the fourth most popular seafood in the United States, trailing only shrimp, cod, and Alaskan pollack, came from the Mississippi Delta. Between 1970 and 1993 there would be an astounding hundredfold increase in catfish production in the Delta, from 5.7 million to 460 million pounds. Even intellectual gourmands in restaurants on the Upper East Side of Manhattan and the Sunset Strip of Los Angeles were extolling the piquant delicacies of Delta catfish.

January 10, 1978, would be one of the saddest days in MCC memory. On that date a company plane returning from Ohio crashed near Barrier Field in Yazoo City, only a few miles from the company headquarters, and killed all five company employees on board, including my beloved young friend Dee Graeber, one of the pilots, who had grown up next door to me on Grand Avenue. The tragic crash was heard all over town and was accompanied by a partial power outage. On that same day fifty thousand American farmers converged on Washington, D.C., to *protest steeply failing farm prices. The following year hundreds of farm-ers from all over the United States drove their tractors to the Washington Mall and lined up there. The next day it snowed twenty inches and the tractors were summoned to help plow out the District of Columbia.*

The taking of fifty-two American hostages in Iran cast a shadow over the final year of the Carter administration, 1980. Americans were con-fronted daily by television films of the grim-visaged Ayatollah Khomeini in his flowing black robes hurling his murky invectives against the United States. A secret military attempt to free the hostages ended in calamity. Ronald Reagan defeated Carter for President in 1980, and the announcement of the freeing of the captives came only minutes after Reagan's inaugural ceremony.

In 1980, I had the good sense to return to Mississippi from Long Island—to live and die in Dixie—and it was about time. I would be writer-in-residence at Ole Miss. I brought with me my Yankee Black Lab, Pete. The governor, William Winter, one of the most enlightened governors of the new South, was a civilizing example in the state. Governor Winter oversaw the adoption of his watershed Education Reform Act, which made public kindergartens for every school district in the state manda-tory rather than optional, restored compulsory public school attendance laws, and instituted higher standards for school accreditation and teacher certification. MCC vice president Gene Triggs took the lead in organizing the Public Education Forum of Mississippi, a think-tank lob-bying group composed of influential leaders of the state's blue-chip industries to promote public school innovation and funding. But Reagan's influence would be felt even more strongly than that of the governor, in Mississippi as in the rest of the country.

Each decade creates its own myth, Murray Kempton wrote in Part of Our Time, *his memoir about America in the 1930s, while ensuing decades wait with knives in hands to kill the old myths and carve new*

ones suitable for their times. "The same can be said of America in the 1980s," Haynes Johnson has added. "It was an age of illusions when America lived on borrowed time and squandered opportunities to put its house in order. . . . In their impact on social, political/governmental life, and on the attitudes and personal values of Americans, the eighties were the most important years since World War II." For Mississippi Chemical the first six years of that decade were the gloomiest in its history, its very survival in question.

The Reagan Revolution in economic policies and rigorous conser-vatism on social issues held sway. The following years would be molded by its catchwords, as all decades are: supply-siders, deregulation, yuppies, cocaine-sniffing, junk bonds, Moral Majority. The big-deal climate of Wall Street seemed pervasive, as did the depression in oil, steel, cars, ore, fer-tilizer, and the entire agricultural sector. Ten million Americans would lose their jobs to plant closings alone between 1983 and 1988, including more than one thousand Mississippi Chemical employees. The national debt was tripling. There were tax cuts for individuals and corporations. Protective mechanisms established in the wake of the Great Depression were being dismantled.

American farm spending reached its lowest level since the 1930s, with a stunning 40 percent of farm acres left idle because of federal monetary policies. The Great Depression was being evoked in a chronol-ogy of farm bankruptcies, foreclosures, forced auctions. Tom Parry of MCC would give spirited testimony before the U.S. Secretary of Agriculture urging the administration to reverse the policies that were devastating farm exports. Jim Buck Ross, Mississippi's agriculture com-missioner, organized a special mediation division to help alleviate the credit crisis which pitted banks against farmers. In the midst of this caul-dron, Mississippi Chemical tried to cope with what soon came to be called "the Great Fertilizer Depression," which eventually led to the ter-mination of nearly one-half of its total work force and the closing of its

Pascagoula and Carlsbad facilities. These were sorrowful times for MCC, and I could feel the gloom in Yazoo City when I came down from Oxford. People were beginning to move away.

As private schools continued to proliferate throughout Mississippi and the South, the integration of Yazoo's public schools was gradually entering a saddening decline. More and more white families in Yazoo City were dispatching their children to the private academy. "It was an experiment, and experiments are exciting, and you'll give up a certain amount of comfort for a while," Mike Espy would reflect. "But at some point, you decide whether it's succeeding or failing, and you move on. Apparently, the whites had decided it had failed." By 1985 the number of white students in Yazoo's public schools had decreased to 954 from 1,394 in 1970, making the black-white ratio about 70 percent black, 30 percent white.

Civil war erupted in El Salvador. In Panama, President Manuel Noriega was turning that quirky nation into a limitless open venue for drug smuggling into the United States and was believed to be aiding the "contras" in Nicaragua. Ronald Reagan defeated Walter Mondale, carrying Mississippi with ease, and became the first president since Eisenhower to serve for eight years. His second term would be distracted by reports of secret arms shipments to Iran. Were funds for those arms sales being diverted to the Nicaraguan contras?

The radical fluctuations of the American dollar in relation to other world currencies played havoc with U.S. trade, and the debt situation worsened. These were the nadir years for MCC, which recorded its first deficit in history, $12.5 million, followed in 1986–87 by an even larger loss, $27.4 million. A pall had fallen on loyal Yazoo City, Pascagoula, Donaldsonville, and Carlsbad. On what became known as "Terrible Tuesday," October 20, 1987, came the stock market crash; the Wall Street Journal reported that our financial system was in serious trouble. In that autumn of 1987 MCC was literally running out of money.

Then, in the shadows of adversity, the fertilizer market suddenly began to turn around and headed upward for the first time in six years, thus saving MCC.

Congressman Trent Lott of Pascagoula succeeded John Stennis as U.S. Senator and joined Mississippi's other Republican senator, Thad Cochran. Ray Mabus of Choctaw County was elected governor of Mississippi in 1986 and was defeated four years later by Kirk Fordice, the first Republican governor since Reconstruction. Reagan's vice president, George Bush, defeated Walter Mondale for President by 54 percent of the votes cast, taking Mississippi's electoral votes in a national voter turnout that was the lowest percentage since Calvin Coolidge was elected in 1924. By the 1990s forty-two blacks were serving in the Mississippi legislature, a record number, and Mississippi surpassed all other states in the number of African Americans in elective office.

The most significant global development was the startling new leadership in the Soviet Union resulting in Mikhail Gorbachev's glasnost and perestroika. The Berlin Wall went down and in Tiananmen Square in Beijing thousands of students demonstrated against the cruelly repressive Chinese regime. As we entered the 1990s the Soviet system, its foreign and Iron Curtain alliances disintegrating, continued to be riven with internal dissent and collapse. After half a century of a dangerous Cold War, in which both the Soviets and the Americans had devoted megabillions to destructive weapons at the expense of their mutual societies' greatly needed internal improvements, the United States was clearly the victor in the worldwide ideological mano-y-mano. "Yet neither could America assert as strong a claim to preeminence as in the past," Haynes Johnson observed. "While the American idea of freedom and democracy had prevailed, its own economic power had diminished.... New questions existed about whether America was still capable of achieving its goals and fulfilling its ideals." There were increasing job eliminations, and from 1990 to 1992 the national debt increased from $220 billion to $362 billion. The United States resoundingly defeated brutal and isolated Iraq in the short-lived Persian Gulf War. The Yugoslavian war expanded to Bosnia. There were bloody riots in L.A. following the Rodney King verdict.

At MCC, however, the economic turnabout was impressive; in 1988–89 the company enjoyed its highest earnings ever, $46.9 million. The Carlsbad facility reopened, and the $350 million Newsprint South paper mill was completed in Grenada, Mississippi, eighty miles from Yazoo. MCC found new partners in phosphate mining in Casablanca, Morocco. In this renewed climate of economic optimism at the company, the Pascagoula facility was finally reopened. Mississippi Chemical was poised before its golden anniversary as our beloved nation entered the waning years of the Twentieth Century. As the company approached its auspicious milestone, exhilarating times for the old Yazoo City firm lay ahead.

W. M.

CHAPTER SIX

Becoming Basic in Raw Materials

Mississippi Chemical's second quarter-century opened with a honeymoon period for the company and its new president Tom Parry. Sales and profits soared. Bold expansions ensued, one after another. Enormous manpower and funds were committed to environmental and equal opportunity training programs. Dozens of new professionals joined the cooperative enterprise. Substantial investments were made to improve the quality of life in those communities in which Mississippi Chemical had plants. And President Jimmy Carter dropped by from the White House to pay Yazoo City a visit. There seemed scant limits to Mississippi Chemical's possibilities during this stimulating era, despite its interruption by a brief recession in 1977–78. The company's bright prospects would not be

Potash from Mississippi Chemical's mine in Carlsbad, New Mexico, is unloaded at Pascagoula for use in making NPK fertilizers.

questioned until the only traumatic chapter in the company's fifty-year history would descend in 1981, unforeseen and of horrific force.

In the early 1970s the ranking priority for Mississippi Chemical was choosing a new president to succeed Owen Cooper, and the second, mounting an all-encompassing campaign to secure the critical raw materials needed for fertilizers. The company would also invest over $50 million to design and install elaborate environmental protection systems to comply with new federal air and water standards, and it would cope with shortages in both natural gas and skilled minority employees.

By late 1971 the time had arrived for Mississippi Chemical to select a successor to Owen Cooper, who would retire in 1973 at age sixty-five. The MCC board of directors appointed a committee to conduct an extensive search for an executive vice president to

become president upon Cooper's retirement. This panel interviewed many applicants from outside the company and several company officers. No one in the company had any notion whom the committee members preferred, or whether they had made a final choice at all.

In January 1972, at the National Council of Farmer Cooperatives meeting in Tucson, Arizona, word of the committee's decision was mysteriously revealed in, of all things, a Chinese fortune cookie. Key members of the company board, along with Owen Cooper, vice president of finance Tom Parry, and their wives, were attending the annual meeting of cooperative leaders from across the United States. Elizabeth Cooper, a devotee of Chinese food, persuaded the Mississippians to stroll to a Chinese restaurant near the Tucson hotel for dinner. After dinner everyone was given a fortune cookie, and the members of the MCC delegation in turn

Tom C. Parry: The Company's New Leader

When Tom Parry was chosen to succeed Owen Cooper as Mississippi Chemical's president in 1973, he was a seventeen-year company veteran with enough acumen to differentiate his own style and role from that of the legend he followed. In his first interview as president, for the employee newsletter, he was explicit on that point: "Taking Owen Cooper's place is as impossible as taking Bear Bryant's [the legendary University of Alabama football coach]. That's not my job or goal. Mississippi Chemical has grown to the extent that it needs and must have a team management concept, and my job is to ensure that we have a strong team approach. We've grown so big that it's imperative that we delegate responsibility and authority further down our chain of command and ask and expect folks to take the ball and run with it. That's the way I intend to operate as president."

Parry knew the company well, its shareholders and its employees. Beginning in 1955 he had served first as assistant to the general sales manager and later as director and vice president of finance. His reputation was that of an executive who could devise workable solutions to thorny problems. "Tom had as quick an analytical mind as I ever met," Bill Hawkins, who was vice president of finance throughout Parry's presidency, would remember. "I could give him a twenty-page set of financials and he could spot the one key fact or the one key error in minutes, sometimes seconds."

Parry was a warm, gregarious man, well-liked up and down the corporate ladder. "The trust and integrity founded by Owen Cooper didn't miss a beat when Tom Parry took over," senior vice president Robert Jones would observe. "I'm forever grateful for the trust he showed in me. It made my career."

While his predecessor was known for making all important decisions himself, Parry gave his managers considerable leeway to use their own judgment. He insisted that Mississippi Chemical use sophisticated modern business tools. Budgets and performance reports, strategic planning, and detailed economic analyses of all critical capital expansion projects became under Parry standard operating procedures. The company expanded sales promotion programs, strengthened employee and management training, and updated pay, benefit, and performance management programs. "Tom did more for the employees of this company in terms of pay and benefits than anyone before or since," Bill

Hawkins, who retired in 1996, would reflect. "Mr. Cooper didn't believe co-ops could pay competitive salaries. I disagreed, and thank goodness Tom Parry did too. It's harder to run a co-op than managing a regular corporation. Tom's major weakness was not tempering his undying optimism with the tough realities that sometimes surfaced. There isn't a mean bone in his body, and it was difficult for him to get tough with people, even when it might have been warranted." Sue Tatum would echo Hawkins's view: "I probably could never have afforded to retire had it not been for the thrift plan and new salary programs Tom Parry initiated."

"Whereas Owen Cooper always moved with speed and dispatch, Tom loved nothing better than taking time to visit with employees, sitting down in their offices and engaging them in a conversation about how to solve the next problem," Lina Farrish, executive secretary to both Parry and Cooper, would recall. "Tom really believed in conducting business through conversations, not written memos or formal documents. We had the hardest time getting him to sit down and deal with the documents he had to approve. He much preferred to be talking to employees about the next big project."

Parry's eventual connection with MCC began with a blind date with Dot McNeil of Jackson in 1953. Parry, a young CPA with Ernst and Ernst in Atlanta, was working in Jackson when he met his future wife. When they married, Parry had never so much as heard of Mississippi Chemical or Yazoo City, but his new father-in-law, Charles McNeil, was executive director of Mississippi Federated Cooperatives and vice president of the Mississippi Chemical board. After Parry left Ernst and Ernst to manage a family-owned telephone company in his hometown of Moultrie, Georgia, he soon tired of the owners' squabbles among themselves. McNeil encouraged him to interview with Cooper.

Parry's first job at Mississippi Chemical was assistant to general sales manager Ward Seat, helping the sales division install needed financial controls and record-keeping systems, as well as traveling the Southeast to sell stock to farmers to finance plant expansions. "Mississippi Chemical was unique among cooperatives in America in believing that farmers had the good sense to put up half the money for any expansion project on the front end, and for requiring them to do so, before we'd build the plant. That meant we only had to borrow half the money needed, and were always strongly capitalized. Most cooperatives, on the other hand, never had enough capital to operate successfully," Parry later reflected. To capitalize on Parry's own uncanny financial knack, Owen Cooper named him head of the company's finance division in 1967. Six years later he was chosen to succeed Cooper.

read their fortunes. When Tom Parry broke open his cookie, he read his future aloud: "An announcement will be made in the immediate future and you will become the top dog." A silence fell on the group. People glanced at each other. No one said a word. The party awkwardly adjourned and walked quietly back to the hotel. One of the directors approached Parry and whispered, "Tom, how the heck did you find out we had picked you to succeed Owen?"

"They thought I simply made up that fortune," Parry would recall, "but actually I read it word for word right out of the cookie. Ever since then I've believed in fortune cookies. I keep a secret supply of fortune cookies in my office, and when we have a hard decision, I'm tempted to break one open and read it."

Soon after Parry was named executive vice president, he would participate in a very difficult decision. He and Cooper combined in an aggressive move that would fortify MCC solidly for the turbulent two decades about to face Parry, the company, and the entire American fertilizer industry.

The source of MCC's future advantage then lay twenty-two thousand feet below the surface of the campus at the Piney Woods Country Life School, an austere boarding school for black teenagers in remote Rankin County, Mississippi. The school had been made famous when its founder, Dr. Lawrence Jones, appeared on Ralph Edwards's *This Is Your Life* television show in 1954. Dr. Jones appealed to viewers to send one dollar donations to help the school in its mission of educating poor rural Negro youth. Soon

When Mississippi Chemical purchased the output of Shell Oil's natural gas fields south of Jackson in 1972, a sixty-mile pipeline was constructed to transport natural gas to Mississippi Chemical's Yazoo City production complex. In the 1990s, MCC would acquire ownership of this pipeline that still delivers essential gas to its Yazoo City ammonia plants.

sacks of mail containing seven hundred thousand dollars flooded the premises.

The school was hurled back into the limelight when the Shell Oil Company's Cox No. 1 well hit a massive and violent natural gas deposit on the Piney Woods School property. The four-mile-deep well blew out of control, spewing natural gas with a concentration of hydrogen sulfide so lethal it killed one man and forced the entire school and surrounding areas to be hastily evacuated. For a while it appeared the entire city of Jackson would be threatened, but

suddenly the sides of the twenty-two-thousand-foot-deep hole caved in, shutting off the gas flow. Shell Oil's auspicious discovery of the rich gas field beneath the school grounds was to produce millions of dollars—enough to make the Piney Woods School the most heavily endowed Negro secondary school in America. And the gas field would endow Mississippi Chemical with critical natural gas for Tom Parry's entire twenty-year tenure as president.

The OPEC-led "oil crisis" had just begun in 1972, and natural gas supplies were dangerously low nationwide. There was growing speculation that the price of natural gas—the largest single component of nitrogen fertilizer costs—was about to increase sharply. No one knew when or by how much the prices of gas or ammonia would actually escalate. Parry was convinced that prices were heading upward quickly, and he was determined to pursue Shell Oil regarding its stunning new gas discovery in Mississippi. Shell's three new gas fields—Piney Woods, Southwest Piney Woods, and Thomasville—were only sixty miles southwest of MCC's Yazoo City headquarters. Because the price of interstate gas sales—gas transported across state lines—was regulated by the federal government and held artificially low, Shell resolved to command a premium price by selling the gas inside the state of Mississippi. Wishing to double the then current interstate price of twenty-four cents per one thousand cubic feet (MCF), it sought bids for its Piney Woods reserves from Mississippi firms which used large quantities of gas. Each company was to submit a sealed bid stating the price it was willing to pay for the

natural gas over the next twenty years. "We talked with Shell for months," Parry remembered. "It was like playing poker for extremely high stakes. In fact, we had no idea at that time what really huge stakes we were playing for. We didn't know what anybody else would bid or what the national or world market would go to in the months and years ahead. Finally, after burning the midnight oil for days and sweating blood, we submitted a bid of 53¢ per MCF for the expected delivery quantity of 15 million MCF per year. We agreed to increase our price to 54.9¢ for all gas over 15 million MCF per year. This was more than double what we were paying." When Shell opened the bids, MCC's had edged out Mississippi Power and Light's by a half-cent per MCF.

Now Mississippi Chemical and Shell had to agree on the terms of their historic contract. Lowndes Daniel, director of raw material procurement, and lawyer Holly Raney, a skilled negotiator later to become general counsel, represented MCC in the negotiations with Shell. "Lowndes Daniel was a very meticulous, thorough contract man," Tom Parry would recall with considerable amusement. "You know he worked for Howard Hughes before coming to Mississippi Chemical, and we kidded Lowndes that his penchant for detail may have contributed to Hughes's demise." Daniel filled dozens of legal pads with copious notes during the laborious negotiations with Shell. When a Shell representative made a statement, Daniel wrote it down verbatim. Daniel suffered much good-natured teasing for his incessant scribbling in 1972, but twelve years

Owen Cooper signs a natural gas purchase agreement between MCC and Shell Oil in 1972. Also on hand for the signing are, from left, M. J. Edwardson of Shell; Holly Raney, MCC's assistant general counsel; and Sue Tatum, corporate secretary. When natural gas prices skyrocketed in the mid-1970s, this Shell agreement, which provided low-cost gas to make ammonia at Yazoo City, became one of the company's most valuable assets.

Mississippi Chemical's new president, Tom C. Parry, right, announces a $43 million expansion of the company's Yazoo City and Pascagoula facilities at a press conference at the state capitol in June 1973. Joining Parry for the announcement was Mississippi Governor Bill Waller. Below, C. T. Collins, center, at a retirement party in his honor, November 1972, receives the best wishes of his fellow Yazoo City instrument mechanics, from left, Charles Hoof, James Bell, Richard Jones, Jimmy Evans, Buddy Moore, and James Whitescarver.

later, during contract negotiations with Shell, his voluminous notes would be of great assistance to MCC.

On May 31, 1972, an excited ensemble of Mississippi Chemical officials went to New Orleans for the signing of the agreement at the handsome new Shell Oil Building. "It was a festive day," Tom Parry would recall. "Both sides were elated to get the contract finalized, but frankly we were somewhat nervous over the high price we had agreed to pay to assure ourselves of a firm supply of gas for our Yazoo City ammonia plant." The day after signing, the New Orleans *Times-Picayune* headline proclaimed: "Price for Gas Believed Highest Ever." Tom Parry remembered, "We felt we had done the right thing, but articles like that made us a little nervous."

No sooner had the agreement been signed than a nationwide dearth of natural gas in late 1972 forced the federal government to begin rationing gas supplies. Mississippi Chemical's Pascagoula ammonia plant was allowed enough gas for the 1972–73 year to run at only 65 percent of capacity, losing eighty thousand tons of ammonia production because of the shortage.

The decreasing availability of natural gas and other basic raw materials did not prevent Parry's first years as company president from being emphatically lucrative. The company's 1972–73 annual report noted a "fantastic increase in customer demand." All over the United States shortages in raw materials and unprecedentedly high farm prices and demand contributed to the biggest fertilizer shortage since the company was founded in

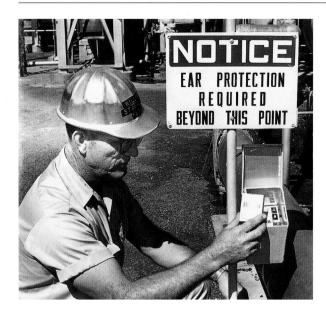

Above, William T. Stanford checks the supply of ear plugs that employees were asked to use in high-noise areas. In the 1970s the company gave increasing attention to employee health and safety, including the prevention of hearing loss. Right: The company's Yazoo City safety staff, from left, Phillip Dixon, Art Gentry, and Petie Neely, review hearing test results.

1948. Mississippi Chemical responded by producing and selling a combined total of more than two million tons of all fertilizer products and pledging to produce even more.

In a June 1973 press conference (competing for headlines with the heightening Watergate scandal), Parry and Mississippi Governor Bill Waller disclosed plans for a $43 million expansion program to increase ammonium nitrate production at Yazoo City from 400,000 to 550,000 tons a year and to augment NPK output at Pascagoula from 800,000 to 1,000,000 tons annually. A sizeable portion of this investment would be used to satisfy the federal air and water stan-

dards recently set forth by the Environmental Protection Agency.

The company also announced new members of its management. Jack Phillips, who had come to Yazoo City in 1950 with the Girdler Corporation to construct the initial plants, was promoted to operations vice president; he would oversee all company production. Bill Hawkins succeeded Tom Parry as vice president of finance, and Holly Raney followed John Satterfield as general counsel. MCC also unveiled a uniform trademark for all its products and its new slogan, "We Make Things Grow." For the previous two decades a red MCC rainbow had been on all nitrogen products, while

Coastal's trademark for NPK products had been a black and green swirl.

In one of his first acts as president, Parry got board approval to begin a new benefit program that would prove highly advantageous to MCC's work force—an "employee thrift plan." Initiated in July 1973, the plan called for the company to match every dollar an employee placed in his account in the savings and investment plan (up to a maximum of 6 percent of the employee's base salary) with a fifty-cent contribution from the company. More than 90 percent of the workers chose to join the thrift plan. By 1998 employee assets in this plan would exceed $75 million dollars. "Tom will always be known as the Robin Hood of MCC for starting that thrift plan: it was a God-send to the working folks!" said Jerry Clower, long-time MCC salesman turned entertainer.

The rampant shortages and mounting prices for raw materials motivated Mississippi Chemical to intensify its efforts to secure for itself the essential ingredients for producing fertilizers: phosphate rock, potash, natural gas, and, later, electric power. In 1972 Mississippi Chemical successfully obtained a five-year, low-cost supply for much of its phosphate rock, the largest single expense of NPK fertilizer production. It traded its undeveloped but promising forty-five-million-ton phosphate rock reserve in Central Florida, acquired in the late 1960s, to the Mobil Oil Company in exchange for rock mined and delivered by Mobil from the

Jerry Martin, left, and Tommy Galloway of MCC's Pascagoula distribution staff watch the Russian ship *Jean Labourbe* edge up to the Pascagoula dock to deliver 10,400 tons of Russian potash to Mississippi Chemical. The docking required special clearance from the U.S. government, and its Russian crew members were not allowed to leave the ship and were monitored twenty-four hours a day by the FBI.

In 1973 a new corporate logo and slogan, "We Make Things Grow," replaced the familiar red MCC rainbow.

former MCC reserve at a very favorable price. In 1973 and 1974 the wisdom of that decision became apparent when phosphate rock prices escalated 156 percent. In addition, sulfur prices increased 70 percent, potash rose 60 percent, and electric power rates doubled. The following year, 1974–75, witnessed even more increases in the expense of these ingredients: rock prices rose by *another* 95 percent, sulfur by *another* 73 percent, and potash by *another* 60 percent.

The company's annual report called fiscal year 1974 "The Year of Shortages." The diminishing availability of potash grew so

troublesome that Mississippi Chemical was forced to order four shiploads of potash from the Soviet Union, through the Occidental Chemical Corporation, to keep its Pascagoula plants running. MCC insisted that the delivery not be made by Russian flag vessels. The Cold War was still in high flourish, and the U.S. government carefully controlled ports of call for Russian ships. On the first day of March Tom Parry received calls from the Coast Guard and the CIA reporting that a Russian ship, the *Jean Labourbe*, was steaming toward the Pascagoula plant loaded with 10,400 tons of potash, and that it would not be allowed to land. "Later I learned that Admiral Hyman Rickover, commander of America's nuclear submarine fleet, advised halting the ship because he was afraid the Russians might learn something about our nuclear submarines, which are built at Ingalls there in Pascagoula," Parry would recall. "That's pretty far-fetched, because you can't see any secrets that lie inside a submarine from a ship several miles away, but the CIA would not budge. 'They absolutely cannot land,' they kept telling me."

Parry dispatched Gene Triggs and Jerry Martin, Pascagoula sales and distribution manager, to Washington late that afternoon with instructions not to come home until they found a way for the Russian ship to land. When Triggs and Martin arrived in Washington, they met with Occidental's attorneys, who had been working for two weeks trying to get permission for the ship to dock at Pascagoula. Triggs, Martin, and the two attorneys then went to see a man who could not be ignored: Senator Jim Eastland of Mississippi, president pro tempore of the U.S. Senate. "We explained our problem to the senator and his aide Bill Simpson at nine o'clock that next morning," Triggs would remember. "Big Jim listened carefully, then asked us to give him thirty minutes. In thirty minutes the Senator invited us back into his inner office. 'I got you a clearance from the U.S. Navy to land your Russian ship in Pascagoula, boys. You see, when we passed the legislation designating approved ports, I told the secretary of the navy I was reserving the right to add some if I ever

In 1975 the company installed a huge French-designed absorption tower to reduce yellow nitrogen oxide emissions from its Yazoo City nitric acid plants. Over the next two decades MCC would install a series of these advanced towers, until, in 1997, traces of the yellowish nitrogen oxide emissions were eliminated.

needed to. Well, I just added one.'" Outside the Dirkson Building waiting for a taxi, one of the Occidental lawyers commented, "This beats anything I have ever seen. We have worked on this for weeks, and Triggs gets it done in thirty minutes!"

But neither the CIA nor the Coast Guard was finished with Mississippi Chemical. They demanded that the company build a small house for them on the Jackson County dock so they could observe the Russians

around the clock. They stopped the *Jean Labourbe* three miles off the coast for a search and went over the entire ship with Geiger counters. When the Russians arrived in Pascagoula on March 6, only the captain was allowed to disembark. As it turned out, the visit by the Russians was memorable not only because of the threat of Cold War intrigue but also for two amusing reactions that would cause Parry to smile years later. "Since our government wouldn't let the crew leave the boat," he recalled, "they decided to relax, took off their shirts, and worked on a Gulf Coast tan. They looked like a bunch of Olympians, and the girls who'd come down to the dock to see what Russians looked like seemed pleased about the state of Russian men."

The second incident involved Captain Mikhail Pastukhov, an engaging, articulate man, who in a show of friendship to the wary Americans invited the press for a tour of his 507-foot freighter named for a Frenchman active in the 1917 Russian revolution. "Everyone called him Captain Mike for short," Parry remembered. "Captain Mike almost killed them with charm, polish, caviar, and vodka. He served vodka in these tiny little glasses. Everyone was expected to drink the vodka down in a gulp and then turn the glass upside down. Some of those press folks had so many of those little glasses of vodka they had a hard time walking the gangplank to get back on shore." The next day the *Mississippi Press Register* in a full-page story under the headline, "Russians Show Some of Their Own 'Southern Hospitality,'" noted that Russia had sent its first ambassador to Pascagoula in sixty years and that Captain Mikhail Pastukhov and his crew scored several victories for international amity.

In April of 1974, about a month after his emergency trip to Washington, Triggs got a call in his Yazoo City office from Senator Eastland, who was a Mississippi Chemical shareholder and ammonia customer. Eastland, like so many other farmers facing the nitrogen shortage, was concerned about his own fertilizer delivery problems. "Gene," the senator said, "your sales folks tell me I can't get a tank of ammonia to put on my cotton for two more weeks. Two weeks will be too late. I need your help now with my ammonia." Promising the senator he would do what he could, Triggs went to sales vice president Charles Jackson's office to explain the quandary. Jackson, who had spent a year in Washington in the early 1950s working for Mississippi's other senator, John Stennis, understood the importance of appeasing Eastland. He paused a few seconds, then told Triggs: "Call the senator and tell him there will be a truckload of ammonia at his farm by two o'clock this afternoon, if I have to drive it myself."

In 1974 the Shell gas was not yet ready to be delivered to Yazoo City. MCC went before the Federal Power Commission (FPC) in Washington to argue that Pascagoula and Yazoo City deserved full supplies of natural gas to produce the ammonia urgently needed by American farmers. Led by a brilliant five-foot, one-inch Washington lawyer, Reuben Goldberg, Mississippi Chemical presented as compelling an appeal as ever before heard by the FPC. He contended that the farmers' need for natural gas to grow food for a hungry world represented a "higher and better" use of the scant gas supply than "merely" burning it to provide industrial and residential heat. The FPC was so impressed by Goldberg's argument that it ruled in favor of the company with respect to both its Yazoo City and Pascagoula cases, and in so doing set a precedent that other gas users appealing to the FPC were forced to follow.

This action permitted Pascagoula to increase its ammonia output from 65 percent of full capacity to 80 percent. In Yazoo City ammonia production was so necessary that the company restarted a part of its initial 120-ton-a-day ammonia plant, idle since the addition of a more modern plant and a fertilizer price decline that forced its closure in 1969. To alleviate the short gas supplies, Tom Parry was chosen to represent the U.S. fertilizer industry in Washington hearings called to establish national priorities for distribution of the scarce gas.

Under President Nixon the federal government not only was involved intimately in energy matters but had established far-reaching environmental standards for all of American industry. MCC's fiscal 1974 annual report stressed the company's $30 million drive to comply with the stringent new federal standards for cleaner air and water. The first federal deadlines on air quality were set for 1975, while water quality standards had to be met by 1977. Eighty new processes were hastened into use, including three that were particularly significant. After a decade of applied research and development, Mississippi Chemical's Gerald Tucker, Toby Cook, and Marion Brown patented a novel ammonium nitrate neutralizer design that curtailed the escape of tiny fertilizer particles into the air, and the company chose to make this design available to the industry by licensing its know-how to other manufacturers. (This innovation would be awarded the national John C. Vaaler Award for the best emission control invention of 1974.) The

Carlsbad: Caverns, Cowboys and Potash

If Yazoo City is shaped by its abrupt hill-to-Delta landscape, blues, cotton, and catfish; Pascagoula by the Gulf's winds and waves; Donaldsonville by the Mississippi River and fun-loving Cajuns; then Carlsbad, New Mexico, is molded by its open desert terrain and vast caverns, cowboys, country music, and spicy Mexican foods. Carlsbad, with its three hundred sunny days each year, is the home of ranchers driving pickups, friendly Hispanics, crusty miners, and high school students called Cave Men and Cave Girls.

Located over three thousand feet above sea level in the Chihuahuan desert, Carlsbad is named for its natural springs, which along with the Pecos River, led hardy and thirsty settlers to locate there in the 1800s. Today its sunny, warm, arid climate and affordable housing attract hundreds of retirees along with millions of tourists who come to visit Carlsbad Caverns, the world's largest underground caverns, located twenty miles southwest of the city. While water is a plentiful and abundant resource at Mississippi Chemical's sites in Yazoo City, Pascagoula, and Donaldsonville, in Carlsbad water is a scarce and precious commodity, carefully allocated to citizens, ranchers, mines, and farmers by the Interstate Streams Commission through the state engineer and other government agencies. For decades, disputes about water rights have led to shootouts and court fights. Still its irrigated fields all around produce the finest in alfalfa hay, chili peppers, and pecans.

On a clear day, and most of them are in Carlsbad, one can see seventy miles across the rough, hilly landscape. That's about halfway to the nearest city, Midland-Odessa, Texas, to the east. Lubbock and El Paso, Texas, are 180 and 163 miles in opposite directions (northeast and west), and Yazoo City lies some 980 miles due east.

Carlsbad's three major industries are all based on the region's unusual, underground resources: the Carlsbad Caverns, its potash mines, and the new federal Waste Isolation Pilot Plant (WIPP), which employs nearly eight hundred people in safely storing nuclear waste 2,100 feet below the arid surface.

The company's personnel and benefits administrator Glen Moore, a transplant from Mississippi, is effusive in his praise of Carlsbad: "We have a terrific climate, a high school and community college that are among the finest in America, youth parks on every corner, riding horses in nearly every backyard, and twenty-six thousand of the most tolerant, friendly, cooperative, and laid-back souls one could ever hope to meet."

Pascagoula, the world's largest single train unit, drew on exceptional German technology and several radical innovations to make it the most pollution-free sulfuric acid plant in the world. Between 1974 and 1976 the number of company engineers and other professionals devoted exclusively to achieving full compliance with air and water standards grew from fifteen to twenty.

Over the next thirteen months the company would swiftly move to solve its long-term needs for potash, natural gas, and phosphate rock. The incident with the Russians had convinced Parry that if Mississippi Chemical were to remain competitive in making NPK fertilizers it had to have dependable supplies of raw materials. In July 1974, four months after the Russians departed, Mississippi Chemical acquired the oldest and largest U.S. potash reserve and mine at Carlsbad, New Mexico, from Teledyne, Inc., for a price of $20 million. The purchase of this historic property, the site of America's first potash mine in 1930, included 9,480 acres of reserves, the right to mine 47,500 acres of land owned by the state and federal governments, valuable water rights, and all mining and above-ground processing facilities. Mississippi Chemical immediately proceeded to reopen the mine, which had been closed for a year, and to undertake a $10 million expansion to double output of the facility.

Working night and day, Mississippi Chemical personnel were able to bring the

company also purchased and installed equipment using innovative French technologies, which reduced significantly the yellow nitrogen oxides, the source of the brilliantly colored plume so long a landmark at its Yazoo City nitric acid plants. (The nitrogen oxide emissions would be virtually eliminated in the 1990s by the use of even newer techniques.) Finally, Mississippi Chemical's 1,500-ton-a-day sulfuric acid plant at old mine and processing plant back into operation in December 1974. Instrumental in this speedy reopening was John Yankovich, the most famous mining superintendent in the Carlsbad Basin. "Mr. Yank," as his Carlsbad co-workers called him, had all but lived in that mine since 1938 and came with the purchase. He knew every foot of the one thousand miles of underground tunnels deep beneath the parched New Mexico soil and more about mining them than any man then alive. The mine, where temperatures remain a constant 72 degrees year round, was soon producing at a rate of a hundred thousand tons annually. It was hoped that expansions would soon triple the output to meet MCC's full requirements for three hundred thousand tons of potash.

Producing potash requires an abundant water supply to float out impurities, and unlike Mississippi's plentiful water supply, usually taken for granted, water in arid Carlsbad is a precious resource and the object of frequent fierce struggles between and among competing users. Tom Parry recalls that the fight to get enough water for the mining operation finally involved Native Americans. "Technically we had the oldest and first water rights to the Pecos River that flows through the heart of Carlsbad and is the very life-blood of the city. But New Mexico and Texas were already in a heated battle over who had the right to that water, so we didn't dare get in the middle of that hot and emotional debate." Instead, Mississippi Chemical decided to build a pipeline to bring water to the plant from the Caprock mountain area, where it also owned water

The flotation unit of the Carlsbad aboveground processing plant, above, separates the potash from unwanted dirt and other impurities by filling the huge vat with water so saturated with salts that the potash ore is "floated" by millions of air bubbles to the top of vat, where it can be skimmed off and dried.

Long-time Carlsbad mine superintendent John Yankovich, left, explains to MCC president Tom Parry and operations vice president Jack Phillips, right, how bolts are inserted to stabilize the potash mine's ceiling (called "the back" by miners). "Mr. Yank" helped Mississippi Chemical bring its newly acquired mine back into production in December 1974.

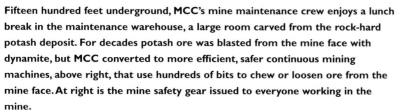

Fifteen hundred feet underground, MCC's mine maintenance crew enjoys a lunch break in the maintenance warehouse, a large room carved from the rock-hard potash deposit. For decades potash ore was blasted from the mine face with dynamite, but MCC converted to more efficient, safer continuous mining machines, above right, that use hundreds of bits to chew or loosen ore from the mine face. At right is the mine safety gear issued to everyone working in the mine.

rights. Construction of the pipeline was soon blocked by Native Americans, or more accurately by ancient Native American artifacts. Directly in the pathway of the waterline were piles of charred rocks, the centuries-old remains of Native American campfires, and preservationists adamantly refused to allow the site to be disturbed. "Finally we hired the state's most noted archeologist," Parry would remember. "She plotted every single black rock and picked them up. We buried the waterline, and then she put every one of those charcoal ruins in the exact spot it originally lay. I think we spent $75,000 to do that, and I wonder if

five people have ever seen those black rocks again. But at last we had water." And the site remained available for future study.

Supplied with water so critical to the next two steps in refining potash ore, MCC was ready to start up its renovated surface refinery for processing the potash ore. First, the ore was scrubbed in a brine solution to remove clay or mud. Next, the clean salts, primarily a mixture of potash (Kcl) and table salt (NaCl), were treated with a reagent that selectively coated the surface of the potash particles. Then the salts were transferred to

brine-filled cells where an ingenious flotation system used millions of air bubbles to separate the valuable potash from the mixture. The air bubbles were attracted to the reagent coating on the potash particles, thereby floating the potash to the top where it could be skimmed off and then dried. The salt (NaCl) particles were removed from the bottom of the flotation cells and discarded as waste.

To supervise the startup of this new flotation unit, the company sent to Carlsbad four veteran company supervisors, Emery Gregory and Walter Richardson from Yazoo City and Carlton Parker and Charlie Roberts from Pascagoula. "When Jack Phillips [then corporate vice president of operations] asked me to go to Carlsbad, I told him I had never seen a potash mine or potash flotation system," Emery Gregory, who for forty-three

Delighted that Mississippi Chemical's Carlsbad potash mine and processing facilities were expanding and providing added jobs were, above left, N. S. Boodie Hurd; above right, Harry Karas; and Ezequiel "Sonny" Salazar.

years has worked in Yazoo City's ammonia plants, remembered. "He said that didn't matter. Jack said my primary job was to spend three months teaching those younger guys and gals how Mississippi Chemical worked and what things we value. I told him I could do that."

Emery Gregory enumerated the company standards he tried to instill in his new Carlsbad counterparts: "Do what you promise you'll do. Always. If you make a mistake, admit it, and learn from it. Always tell the truth. Just tell it like it is. Don't try to play games or cover up problems or mistakes. Pitch in and work together. Help the other guy out. You can buy the fanciest technology, but you can't run it right without honest, helping people. Teamwork is crucial to get a plant running in the middle of the night or any other time. Always strive to

learn more about what you're doing. We can always learn more and get better at our jobs. And, finally, we don't work 'for' each other. We work together. And as my Daddy insisted, never talk negatively about the hand that's feeding you as long as you're on the payroll."

The company also invited its salesman-turned-Grand-Ole-Opry-star, Jerry Clower, to fly to Carlsbad and entertain all the employees and their spouses—"to give them a

Jerry Clower royal welcome into the Mississippi Chemical family," Parry would recall. "What we didn't know was that Clower was going to give away fine new employee benefit programs at Carlsbad. You know Jerry. He didn't want you to tell him what to say or not say. He said, 'Just leave it to ole Jay-ree!'" Clower did not realize that the company's Carlsbad workers had some employee benefits carried over from the company's predecessor, and not available to the rest of the company, and the rest of the company had several fringe benefit programs not yet available in Carlsbad. "Jerry got up there and decided to list every benefit Mississippi Chemical offered. Naturally he went over in great detail those benefits not yet available for Carlsbad. After that, we had no choice but to 'homogenize' Yazoo City and Carlsbad benefits, and pronto! I told Jerry his 'free talk' turned out to be a doggone expensive one, although, really, it just caused us to

MCC's most famous salesman—Jay-Ree Clower

Since 1970 Mississippi Chemical's most famous fertilizer salesman, Jerry Clower, has entertained national audiences with his outlandish tales about growing up poor in RFD Liberty, Mississippi. "Jay-ree," as the Grand Ole Opry star is known on stage and off, has earned the title of *Music City News* Country Comedian of the Year an unprecedented twelve times, recorded more than thirty best-selling comedy albums, and performed for thousands of fans at sold-out events across America.

Clower joined the company's field sales force in 1954 and five years later moved to Yazoo City, where he worked as a field sales director until 1970 when, in his words, he "backed into show business." From 1970 till 1991, Clower maintained an office at MCC and performed several shows a year for the company.

Clower's earliest assignments at MCC were selling stock, first in the brand-new Coastal Chemical Corporation at Pascagoula and then in First Mississippi Corporation. "Charles J. Jackson sold more stock in Mississippi Chemical than any man who lived, but I sold the most Coastal Chemical stock," Jerry recalls. "All of us field men loved selling that initial First Mississippi stock," Clower says, "because we got two cents for every dollar's worth we sold. If I sold 125 shares ($500 worth), I got a ten-dollar commission. I talked a lot of country folks into investing all their MCC patronage in First Mississippi stock, throwing it in the lock box, and letting it grow for a rainy day. And, brother, did it ever grow! Forty years later, not a week goes by that I don't run into somebody who thanks me for selling their Daddy First Mississippi stock back in the late 1950s. It has made them a pile of money, and that sure makes me feel good."

Clower is especially proud of the company's field salesmen he supervised during the 1960s. "For decades, Mississippi Chemical has had the finest sales force of any agribusiness in America. Our field men know agriculture and fertilizers and earn the trust of Southern farmers by giving them and their dealers advice you can count on. I remember the day I walked in and told Charles Jackson [sales vice president] that I was searching for a field man who would work as hard as Fred Sullivan, knew our product like Karl Gillman, was as friendly as Charles Chambers, and could sell like Royal Harrelson. 'Now, Jerry,' Charles exclaimed. 'You're trying to hire somebody good enough to replace me.'"

Clower delights in recounting how a Mississippi Chemical assignment led to his show business debut. He had begun making speeches to farmers when he was on the road selling fertilizer. "I would tell them about how we made 'homogenized, homogeneous, water soluble, pelletized fertilizers,' but I never did get invited back." So he started incorporating country stories into his fertilizer talks. In Lubbock, Texas, in 1970, while representing MCC at a national plant food conference, Clower made a speech that would forever change his life.

"When it come my turn to speak, 80 percent of the audience had gone to sleep. So, I hollered real loud and then told them my "knock him out, John" story just to wake 'em up. Well, the guy taping the conference liked me so much, he mailed a tape to MCA records in Hollywood. Someone from MCA called me on the telephone. "Mr. Clower," he said, "you have some possibilities. We've heard your work. We don't have a humorist on our label, and we'd like very much to negotiate with you. The next time you're in the vicinity of the West Coast, please drop by." I said, "I ain't never gonna be in that vicinity. Fellow, you don't leave Yazoo City, Mississippi, and just drop by Los Angeles." In thirty days, they had flown to Yazoo, signed me to a five-year recording contract, and my record was number 5 in America. Haw! That was something! I'm now in my twenty-eighth year as an MCA artist—the longest in history—and this year we'll bring out my thirty-second MCA album."

When Clower talks about what Mississippi Chemical means to him, he drops his billboard-sized persona, puts all jokes aside, and speaks from the heart. He says he will never forget two examples of the company's immense concern for him and his family. "When they wanted to promote me to the home office in Yazoo City to manage the field sales force, they moved me a whole year early so my son Ray could start first grade in Yazoo and not have to move later and leave his friends," Clower recalls. "Then, when I had an opportunity to try my hand in show business, Owen Cooper and MCC encouraged me to give it a shot and held my job open in case the entertainment career didn't pan out. Most companies would have said, 'Make up your mind whether you're going to sell fertilizer or go into show business.' If Mr. Cooper had said that, I probably would have stayed in fertilizer because I knew I could make a living for my family that way."

"I'm eternally grateful for the opportunity to become associated with the finest company and the finest group of folks God ever put on this earth," Clower says. "Mississippi Chemical ain't perfect, but it's the closest thing to it of any company I've been blessed to see."

Jerry Clower, the mouth of Mississippi Chemical

move a little more quickly than we had planned."

In an attempt to discover and develop its own natural gas reserves, MCC entered a mutual exploration agreement with the Amerada Hess Oil Company in May 1975. The company agreed to invest $5 million in a partnership to discover and drill for natural gas on seventy-eight thousand acres in south Mississippi, south Alabama, and west Florida. Under the agreement Mississippi Chemical would have priority on any gas discovered, and Amerada Hess would have first call on any oil. Bob Hearin, a prominent Jackson banker, introduced Mississippi Chemical to Leon Hess, one of the richest men in the world. Hess owned not only Amerada Hess Oil, but the New York Jets professional football team and diverse other properties, including two personal jets. Tom Parry would remember Leon Hess well: "He was a tiny, eccentric multibillionaire who was so afraid of being kidnapped that he never flew in a commercial airplane. He kept not one but *two* huge personal jets ready to fly him around the globe on a second's notice. Hess never let his crew or anyone else know which plane he would select which day. That way, he figured, no terrorist would know where he'd be, or when."

Hess chose one of his jets, flew south, picked up LeRoy Percy, Tom Parry, Gene Triggs, and Bob Hearin, and took them off to the Caribbean to see his two enormous oil refineries and to discuss the deal. The refineries had been built by Queen Elizabeth of Great Britain, and Bob Hearin had negotiated their purchase for Hess. "He was so proud of those refineries that he kept us up all night touring one refinery, and then he insisted we fly on to see the second one the next morning. On the plane flying home LeRoy Percy began to nod off. Leon Hess hauled off and kicked Mr. Percy in the shins and said, 'Wake up, LeRoy, this is important!' He was an abrupt man, all business."

Two years later, in 1977, the joint enterprise would devote almost all the $10 million invested by the two partners in sinking deep exploratory wells near Foley, Alabama, just north of the Gulf Shores beach vicinity. While these expensive wells failed to discover the vast deposits of natural gas the company had hoped to find, it did unearth small pockets of natural gas at shallow levels. "I've since told folks that our natural gas exploration program was 'successfully unsuccessful,'" Tom Parry would explain. "It was unsuccessful in locating a large enough gas field to allow us to build a new ammonia plant, but it was successful enough for us to recover all the money we invested in it."

In another endeavor to find sufficient gas to build a new ammonia plant, Mississippi Chemical looked as far south as the northeastern coast of South America. "We took a long, hard look at going to Trinidad and building an ammonia plant there using the huge gas reserves that the tiny island nation controlled," Holly Raney, then general counsel, would recall. "Don McGraw [MCC vice president] and I flew to Trinidad twice to work out a deal with their government. I thought the tentative offer we worked out was a very good one, but our board of directors at that time was not willing to risk building in a foreign nation so far from home." Two decades later, in 1995, Mississippi Chemical would reverse that call and decide to become a partner in constructing the world's largest single train ammonia plant in The Republic of Trinidad and Tobago.

In August 1975, encouraged by the $88 million in profits it had amassed in its previous two years, Mississippi Chemical took the boldest step yet in its drive to acquire raw materials. After two years of exhaustive studies, the company agreed to the largest capital project till then: it arranged to buy a major central Florida phosphate rock deposit lying under twenty thousand acres of citrus groves and pasture lands in Hardee County near Wauchula, Florida, and initiated efforts to obtain mining permits and secure a partner to consume a portion of the output of the

Indian ambassador T. N. Kaul, third from right, paid an official visit to MCC's Pascagoula complex in 1973 to salute the company for aid it had given India in producing fertilizers and food. Present were, from left, Pascagoula Mayor Vincent Ross; Eddie Khayat, president of Jackson County board of supervisors; J. B. Ramakrisha, India's minister of economic affairs; Tom Parry, MCC president; Ambassador Kaul; Jerry Martin, manager of sales and distribution for MCC at Pascagoula; and Paul Lacy, general manager of the Pascagoula complex.

Mississippi Chemical dispatched veteran Pascagoula employee Spencer Roberts to open its offices in Wauchula, Florida, in 1975 and to serve as field coordinator for the phosphate rock project for the next seven years. Right: In 1976 Mississippi Chemical vice president Don McGraw, right, and president Tom Parry, second from right, present plans to build a three-million-ton-a-year phosphate rock mine to officials of Hardee County, Florida, where the proposed mine was to be located. The fertilizer depression of the 1980s forced MCC to cancel this project.

mines. Development of these reserves was intended to supply the one million tons a year of phosphate rock Mississippi Chemical needed to produce five million pounds of NPK fertilizer daily at Pascagoula, plus meeting the rock needs of a partner. Estimates placed the price for this reserve and a complete mining operation at $250 million, by far the company's largest undertaking ever. This reserve was far larger than the Florida phosphate reserve MCC acquired in the late 1960s and traded to Mobil Oil in 1972.

The new phosphate reserve was purchased from the Carlton family, whose patriarch had served as governor of Florida and during the depression had accumulated vast holdings of citrus and cattle land in rural Hardee County. Mississippi Chemical negotiated with the governor's son, Doyle Carlton, who had himself made an unsuccessful run for governor and was remembered by many as looking like the original Marlboro man. Carlton had become close friends with Owen Cooper and Gene Triggs while the three men were serving on the board of the New Orleans Baptist Seminary. For years Cooper and then Parry had frequently dis-

cussed with Carlton the likely purchase of his family's holdings for a Mississippi Chemical phosphate rock mine.

In 1974 Parry dispatched Don McGraw and Holly Raney to rural Florida to work out a deal with Doyle Carlton for the purchase of the Hardee County empire. "When you land there, you wonder if you're really in Florida because there are no condos, beaches, or tourist attractions as you would expect of Florida," McGraw recalled. "Hardee County is all orange groves and Brahma cattle ranches and is mostly populated by good country folk, plus quite a few rattlesnakes. One time they invited me to play golf but told me I needed to wear my cowboy boots. I asked why I needed cowboy boots, and they told me the rattlesnakes were the toughest obstacle on their golf course. I told them we were too busy to play golf."

"Doyle picked us up in one of those Mercedes 450 SL convertibles, which was his version of a pickup or Jeep. But it just had two bucket seats and a tiny little luggage area in the back," Holly Raney remembered. "Doyle's wife had inherited the Hav-a-Tampa cigar company, so Doyle was offering everyone generous chews of his new product, Hav-A-Chew chewing tobacco. Doyle and Don McGraw jumped into the front seats with huge plugs in their jaws and motioned for me to squeeze into the back seat. Off we went, top down, sailing along those rural Florida roads with lanes of orange trees whizzing by as far as the eye could see. Pretty soon there were streams of tobacco juice flying back from both front seats, and I was hunkering down lower and lower in the middle trying to become the smallest possible target for their tobacco missiles. It was quite an adventure dealing with Doyle Carlton."

Soon after signing the purchase agreement, Mississippi Chemical sent Spencer Roberts from its Pascagoula offices to become its man in Wauchula. The likeable Roberts would spend years coordinating applications, hearings, and negotiations between the company's technical consultants and local, state, and federal permitting officials. Parry recalls the odd events that occurred when Mississippi Chemical went

before the Hardee County Board of Commissioners seeking approval for the project. "We'd met with the five commissioners for months. Jerry Clower had even flown down and entertained them. All five of them assured us they fully supported the project. Then, just as the official hearing began, up drove two Greyhound buses. When the doors opened, one hundred and twenty-five retired ladies from a Tampa retirement community paraded into the hearing. Before long these ladies, who lived seventy-five miles away, were crying and weeping about how one more mine would ruin the state of Florida." To placate the protestors, the commissioners voted to table the permit while additional studies were done.

None of the company's expansion projects in the 1970s consumed more time or dollars than the effort to open a Florida phosphate rock mine.

To make matter worse, Mississippi Chemical had the dubious distinction of being the first company in Florida's history to seek a mining permit under rigorous new state and federal environmental guidelines and heightened environmental concerns. At almost every step the company had to cope with environmental advocates, as well as with regulations and procedures that were either still unwritten or so new that they had never been applied or interpreted. "It was an unbelievably complex permitting challenge," David Arnold, who as vice president of engineering coordinated the permitting from Yazoo City, recalled. "Spencer Roberts ended up spending so much time in the state capital in Tallahassee meeting with regulatory and elected officials that folks would laughingly tell him he was better known and better liked than anyone short of Governor Graham. There was a lot of truth to that, because Spencer did an incredible job of helping to win the permits we obtained." Florida's Lieutenant Governor at that time, Wayne Mixon, was a farmer and long-time Mississippi Chemical shareholder-customer. He proved a vigorous ally in this six-year marathon.

In early 1975 the new U.S. president, Gerald Ford, phased out President Nixon's freeze on domestic prices and wage levels, and American fertilizer prices raced to catch up with the much higher world prices that the shortage had evoked. Increased prices and the continuing high demand for both nitrogen and NPK helped Mississippi Chemical achieve new records: $43.7 million of patronage earnings in fiscal 1974 and $40 million in fiscal 1975. Total sales jumped from $100 million in fiscal 1973 to $198.6 million only two years later in fiscal 1975.

To help finance the expansions it had undertaken to produce more ammonium nitrate and NPK products, the company made a $30.6 million pro rata stock offering, the largest in its history, in March of 1975. Existing shareholders, anxious to purchase more fertilizer, were quick to exercise their rights to buy this stock. That same month the company announced long-range plans to build both a new Kellogg ammonia plant and a new urea plant. Five months later the company wisely postponed construction of these facilities because of uncertainties about the availability of natural gas and an intervening softening of nitrogen demand. (Mississippi Chemical's kindred corporation, First Mississippi Corporation, would complete its AMPRO ammonia plant in the fall of 1977 and find itself unable to obtain federal approvals for natural gas to operate the plant until 1980. That plant would later come to Mississippi Chemical in its 1996 acquisition of all First Mississippi's fertilizer assets.)

∾

That same year, 1975, a decade after Owen Cooper had explained in careful detail the 1964 Civil Rights Act to its employees, the company reaffirmed its position as an equal opportunity employer and outlined steps it would take to speed the hiring and promotion of blacks, Hispanics, and women. "We've worked hard at finding and hiring qualified minorities. I'm asking you to do even more," Tom Parry would declare. In the

late 1970s Mississippi Chemical established in the Yazoo City plant a school for new and existing employees, including blacks and women, to strengthen their promotional prospects, and it aggressively began recruiting minority and female professionals for entry-level jobs.

Holly Raney, general counsel during this period, recalls that the legal department went all-out to lure its first female attorney, Ethel Truly, to Mississippi Chemical. "Ethel was an incredibly bright Mississippian who wanted to come home from Ohio, and we wanted her on our staff. I was concerned, though, that a couple of our male chauvinist executives might refuse to allow Ethel to assist them. Well, she hadn't been at work three months when two of the worst were insisting that Ethel handle all their work. They didn't want Robert Jones or Chuck Dunn—they wanted Ethel." (In 1996 Truly was named the company's vice president of administration.)

Persuading professional blacks and women to come to Yazoo City, Mississippi, was not easy, especially since those with the greatest potential had lucrative possibilities in larger cities and companies. "The challenge has been so great that on several occasions our board has asked me whether we should relocate some of our headquarters," Parry remembered. "We've even looked at that."

Instead of relocating, however, the company devoted significant effort and investment to strengthen and improve the quality of life in those communities in which the company maintained operations. In Yazoo

MCC president Tom Parry visits the Yazoo City ammonia plant. In one of his first acts as president, Parry instituted an employee thrift plan to benefit all employees. By 1998 employee savings in the plan totaled $75 million.

City a six-hundred-thousand-dollar drive to construct the Triangle Cultural Center, to consist of an expanded Ricks Memorial Library and a museum and community center created in the old Main Street School, succeeded largely because of Mississippi Chemical's leadership and financial contributions. The company also helped found and fund the Yazoo Arts Council, which brought more performing artists to its hometown audiences than any other similar group in the state. For these efforts the company received *Esquire* magazine's "Business in the Arts" award in 1976.

In Pascagoula, Mississippi Chemical helped to found a Boys and Girls Club and in 1975 created for the club's seven hundred young people an eight-acre ranch and nature area on company property just north of its Bayou Casotte plant. The following year the company helped construct and then donate to the city an eighteen-acre nature park and recreation area on newly acquired company lands. Mississippi Chemical also made a ten-thousand-dollar gift to the Jackson County Junior College (now Mississippi Gulf Coast Community College) scholarship fund to aid deserving and needy students. (The company has continued to provide scholarships at the Gulf Coast college over the ensuing quarter-century.)

Mississippi Chemical's substantial tax payments continued to provide considerable benefits in the towns where the company maintained operations. In 1976, for example, Mississippi Chemical paid $742,185 in taxes to Pascagoula and Jackson County, making it the area's third largest taxpayer. In Yazoo County the company was by far the largest taxpayer with annual payments exceeding the half-million dollar mark for the first time in 1977.

The company's civic-minded employees also made important contributions in their communities. At Pascagoula personnel manager Chuck Ueltschey served as president of the Jackson County United Way, general manager Jim Gambrell served as president of the south Mississippi Girl Scout Council, and production manager John Rednour served on the Pascagoula Civil Service Commission. In Yazoo City Gene Triggs and David Arnold each served as president of the Chamber of Commerce, while credit man-

David Arnold, right, who has coordinated dozens of expansions during his thirty-plus years of leadership to Mississippi Chemical's technical group, confers with senior engineer, James Cox, who has four decades of service to the company.

ager Al Allbritton, Charles Jackson, and Floyd Johnson of the sales staff served terms as city aldermen. Arnold also served on the Public Service Commission, and Johnson left the company to become mayor. At Mississippi Chemical's newest installations—Carlsbad, New Mexico, and Wauchula, Florida—the company made generous investments in youth and educational programs and flew in Jerry Clower to keynote the Chamber of Commerce banquets at both sites. In addition, Carlsbad general manager Jim Walls and Florida project coordinator Spencer Roberts provided leadership to numerous civic projects. These men were among many employees throughout the

company dedicated to community service.

To support its recruiting efforts to lure skilled new employees, in 1976 the company produced a full-color movie delineating the opportunities for professionals and minorities at Mississippi Chemical and its Yazoo City community. Two additional films, *The Bountiful Harvest* and *Tomorrow's Harvest*, featuring the company's programs to help feed a hungry world and protect the environment, would be seen by a half-million school children and adults throughout the company's southern trade territory.

In 1975 and 1976 MCC completed two substantial projects at Pascagoula designed to increase production and meet federal environmental standards. In 1975 the company started its second 1,500-ton-a-day sulfuric acid plant, almost a twin to its first, featuring the German double-contact process and a number of radical emission control features. Mississippi Chemical's two sulfuric acid plants rightly boasted the lowest emission rates of any such plants in America. In 1976 the company completed and brought into full service its $22 million waste water treatment and holding unit at Pascagoula. "Building a system to meet all discharge standards at Pascagoula was one of the most comprehensive challenges we've ever taken on," David Arnold, senior vice president of the technical group, would recall. "Pascagoula gets such a huge natural rainfall, and we had to capture, hold, and treat all that rainfall. While we could use some of the rainwater in the plant, we had to treat the excess rainwater, together with any water discharged from our process there, before it could be released." Unfortunately, the expensive water treatment and other environmental requirements substantially increased the cost of the fertilizer—just as the world NPK market took an abrupt downward turn in 1976–77.

∾

The precipitous drop in the NPK market would prove symptomatic of the roller-coaster years of 1977 and 1978. The glut in the world NPK market and the deteriorating nationwide natural gas supply prompted Mississippi Chemical's 1976–77 annual report to note that producing enough nitrogen fertilizer and selling enough NPK fertilizer were serious and vexing problems for the company. Earnings had shrunk by half and totaled only $22 million in 1976–77 and $18 million the next year. At that juncture Tom Parry felt that economy measures were imperative for the company, and he ordered a 10 percent reduction in personnel in 1977. Speaking of this decision, Parry would later say, "I made the decision regarding a reduction in force, and it was a very hard one. We'd undergone a pretty major buildup in employee numbers, some for projects that were not going to come to pass, like a new ammonia plant or cranking up the original Yazoo City ammonia plants. Pascagoula was losing money two years in a row. I simply felt we had to take a step to tighten up our entire crew, to be more efficient and operate leaner."

Severe winter weather in 1977 led to gas curtailments, which cut ammonia output by another forty thousand tons. A second nitrogen production dilemma was to plague Mississippi Chemical for the next four years: interminable delays in finishing the No. 8 nitric acid plant at Yazoo City and the No. 8 plant's repeated failed attempts to achieve satisfactory operating guarantees. MCC was relying on acid from that plant to increase ammonium nitrate production, but this increase would be far into the future. Errors made by the contractor included dropping the huge absorption tower while trying to hoist it into place, destroying a corner of the company's plant office building in the process and extensively damaging the tower itself.

Longtime plant supervisor Harold Keith, now retired, recalls how close the falling tower came to striking him and his car. "I parked behind the plant office and stood outside the plant fence, watching the contractor hoist the tower into place," he would remember. "Just when they got it nearly up, the whole thing started to shake violently, and suddenly I realized it was going to fall. I raced to my Mazda, jumped in, and pulled off, just as the huge vessel toppled toward me. As my car pulled away, the tower smashed down right where I'd been parked, and as it came down, the cable attached to it caught the CB antenna on the back of my car and ripped it off. Thank goodness no one was hurt." Mississippi Chemical eventually fired the contractor on the job, got a court order to force them to leave the plant, and took over the whole project itself. Even when MCC finally completed the acid plant, the new unit's output was limited by the contractor's faulty design of the main compressor, the largest and most expensive part of the plant. The giant rotor vibrated so violently that its metal tips shattered, wrecking the hot gas expander. Ultimately the company had to order a replacement compressor. Litigation over the delays and damages Mississippi Chemical suffered on this project would persist until 1982.

During this same period, 1976–77, MCC officials circled the globe trying to sell the Kellogg ammonia plant MCC had ordered in 1975 but now lacked the natural gas to build. The petroleum-rich OPEC nations seemed the most likely buyers, and Ed Mc-Craw, the youthful engineer charged with the sale, was determined to find an appropriate client. He so interested the Algerian government in the plant that he, Tom Parry, Jack Phillips, and LeRoy Percy were invited to that Mediterranean nation to meet with its Arabic leaders.

"The Algerians could speak five or six languages but insisted that our negotiations take place in French, their language of commerce," Tom Parry would remember. "So we had picked up this French translator in Paris to go with us and speak for us. He was a nice guy and a good linguist, but he knew next to nothing about chemistry or chemical process terms, and that was the subject of our negotiations. One time he was completely puzzled and couldn't translate the question the Algerian minister kept asking. Finally the minister looked at us and spoke in perfect English, 'Please tell us about the carbon dioxide output of this proposed ammonia plant.' Everyone took a deep breath. It was obvious the Algerians had fully understood every word we had said from the start, while we dumb Americans didn't understand a single thing they were saying in Arabic."

The banquet the Algerian cabinet gave to honor LeRoy Percy and Tom Parry later that evening was exotically alien. They felt it could have sprung from the tales of the Arabian Nights, and the evening provided one of the most oft-repeated stories in the company's history. The hosts and their honored guests, Parry and Percy, sat cross-legged on the Oriental carpet for a three-hour meal: ten courses punctuated by Arabic music, dancers, and much revelry. "I was exhausted from the long flight and feeling sort of woozy and was relieved when it looked as if the whole production was finally over,"

"MR. COOPER, IT'S SO NICE AN' QUIET IN YAZOO CITY."

President Jimmy Carter came to Yazoo City on July 21, 1977, at the invitation of his close friend Owen Cooper, to conduct a nationally televised town meeting in Yazoo City's new high school. In the crowd, flanking President Carter were MCC employees Gene Triggs and Hannah Kelly. Ricky Noble's political cartoon captures the excitement surrounding the president's visit.

LeRoy Percy would recall. Then his hosts brought out a huge roasted sheep and placed it in front of Percy. The Algerian minister explained that it was the zenith in Arabic hospitality to offer the guest of honor the most choice morsel of the lamb, and that he was most honored to offer that portion to Percy. "Lo and behold, the minister reached down and plucked out the sheep's eye and put it on my plate. Let me tell you, there was some kind of long pause in the festivities. I was thinking to myself, the sale of this ammonia plant for Mississippi Chemical may ride on whether I offend this Algerian minister or not. So I got up my courage, picked up that sheep eye, threw it in my mouth, closed my eyes, and gulped. Down it went. From that day on I've told Tom Parry if we ever fly to another Arabic country, I'm going as second in command, and he's going as board chair." Despite Percy's sacrifice, the Algerians declined to purchase the Kellogg ammonia plant from Mississippi Chemical.

Still determined, Gene Triggs was soon flying farther into the Mideast in yet another attempt to sell the plant to the United Arab Emirates. "They picked me up in a fancy Mercedes limousine," Triggs remembered, "and it sped down a blacktop road through miles and miles and miles of sand, finally approaching a huge oasis." On that island, utterly encompassed by expanses of sand and oil wells, Triggs tried to persuade the Arabs to buy the plant. "I honestly believe they were very interested in the plant, but in the end we could not reach an agreement."

Triggs recalls being stunned that evening when a large assemblage of young children entered the room. "It looked as if school had been dismissed." Triggs learned that the sheik had many wives and that all these children were his and had come to kiss him goodnight. Again the lengthy Arabian dinner ensued, and again a roasted lamb, complete with its eyes, was ceremoniously placed in front of Triggs as guest of honor. The sheik reached across the table and with one hand placed the sheep's eyeballs in Triggs's now empty plate. The sheik watched to see what Triggs would do. Triggs said, "I looked down at them, and they looked up at me, and I prayed a silent prayer—'Dear Lord, don't let me blow this deal. Help me get them down.' And He did." Tom Parry had warned him this might happen. The next morning a telegram came to Parry in his Yazoo City office. It read: "They did. I did. Gene."

In 1978, unable to sell the ammonia plant, the company wrote off a loss of the project at $3,856,000. "While that was a significant short-term loss, our long-term gain from that project was recognizing what a wonderful talent we had in Ed McCraw," Parry would reflect. Over the next decade McCraw would make a meteoric rise to become the company's youngest vice president of operations ever.

In May 1977 MCC completed what it termed a "stem to stern" modernization of the Carlsbad potash production facilities, a project which doubled the unit's production. Underground, the miners were then able to use more efficient methods. The company also completed a comprehensive water containment and treatment system to bring the Yazoo City complex into compliance with water discharge standards and invested nearly fifty thousand man-hours to improve product quality.

The year 1978 opened with a stunning loss still acutely painful in the memory of employees and many Yazooans. People solemnly speak of the night of January 10, 1978, as without doubt the saddest moment in the company's history, an unmitigated tragedy. At 6:44 p.m. on a cold, clear evening in Yazoo City, the Mississippi Chemical King Air corporate aircraft crashed and burned, killing all five men aboard: engineers Paul Parker, Lee White, and Jim Screws, and pilots, Tom Ishibashi and Dee Graeber.

The airplane had begun a routine descent toward the runway at Yazoo City's Barrier Field, and family members across town were awaiting the safe return of the engineers and pilots from a day's trip to Cincinnati to gather technical information for a plant expansion. A split-second before the plane was to touch down, something went terribly wrong. Pilot Tom Ishibashi tried to pull the plane out of its descent and climb upward, but the right engine apparently failed. He ascended into a steep turn, giving the remaining left engine full throttle. As the plane cleared the end of the runway, struggling to stay airborne, it passed so close to rooftops that MCC employees like Harold Keith later reported fearing the plane would hit their houses.

"I was on my front porch telling a friend goodbye when I saw our plane barely above

Shift Workers: Keeping MCC Going

For a combined one hundred and five years, as of 1998, Emery Gregory, Dallas Powell, and Erie Daniels have been shift workers and later shift supervisors in the Yazoo City production plants. The shift workers have always been Mississippi Chemical's unsung heros. The majority of them serve on rotating shifts, which means they work sometimes all night, all day, all weekend, but never eight to five, Monday through Friday. Emery Gregory reflects on the trials and sacrifices of these workers, and on the improvements they enjoy today: "A shift worker gets tired and sleepy. He gets mad, angry, frustrated, and disappointed. He gets cold, wet, and is buffeted by the wind. He misses anniversaries, holidays, his child's school performances, church services. But he keeps doing his job. Why does he keep going? Because he is dedicated to providing shoes, braces, and a college education for his children and to seeing his company succeed. There's no way a shift worker can do well without the support and understanding of his family. They have to help him get some sleep when he needs it and forgive him for missing so many family functions."

Erie Daniels, who grew up near Benton and has been a shift worker for twenty-six Christmases, agrees. "It can almost break your heart to leave your child on Christmas morning and head to work, but that's a part of the life of a shift worker and his family. Most folks have no appreciation for the stresses and strains that shift work throws on your family." Trying to sleep during the day and missing family events are problems for every shift worker.

"There have been times when I missed Christmas with my family five or six straight years," Dallas Powell says. "But someone has got to keep our plants running right through every holiday if Mississippi Chemical is going to make a profit and keep all our jobs secure."

Gregory, Daniels, and Powell agreed that working nights and during severe cold weather are the toughest times for anyone on shift duty. "When the temperature drops down into the teens or lower," Powell reflects, "it's brutal out there dragging steam hoses to try to keep critical units from freezing up. It takes double shifts [two shifts working instead of the normal one] and leaves everyone exhausted." To keep themselves alert and awake through the endless night hours when things are running smoothly, shift employees swap tall tales, take long walks, rotate assignments, go through "what if" exercises, and have a 1:00 a.m. breakfast.

"I wouldn't want anyone to think everything about shift work is negative," Daniels declares. "Not at all." They work so closely together that shift workers become almost like family to each other. "The people on our shift know everyone's strengths and weaknesses and how to pull together to handle any emergency. There's almost nothing these guys wouldn't do to help each other out."

For decades these employees worked eight-hour stints for seven consecutive days, some weeks working during the day, others in the evening, and others on the "graveyard shift" after midnight. They got off for two days at the end of that period, but only once a month on Saturdays and Sundays as the normal world does. Today most of MCC's shift workers are pleased with the twelve-hour shifts that give them more days, evenings, and weekends with their families. The twelve-hour shifts means that every worker gets two weekends off a month, a big improvement over the old eight-hour ones.

Dan "Ju-Ju" Russell, who in 1998 is third in plant seniority at Yazoo City behind Cottruel Generette and James Hicks, recalls that it required more men to produce three hundred tons of nitrate a day in 1959 than it does to turn out two thousand tons a day in 1998. "Back then it was nasty, grimy, dirty, hard work. We wore rubber boots in the slush every day. Now our plants are so much more modern, cleaner, and automated."

In his forty-three years with MCC, Gregory cites the most salutary advances as the advent of two-way radios and air-conditioned control rooms in the mid-1960s, refined safety equipment, and the evolution of sophisticated process-control computers that were initiated in 1966 and have improved ever since. In the 1950s, the only way operators could communicate with each other in a noisy plant was by hand signals or loud screaming. The two-way radios amounted to a significant breakthrough in making every operator's job easier and safer. Later the ability to control huge plant valves that regulate the flow of all materials electronically instead of by hand was a major step forward. But the most notable change was the computer revolution.

"We've gone from our first computer in the Kellogg ammonia plant in 1966 that could only monitor the plant process and tell us what was happening," Gregory emphasizes, "to today's computers that control all process variables and sound alarms when equipment is acting abnormally." And Powell reflects, "When I came on board in 1965 our production jobs were much more physical. Today there's more mental stress involved in keeping our sophisticated plants running. As great as they are however, computers can't equal a skilled operator in spotting a leak, hearing a bad bearing or pump or gear box, and fixing something that breaks. Computers make our job easier and safer, but they'll never eliminate great operators."

Mississippi Chemical depends upon its many dedicated plant operators willing and ready to work twenty-four hours a day as needed to ensure that farmers around the world get needed fertilizers for their crops.

Ammonia shift supervisors, from left, J. O. Moore, Emery Gregory, and Hugh Adams

From Left, Bubba Smithhart, Emery Gregory, and Dallas Powell have helped keep the Kellogg ammonia plant running smoothly for three decades.

treetop height trying desperately to pull up from what looked like an aborted landing attempt," Marion Brown told the Federal Aviation Agency's crash investigators. "The engine was making this high-pitched, screaming noise, obviously at full throttle as the pilot tried to pull the plane to safety when suddenly the motor coughed, cut off, and the plane fell straight to the earth with a scary thud."

The instant the plane hit the power lines on Lamar Street, electricity flickered or went completely out all over Yazoo City. Don Mc-Graw recalls his lights blinking in Enchanted Hills two miles away, then the telephone ringing with the message that still haunts him twenty years later: "One of Mississippi Chemical's planes just crashed at the corner of Lamar and Thirteenth Streets." McGraw raced to the crash site in a matter of moments. As he arrived, firemen were just extinguishing the flames but were hesitant to open the cabin of the plane for fear it would explode. Sheriff Homer Hood, who had been visiting in a house grazed by the stricken plane, was directing emergency personnel. As they opened the aircraft door and peered inside, a deathly silence gripped the onlookers. Finally came the dreaded but expected words: "No one survived."

A few blocks away Beth Cook and Kathy White were visiting over a cup of coffee when the lights in Beth's home faltered. Minutes later the Yazoo radio station announced that one of Mississippi Chemical's two corporate aircraft had gone down in a reportedly fatal crash. "One of our husbands is dead!" screamed Kathy White, who

During the 1970s the company used two Beech King Air planes to help manage operations from Carlsbad, New Mexico, to Wauchula, Florida. Shown with the planes are MCC pilots, from left, Ray Trotter, Larry Wells, Larry Eldridge, and Tom Ishibashi. On the night of January 10, 1978, tragedy struck MCC when the King Air B-90, at right, crashed while attempting to land at Yazoo City's Barrier Field. The crash, which killed five employees, was one of the lowest points in the company's history.

knew that her husband Lee was returning home on one corporate aircraft and Beth's husband, Owen Cook, was scheduled on the other. (Beth Cook, however, knew that only twenty minutes earlier, Owen had called from Carlsbad to say he would spend the night and return to Yazoo City the following morning.) "Both our company planes took off from Barrier Field early that morning within minutes of each other," Owen Cook would recall. "I was on one plane heading for Carlsbad, and the other plane flew to Cincinnati. At the airport we were all joking and kidding like we normally do. Never did we imagine that it was the last time we'd see those guys alive."

Hundreds of company employees and

their family members did everything they could to support the five families devastated by the crash. Tom Parry would recall, "Going to those five funerals in two days was the saddest thing I ever had to do." Fortunately the company had comprehensive insurance programs in place. "The way Mississippi Chemical cared for and supported the families of those five men—including my family—was to me a defining moment in its history," Griffin Norquist, Jr., whose first cousin, Dee Graeber, was co-pilot of the plane, would recall. "MCC proved what kind of company and what kind of people they were, and we'll never forget it."

The Federal Aviation Agency's prolonged and meticulous investigation began immedi-

ately and months later concluded that the cause of the crash was equipment failure in the right engine. The engine failed as the plane was about to land, and the left engine was unable by itself to lift the plane back to safety. Less than a month before, the aircraft had passed its annual inspection at the manufacturer's plant in Kansas. The manufacturer settled with the victims' families.

In the spring of 1978 the nation and the fertilizer industry faced a crippling shortage of railroad cars. The government had ordered half of American rail cars devoted to hauling domestic grain shipments to ports for shipments to the Soviets. Fortunately MCC had in the previous two years added seven water-based storage terminals and was therefore able to move products by barge freight. Twenty-one of the company's twenty-eight regional terminals were now situated on navigable waterways and over half the company's sales—more than a million tons—were delivered by water.

The company continued to work to clear the long list of permitting hurdles for the Florida phosphate rock mine throughout 1978 and to seek partners in that endeavor. "To be economical, a phosphate mine had to be sized to produce nearly three million tons of rock a year, and we only needed one million tons to supply Pascagoula," David Arnold would explain. "We were courting other major rock users, hoping to persuade them to become our partner in a three-million-ton-a-year mine and commit to take some of that mine's output. While we had serious discussions, we were unable to secure a committed partner to share the investment and the risk."

Mississippi Chemical and its employees got some good news in October of 1978. At a statewide banquet that month, the company was the first industry ever to be awarded the Mississippi Wildlife Federation Conservationist of the Year Award in recognition of MCC's investment of nearly $50 million to protect the environment and its far-reaching efforts to be a conscientious environmental steward. This award for environmental stewardship would not be the company's last.

On its thirtieth birthday, October 27, 1978, the company possessed the capacity to produce 2.5 million tons of fertilizer a year, or 12 million pounds a day—thirty times the eighty thousand tons a year it had produced at its original Yazoo City plants. Assets had grown to $350 million, thirty-five times the initial company capitalization of $10 million. Cumulative patronage refunds paid to owners through the company's first three decades had passed the $250 million mark.

While nitrogen sales and profits remained steady, the NPK market was still depressed throughout 1978 and 1979, causing the company to absorb losses on its mixed fertilizer business for both years. To bolster NPK sales and earnings, MCC introduced additional fertilizer grades tailored specifically for corn, soybeans, and peanuts, and widened educational and advertising programs to emphasize the return farmers could realize from investments in aggressive fertilization practices. In late 1979 prices in the NPK export market were starting to rise—only to spiral downward again when President Carter em-

bargoed shipments of grain and soybeans to the U.S.S.R. The embargo, a retaliation against the Soviet invasion of Afghanistan, also halted Occidental Chemical Corporation's shipments of a million tons of phosphate products to the Soviets and caused that large and unexpected tonnage to enter the already sluggish domestic market. Earlier that year Mississippi Chemical had been forced to ration potash sales from Carlsbad because of world delivery problems on potash shipments from the Soviet Union and Canada. The company had also been keenly disappointed that its deep exploratory gas wells in Baldwin County, Alabama, had not tapped the anticipated natural gas reserves.

The concluding two years of this chapter, 1979–80 and 1980–81, would be among the

most salutary in MCC's history: the company attained new records for sales revenues, tons sold, and patronage earned. But 1979 had commenced with a major scare and the first real-life test of the company's elite hurricane task force, formed to oversee the Pascagoula complex through hurricanes after 1969's Hurricane Camille. In August 1979 Hurricane Frederick sped northward through the Caribbean, gaining velocity as it headed directly for Pascagoula. Almost the entire population of the city boarded up and fled inland—virtually everyone but the two dozen members of Mississippi Chemical's hurricane task force, who moved into emergency quarters at the LaFont Inn from which they were in contact with disaster officials by radio. Using carefully rehearsed hurricane

At MCC's Carlsbad mine a crew prepares to descend the No. 2 mine shaft for a day of work in the miles of tunnels burrowed underground. The temperature underground is a constant 72 degrees year-round.

Above, Carl Hicks, chair of the MCC Community Charity Fund to which hundreds of MCC employees at Yazoo City contributed one day's pay per year, gives a check to the 1975 Yazoo County United Way chair Griffin Norquist, Jr., right. At left, Dot Hatchett collects donations from MCC employees to aid families devastated by tornadoes that swept through Mississippi in February 1971. In 1979 employees at Pascagoula and Yazoo City donated over $18,000 in a special drive to assist victims of the massive Easter flood that inundated much of Jackson, Mississippi.

procedures, the team battened down the plants at the last minute and then huddled at their LaFont command post ready to go to work when the winds and waters receded. At the last moment Frederick veered slightly to the east of Mississippi Chemical's complex, hurling its worst wrath eastward where flood tides caused death and substantial property damage in Mobile and adjacent Baldwin County, Alabama.

Although Mississippi Chemical had escaped the brunt of the waters, high winds had smashed nearly every major conveyor system in the plant and destroyed all regular

communications links. Within minutes the hurricane crew was in the plant, surveying damage and plotting their actions. "Our team responded like champions," Jim Gambrell, plant manager at the time, would recall. "With great skill, determination, and courage, those guys took the lead in getting our plants back into operation in just twelve days. Without all the planning and the great performance our team turned in, we could easily have been down for weeks."

Buoyed by the strongest harvest of the decade in the fall of 1979, both demand and prices for nitrogen and NPK fertilizer esca-

lated dramatically. NPK prices jumped 34 percent nationwide while nitrogen prices advanced 27 percent. Largely because of the favorable agreements Mississippi Chemical had negotiated for Yazoo City with Shell Oil and for Triad Chemical with Texaco, the company's natural gas costs were far less than those common to the industry. These savings on natural gas costs—the largest cost component of nitrogen production—generated for Mississippi Chemical nitrogen earnings that were the highest in the company's history. While 80 percent of the nation's ammonia plants confronted gas costs of more than two dollars per MCF, Mississippi Chemical paid only twenty-three cents at Triad and fifty-three cents at Yazoo City. The boom spilled over into 1980–81. Mississippi Chemical paid out patronage earnings of $53.6 million on sales of $395 million dollars, both company records.

Anticipating that prosperous and expansionary times would continue, in July 1981 the company held a series of town meetings with community leaders in Yazoo City, at which president Tom Parry announced plans to construct a $6 million addition to the corporate headquarters (later canceled during the fertilizer depression) and challenged Yazoo County leaders to improve the community's medical services, recreation, retail opportunities, industrial development, and public schools. After hearing Parry's plans and plea, Yazoo City mayor Charles Fulgham said, "I'm overjoyed! I endorse all these plans. Everyone I've talked to is thrilled to death." Chamber of Commerce executive vice president Tom Gillis echoed his endorsement. "It's almost unbelievable, the amount of support Mississippi Chemical has given and is giving the community to improve itself." To launch the self-improvement efforts, the company paid for consultants, Dr. William Deaton and Dr. W. L. Davis from Auburn University, to conduct a comprehensive study of Yazoo City's public elementary and secondary schools. Then, the company agreed to help fund one of the study's major recommendations: the employment by the city school system of an assistant superintendent to strengthen curriculum development. In recognition of the company's extensive efforts to improve its headquarters community, Governor William Winter presented to Mississippi Chemical a special "Salute to Industry Award" in 1981.

Little did the company or its headquarters community know what arduous times and unforeseen difficulties were lurking just beyond the horizon.

In August 1979 Hurricane Frederick slammed ashore just east of Mississippi Chemical's Pascagoula complex, leaving every conveyor in the plant in twisted ruins. Because of the rapid and skilled response of MCC's well-prepared hurricane task force, the Pascagoula plants were back on line in just twelve days.

CHAPTER SEVEN

Depression and Comeback

In the decade of the 1980s, a succession of harsh and complex economic events, including the U.S. government's attempts to stem inflation, would doom America's farmers, its fertilizer industry, and Mississippi Chemical to a desperate struggle for survival. These were the most traumatic years in the company's history. Employees, shareholder-customers, and the communities where Mississippi Chemical had facilities all suffered substantial losses. That Mississippi Chemical outlasted this calamitous period—in which more than half of the nation's fertilizer producers and many of its farming operations faded from existence—would be a tribute to the character and abilities of its people.

The severe agricultural depression of 1982–87 was the darkest hour in the company's history and saw America's farmers, its fertilizer industry, and Mississippi Chemical in a desperate struggle for survival.

From the mid-1960s until 1980 American agriculture had grown more and more successful with immense export sales of its grains and soybeans to foreign customers such as Russia, Japan, and India, who were eager to obtain affordable American foodstuffs for their growing populations. With this upsurge in exports America's agricultural economy became increasingly dependent on foreign markets and therefore vulnerable to sudden shifts in that market. In the 1980s an unforeseen change in the export market severely crippled and threatened to destroy the American farmer and those who supplied him fertilizers.

To halt the domestic inflation that had troubled the nation under Nixon and had reached record highs under Carter, President Reagan and the Federal Reserve Board in 1980 initiated sweeping transformations in U.S. monetary policy, taking vigorous action to strengthen the American dollar against other world currencies. "Those sharp increases in Federal Reserve discount rates were a salvation for America's banks but a disaster for agriculture," Tom Parry reflects in 1998. As the dollar rose in value, so did the price of American products to international customers, then buying nearly half of America's grain harvest. Overnight almost, American grains, soybeans, and fertilizers were priced out of critical world markets, and the country's entire farm economy experienced a menacing nosedive. Though Reaganomics did check inflation and spurred growth in the economy generally, for the American farmer and fertilizer industry the cure proved to be bitter medicine indeed, far more life-threatening than the illness itself. World demand for America's grains and fertilizers collapsed suddenly and violently in late 1981 and early 1982 and would remain frighteningly low until 1987.

Although the serious American agricultural depression was caused in part by the sharp jump in the international value of the U.S. dollar, a number of other factors contributed to the downturn. Offshore grain and fertilizer production had surged. Foreign nations had increased grain acreage in response to President Carter's politically motivated grain embargo. There was an overbuilding of new fertilizer capacity around the world, especially by state-controlled economies eager to convert natural gas to marketable fertilizers. A worldwide oil shortage and the highest interest rates in fifty years also propelled the sudden downturn.

This great agricultural depression would throw Mississippi Chemical into a prolonged downward spiral. The company would be forced to close its Pascagoula plant and the Carlsbad potash mine, cancel its Florida rock project, terminate the employment of more than half its work force, suffer the only two net losses in its fifty-year history, and come perilously close to running out of funds with which to operate.

The effects of the U.S. Federal Reserve Board's monetary policies and the sudden shift in exports and imports struck Mississippi Chemical and United States agribusinesses with crippling force during the fiscal 1981–82 year. The company's earnings plummeted $50 million from a record high in 1980–81 to only $4.5 million in 1981–82; MCC's entire NPK operation incurred a loss. Nationwide, NPK fertilizer sales plunged nearly 20 percent, prices dropped 25 percent, and surpluses mounted as export sales diminished. Nitrogen imports from the Soviet Union and Mexico, aided by the

America's fertilizer market suffered a disastrous collapse during 1982 and 1983, forcing MCC and the entire U.S. fertilizer industry to idle production plants and terminate the employment of thousands of employees.

stronger dollar, however, mushroomed, making America a net importer of nitrogen fertilizers. This caused nitrogen prices to slump, while shortages of natural gas continued to plague domestic producers, including Mississippi Chemical.

Mississippi Chemical and its fellow American fertilizer-makers were forced to take extreme measures to survive the collapsed markets. Thirty-six ammonia plants with an annual capacity of five million tons were closed because of the rising natural gas prices and stiff import competition. Among those

shut down were MCC's own ammonia plant at Pascagoula. "We could buy ammonia much more cheaply than we could make it in our own Pascagoula plant," Tom Parry would remember. "Sadly, we had no choice but to halt ammonia production at Pascagoula."

The NPK arena was even harder hit. In August 1981 Mississippi Chemical curtailed Pascagoula's NPK production because of accumulating inventories and declining sales. Prospects worsened over the next ten months. The company had a huge investment in the Pascagoula plant, which produced high quality but higher cost NPK fertilizers. As the depression worsened, farmers were less willing and able to pay premium prices for the company's premium quality NPK product. There was heated debate and little consensus among the company's top management about what could be done to arrest the mounting NPK losses. "The greatest sin a company can commit is failing to earn a profit," John Rednour, then the Pascagoula production manager, would note. "If you can't earn a profit, no one has a job."

On June 2, 1982, half the total Pascagoula work force, some 255 employees, were dismissed in the biggest work force reduction in company history. "There's nothing in the world worse than having to tell loyal, dedicated employees that their job has ended through absolutely no fault of their own," Paul Lacy, who had served as Pascagoula general manager for more than a decade, would recall. "It was one of the saddest days of my life. These were friends and co-workers who had dedicated their lives to

In the mid-1980s, collapsing markets, idled plants, and work force reductions cast dark clouds over the company's Yazoo City headquarters and its employees.

Mississippi Chemical. It broke my heart." The company offered a range of services to help the employees and their families, including opening a job placement center and providing special severance benefits and health insurance coverage. "We were stunned," Shirley Speights, long-time Pascagoula employee, reflected. "Our whole

office and plant felt like a morgue for days. It was like a huge death."

Three weeks later, on June 28, Mississippi Chemical terminated the employment of thirty-eight employees at its Yazoo City headquarters and closed the distribution plants at Canton and Meridian, Mississippi, whose workers were discharged as well. The

dazzling euphoria of the 1970s had capitulated to the grim reality of economic forces well beyond the company's power to control.

Less than a month later, in July 1982, the company ended its Florida phosphate project, dismissing the entire Florida work force, and agreed to trade its Hardee County rock reserve to the International Minerals and

Chemical Corporation (IMC) in exchange for rock IMC would sell to the company over the next twenty-two years. "It was a sound decision," Rex Brown, who had moved from Yazoo City to Lakeland, Florida, to oversee the design of the mine and its equipment, recalled. "The phosphate fertilizer and rock market had collapsed to the point where it could have been economic suicide for us to proceed." Reflecting on that resolution to abandon MCC's own phosphate rock mine, current president Chuck Dunn would call it "the most fortunate decision in Mississippi Chemical's fifty-year history. Phosphate rock prices had to be more than forty dollars per ton for operating the mine to be feasible. Prices never approached that in the 1980s or 1990s. Had we proceeded with that mine it could have bankrupted the company."

The plight of American agriculture continued to worsen. In January 1983, in an attempt to reduce the vast stockpiles and surpluses of American farm products that had built up as export sales collapsed, the Reagan administration offered a Payment in Kind (PIK) program to America's farmers. Under PIK the federal government offered to pay farmers not to plant some of their acres, much as Roosevelt has done in the 1930s. The farmers responded by choosing to allow 39 percent of all their cropland—some eighty million acres—to remain idle during the 1982 farm year. The fertilizer industry, already reeling under deflated export markets and rising import competition, now watched impotently as the demand for fertilizer was further diminished by actions of its own government.

"I don't blame the American farmer. His purchasing power was at the lowest level since the Great Depression of the 1930s. I put the blame squarely on the Reagan administration and the Federal Reserve Board," Tom Parry, company president during the PIK program, would declare. "Instead of dealing with the root cause of the problem, which was the loss of vital export markets and the ridiculously high value of the American dollar, our government dealt only with the symptom. And they devised a short-term and shortsighted solution that did nothing about the problem of reopening crucial export markets."

The introduction of the PIK program signaled the end of MCC's efforts to keep the Carlsbad potash mine running during that unnerving crisis. With the collapse in American fertilizer usage, Mississippi Chemical had already stockpiled nearly a year's inventory of potash. Now it was obvious that the potash market and potash prices would tumble even lower. "We simply had to halt production at Carlsbad or accumulate even larger inventories and losses," Parry remembered. On January 21, 1983, the company closed its Carlsbad mine and processing facilities which it had opened so optimistically half a decade earlier. Two hundred Carlsbad employees were dismissed as production ceased. The company retained only a skeleton crew of twenty employees to deal with existing inventory, ongoing maintenance, and regulatory requirements and to be ready for the day the market revived. That day was not to come for almost six years.

In August of that year, frustrated by the losses shareholders, farmers, and innocent employees were experiencing, Tom Parry delivered blistering testimony on behalf of the company and American farmers at hearings held in Washington by U.S. secretary of agriculture John Block to find solutions to the widening crisis:

> Reducing American production is a quick-fix remedy that favors our foreign competitors

The company's one bright spot during the great fertilizer depression was low-cost natural gas contracts that allowed its Yazoo City and Triad units to produce nitrogen fertilizers profitably. Mississippi Chemical negotiators devised creative new contracts with Shell and Texaco to assure continued and economical deliveries of this essential gas.

and weakens our trading position. Instead, we should immediately use every diplomatic means available to open markets for U.S. produced farm commodities. . . . Most importantly, we must get our national economy in order and thereby allow U.S. agricultural commodities to be priced competitively in the world market. Our U.S. government should help, not hinder, and then step back and let the American farmer show he is still the best in the world.

Trapped in a global economic tempest they could not influence, thousands upon thousands of American farmers sought bankruptcy protection. More than one-third of the Farmers Home Administration loans in the nation were delinquent. Before the depression turned, nearly one-third of U.S. farmers would go out of business.

Mississippi Chemical soon found itself not only confronting shrinking fertilizer markets, but also drawn into a bitter dispute with two of the world's most powerful petrochemical giants, Shell and Texaco, over dwindling deliveries of natural gas. In 1967 and 1972, respectively, the company had negotiated a twenty-year contract with Texaco and a fifteen-year contract with Shell for the delivery of essential natural gas to its Donaldsonville and Yazoo City nitrogen facilities at what would later be considered "*very* low prices." When prices for new gas sales shot up to six and then eight dollars per thousand cubic feet (MCF) in the late 1970s, Shell and Texaco warned Mississippi Chemical that they could no longer supply contract gas volumes at the prices agreed to in the contracts.

The 1980s brought a series of setbacks for Mississippi Chemical and its top management. Wrestling with these major challenges were, seated from left, Bill Hawkins, vice president of finance; Charles Jackson, senior sales vice president; Jack Phillips, vice president of operations; and Tom Parry, president. Standing were corporate secretary Sue Tatum and vice president of research Marion Brown.

Mississippi Chemical's general counsel, Holly Raney, would vividly remember this dispute. "While we were dwarfed in size by these two international oil giants, we didn't shy away from a confrontation to protect our rights." Mississippi Chemical filed lawsuits against both Shell and Texaco and asked the courts to order the two oil companies to deliver the full quantities of gas they had contracted to provide. "The disputed gas supplies were worth hundreds of millions of dollars to our nitrogen fertilizer costs and

profits," Tom Parry recalled. "We've never had so much riding on a lawsuit before or since."

In the Shell altercation, Mississippi Chemical methodically developed a strong case that its adversary was legally obligated to employ new gas wells it had drilled in Rankin County to supply Mississippi Chemical. Shell was adamantly refusing to allow the company access to the output of these new wells, preferring to hold it in hopes of selling it on the open market at prices then nearing eight dollars per MCF. The voluminous notes taken by MCC procurement director Lowndes Daniel during the 1972 contract negotiations substantiated that Shell had in fact committed itself to employ the entire output of its three Rankin County fields to satisfy its agreement with Mississippi Chemical. In the end MCC's attorney Robert Jones devised a strategy that gave both sides the results they wanted—and produced a settlement in mid-1982. Jones would later describe his inventive plan:

> During 1982 prices of new unregulated gas had reached all-time highs ranging from eight to ten dollars per MCF. But Southern Natural Gas Company, a regulated interstate pipeline company, was required to sell us gas at Yazoo City for approximately three dollars per MCF, because they had a mixture of gas bought over thirty years in their system. So I came up with this idea:
> • Mississippi Chemical would take only twenty-five million cubic feet of gas a day from Shell at a price of $1.10. This would allow Shell to sell the balance of their other new gas on the open market for eight to ten dollars.
> • Mississippi Chemical would buy the extra twenty-one million cubic feet a day of gas needed for Yazoo City for approximately three dollars per MCF from Southern Natural.
> • Shell would pay to Mississippi Chemical enough money (approximately $1.90 per MCF) to lower the three dollars we paid Southern Natural down to the $1.10 figure of our Shell agreement.
> • This would give us the extra twenty million cubic feet we urgently needed at $1.10 per

MCF while Shell could profit on its new gas in the open market.
> • Finally, the new contract was extended to April 1989.

Shell agreed to the resolution of the dispute on the first day the plan was proposed to them. Thus, Mississippi Chemical got not only the amount of gas it needed for $1.10 per MCF, but also two more years added to the contract term.

Mississippi Chemical would use similar negotiating skills to favorably resolve its dispute over gas deliveries with Texaco. "Our lawyer in the Texaco case was simply brilliant," Holly Raney would recall. "He figured out a way to settle the dispute with Texaco where we came out even better than if we'd won the law suit, and Texaco was better off, too. It was another 'win-win' proposal and Texaco agreed to it." Tom Parry was likewise pleased. "I can't say enough about the incredible job our team did with both the Shell and Texaco cases," he reflected. "I've never been prouder of the way Mississippi Chemical representatives handled themselves." It was a substantial victory for Mississippi Chemical and another in a long chronology of legal and negotiating triumphs over the company's fifty-year history.

Chuck Dunn would later explain why MCC was historically so successful in its big legal cases:

> There are several reasons. First, Mississippi Chemical involves our legal team closely in making key decisions. Unlike some firms who avoid using attorneys until they encounter a

problem, our legal staff is integrally involved in our strategic deliberations and decisions. Second, Mississippi Chemical is very ethical. We genuinely try to treat other companies fairly and to work out any disputes. If we resort to a lawsuit, it is because we believe we have been wronged and will prevail. Finally, Mississippi Chemical has had an outstanding legal staff throughout its entire history. That began with John Satterfield, continued with Holly Raney, Robert Jones, and Ethel Truly, and continues with our legal staff today.

Bill Hawkins, Mississippi Chemical vice president of finance during the difficult 1980s, would later summarize the decade.

> Many factors—not just government actions—contributed to our serious problems. We, along with the entire American fertilizer industry, got swept up in the drive to feed the world and expanded too rapidly from 1965 to 1980. Then, the world economy dealt us a harsh dose of reality. We lost millions on our Pascagoula NPK operations because we kept making premium quality NPK products while farmers' preference was shifting to cheaper DAP. Then, we purchased the Carlsbad property and the Florida rock reserves, both of which look good in expansionary times, but neither of which was economically feasible when the world market collapsed. Fortunately, we were making huge profits on our nitrogen fertilizers because of our great gas contracts with Shell and Texaco. Those nitrogen profits were more than offsetting our NPK losses, and they kept the company afloat. I only wish we had retained more of the earnings to strengthen our company.

In 1985 Mississippi Chemical completed the U.S. fertilizer industry's first co-generation unit, above, which produced most of the electricity and much of the steam needed at its Yazoo City complex at significant savings. Later in the decade obtaining low cost electric power would be crucial to the feasibility of the company's massive new papermill project, Newsprint South. Power for the new Grenada county mill, equal to that consumed by a city of 100,000, was purchased from the Tennessee Valley Authority. At left, engineer Danny Hood inspects the TVA substation at the company's Newsprint South mill.

In 1984 Triad's Donaldsonville, Louisiana, employees won safety citations for operating over one million hours without a lost-time accident. Celebrating the accident-free landmark are, front row, from left: Dale Andrews, Pam Gregoire, Jack Phillips (MCC's vice president of operations), Triad general manager J. F. Acardo, and safety director Harold Capello. Back row, from left: Bob McKee, Tom Newchurch, Tippy Torres, and Larry Savell. In 1997 Triad surpassed the nine-million-hour mark without an accident.

To strengthen its nitrogen earnings and product quality, the company made a series of investments to augment the efficiency of its two nitrogen complexes. In 1984–85 it invested $20 million at Yazoo City to build a 20.5 megawatt co-generation plant that produced electricity at one-third the cost of purchasing it from Mississippi Power and Light Company and also efficiently generated steam for the Yazoo City complex. Termed "co-generation" because the huge gas-fired unit generated both electricity and steam, Mississippi Chemical's unit was the first ever built in an American fertilizer plant and the first constructed in the state of Mississippi by any industry. The unit produced enough

electrical energy for the entire Yazoo City fertilizer complex or one and a half times the electricity consumed by all the residents of Yazoo City on an average day. In doing so, it utilized a mammoth General Electric LM 2500 gas turbine, a derivative of the jet engines which power modern aircraft and naval vessels. The co-gen unit proved so successful that the savings in electricity and steam costs recouped the company's full investment in only two years. As the cost of energy increased, so also would the savings from this new unit. Bill Hawkins, the company's conservative chief financial officer, said, "We want to find and fund more projects with payouts like this co-generation unit."

Simultaneously, the company installed additional equipment at the ammonium nitrate plants in Yazoo City to facilitate the use of a new additive and coating agent developed by Mississippi Chemical researchers. This proprietary innovation produced "free-flowing prills," that is, prills which did not break down to form dust or stick together in lumps, and thus could be handled and stored more easily. In 1985 the company also began a "retrofit" program to reduce the amount of natural gas required to make nitrogen fertilizers at both Yazoo City and Donaldsonville.

As the American phosphate market steadily weakened in 1985, the rock agreement Mississippi Chemical had executed with IMC in 1982 turned into a veritable nightmare. "We'd agreed to pay IMC 'cost plus' for their rock, including trading them part of our Hardee County reserve," Bill Hawkins would explain. "But as the market price continued to collapse, IMC insisted that their costs were higher than the depressed world market price. We were stuck having to pay them much more than the market price. It was horrible. It was absolutely critical that we get out of that IMC rock contract. It could have sunk the company. Chuck Dunn, then a corporate attorney, did a wonderful job of negotiating Mississippi Chemical out of that contract. We had to pay a substantial penalty, but it was worth it."

Robert Jones, then the company's general counsel, and Hawkins likewise had to deal with the long-term potash supply contract Mississippi Chemical had signed with Israel's

Dead Sea Works in 1982. "We tried our best to sell our Carlsbad potash to the Israelis in 1982 so we could keep Carlsbad running," Hawkins remembered. "But the American dollar was so strong that the Israelis offered to sell us their potash much cheaper than we could mine our own." Israel did not mine potash, but extracted it from the Dead Sea by an evaporation process. After touring the Holy Land and inspecting its production facilities, MCC representatives agreed to buy from the Israelis. But the Israeli potash turned out to have grave faults. It arrived in Pascagoula so dusty that it would not granulate into a high-grade NPK product, and it was gray in color. "Our farmers simply refused to take gray potash," Don McGraw, then sales vice president, later explained. "If it wasn't red, they didn't think it was potash." After trying to use and sell the dusty inferior product for three years, Hawkins and Jones met with the Israelis and succeeded in negotiating a means of extricating the company from the agreement.

Eliminating the company's deepening losses on NPK operations was a serious business. "I spent many a sleepless night during those six years trying to figure out how we could sell more NPK products," McGraw would confess. "We tried innumerable different approaches. We experimented with making diammonium phosphates. We experimented with making lawn and garden fertilizers. But there was no way we could overcome the economic forces that were creating huge losses, not just for us, but for virtually every American NPK producer."

Mississippi Chemical's management and

In 1987 **Mississippi Chemical and its president Tom Parry, right, hosted President Gerald Ford's visit to Mississippi to recognize the state's outstanding farm families. At center is Parry's grandson, Matthew Van Landingham.**

board remained hopeful that the NPK situation would improve, but instead it continued to worsen. Mississippi Chemical was caught not only by the deep slump in U.S. demand for phosphate and potash products, but by a growing market shift to cheaper mixtures of nitrogen, phosphate, and potash blended at the dealer's terminal (termed "bulk blends"). The "mixed" NPK fertilizer made at Pascagoula granulated the plant nutrients together in every prill, previously a significant advantage over bulk blends which were prone to uneven effects in the field. However, by the mid-80s the equipment and techniques for bulk blending had improved and farmers could not justify paying a pre-

mium price for MCC's product that could no longer be considered that much superior to its cheaper competition.

In the spring of 1985 the market prospects for fertilizers were so bleak the company had to take further drastic measures to stay afloat in the ocean of red ink threatening to drown American farmers, fertilizer-makers, and all of agribusiness. Mississippi Chemical terminated the employment of another 300 people across the company in several steps. In April the payroll was reduced by the early retirement of more than 100 workers. Then on May 1, 1985, three years after the Pascagoula work force had been cut in half, the company stopped production at the

Pascagoula plant altogether and terminated another 133 workers. A week later the Yazoo City force was trimmed by 31 more employees. Only 100 employees remained at Pascagoula, retained there to maintain the plant and produce limited tonnages of NPK if and when ordered by a customer.

"I'll never forget the day we met with those Pascagoula employees one at a time to tell them their jobs had ended through no fault of their own," Chuck Dunn would recall. "It was incredibly sad. It got so tough I walked out in the hall to take a break and saw Lamar Peyton, corporate personnel director, and Ethel Truly, corporate attorney, both of them very tough people, standing there with tears streaming down their cheeks. I'll bet I didn't sleep two hours a night for the next month thinking about those people and what they were going to do. It left me with a conviction that I never wanted to be responsible for people losing their jobs because I failed to do mine as well as I possibly could."

Over the next two fiscal years, 1985–86 and 1986–87, the American fertilizer market receded to its lowest ebb in history and pulled Mississippi Chemical down with it. With Pascagoula closed, the company's sales in 1985–86 fell to $226 million, a decrease of $99 million from the prior already poor year, and for the first time Mississippi Chemical suffered a loss—$12.5 million.

In 1985–86 the company took three positive actions that in the long-run would have great significance for the company but in the short-run could not erase its current losses.

It elected three new young corporate officers, Charles Dunn and Ed McCraw as vice presidents and Robert Jones as vice president and the company's third general counsel. This triumvirate would play key roles in restoring MCC's fortunes in the ensuing decade. Second, the company began feasibility studies for a huge paper mill project which would eventually materialize as Newsprint South, Inc. Finally, Robert Jones organized a complicated re-negotiation of the Shell Oil natural gas contract for Yazoo City, which he had devised in 1982; the new agreement would reap substantial dividends from 1989 to 1992. "As the natural gas market fell from its all-time highs of around ten dollars to approximately two dollars per MCF, Shell was caught in a whip-saw and the 1982 contract was costing it a tremendous amount of money," Jones would explain. Mississippi Chemical's negotiators Robert Jones, Ed McCraw, Bill Hawkins, and Paul Lacy formulated a solution that would save Shell millions in the short-run and in return obligate them to extend their agreement to supply gas to MCC for four more years. "The formula our guys devised was so sophisticated and so complicated that it had to be put on a computer disk that was kept in a lock-box at Deposit Guaranty Bank in Jackson," Tom Parry remembered. Neither Shell nor Mississippi Chemical could remove the computer disk from the lock-box without the other party present. In the early 1990s the accord contained in that computer program would be a major factor in propelling Mississippi Chemical to record-breaking profits. In 1987, however, profits were nowhere to be seen.

"1987 marked the sixth year of the worst depression for agriculture since the 1930s and was Mississippi Chemical's darkest hour," Parry informed shareholders in the annual report. Nitrogen prices plummeted another 30 percent, creating an even larger loss—$27.4 million. "We were the nation's lowest-cost nitrogen producer, and we lost $40 million in those two years," Parry would say. "You can only imagine how much money the rest of our industry was losing."

Those six depressed years had taken a dreadful toll. The Pascagoula plants, which produced one million tons of NPK fertilizer in 1980–81, were now completely shut down and Mississippi Chemical was seeking a buyer for the Gulf Coast complex. The Carlsbad mining operation was idle, and the Florida phosphate mine had been canceled. The reduction of another 34 headquarters employees in May 1987 left the company's work force reduced by 1,034 employees, or 61.7 percent, since January 1982. From January 1982 to January 1988, ten of Mississippi Chemical's seventeen vice presidents would leave the company, either taking early retirement or suffering the elimination of their positions.

The American fertilizer industry was decimated. Fifty-one of its ninety ammonia plants had closed or been sold, thirteen of the twenty-five phosphate plants had been shut down or sold, and more than half the nation's potash capacity was idled. Agrico, Allied Chemical, Beker, Estech, Gardinier, and Grace—all substantial forces in the industry during the 1970s—had suffered irreversible losses and had exited the fertilizer business, in some cases after filing bankruptcy. Circumstances were as bad or worse for American farmers. Thousands of farm families faced the insufferable anguish of losing land that had been handed down in their families for generations. Hundreds of Mississippi Chemical stockholders, either by choice or necessity, had given up farming.

The wave of farm bankruptcies and foreclosures in the state rose so rapidly that a group of concerned leaders convened to help lessen the human suffering brought on by the crisis. Mississippi's commissioner of agriculture, Jim Buck Ross, was persuaded to hire mediators to help farmers and bankers resolve financial foreclosures with a minimum of violence, suicides, and breakup of families. The Mississippi legislature passed a law supporting voluntary mediation in farm bankruptcies. A farm credit crisis hotline was set up in Mississippi to serve farmers and lenders.

During this bleak time, Mississippi Chemical moved forward with an aggressiveness evocative of its founding forty years before. Rather than retreat after the largest loss in its history, in 1986 Mississippi Chemical created a new subsidiary, Newsprint South, Inc. (NSI), and in 1987 the company's board voted to support the construction of a state-of-the-art newsprint mill that was to be both the largest capital project and the most daring diversification the company had ever attempted. The project's expected cost of $350 million was 50 percent more than the company's total assets of $230 million in 1987. The new facility, designed to be the most

modern, efficient, and pollution-free mill in the U.S., would produce 225,000 tons of newsprint a year—nearly two million pounds a day—at NSI's new complex in Grenada County, Mississippi.

In certain ways the newsprint enterprise paralleled the company's fertilizer business. Mississippi Chemical had been approached about a newsprint project in 1986 by Don Branch, an officer of the company's longtime lender, the Jackson Bank for Cooperatives (CoBank). Branch had been involved with an earlier, unsuccessful paper mill project attempted by Owen Cooper and others in the early 1980s, and he suggested that Mississippi Chemical would be an ideal sponsor for a similar project. If successful the mill would increase Mississippi landowners'

returns and profits from their timber operations. Like Mississippi Chemical's other plants, the newsprint mill would draw on advanced technology and large-scale process plants to reach maximum efficiencies. From the beginning the project piqued the interest of Mississippi publishers as well as major American newspapers, newsprint representing about a third of their costs. And, as they had once predicted about Mississippi Chemical, skeptics scoffed that the newsprint mill could never reach fruition.

"This newsprint mill had been a dream of Mississippi Chemical's founder Owen Cooper for years, if not decades," recalled Chuck Dunn, the able executive chosen by Tom Parry to coordinate this massive project for the company. In the face of the dire con-

In 1987 Mississippi Chemical committed to construct Newsprint South (NSI), a $350 million project, the largest in MCC's history. Above, Paul Herbert (in the light suit), construction manager for Rust Engineering, project contractor, discusses a model of the paper mill with John Sharp Howie, MCC board member, as Chuck Dunn, NSI's president, looks on.

ditions in the agricultural economy, the Mississippi Chemical board of directors approved the project but would authorize an equity investment of only $22 million. This presented a daunting challenge for those involved in the project. Securing the additional financing demanded that Chuck Dunn, finance director Tim Dawson, and attorney Ethel Truly spend more than a year constantly going back and forth to New York. Meanwhile, Mississippi Chemical had contracted to provide many services for Newsprint South, just as it had decades earlier for Coastal Chemical, and soon employees from every department were involved with the mill project. The engineering division, led by Dr. David Arnold, spent numerous hours selecting a construction contractor and choosing among alternative pulping and papermaking technologies, vendors, and equipment. Tommy McKiernon moved from MCC's headquarters to Grenada to serve as NSI's administrative manager and first employee and set about winning community support and recruiting employees for the project. Throughout Mississippi Chemical, people supporting the newsprint project found they were investing their pride and their hearts, as well as their time, in the new venture.

Amidst the flurry of activities surrounding the mill project, Dunn received a disturbing telephone call during one marathon Wall Street meeting he would never forget. It came from the company's vice president of finance, Bill Hawkins, in Yazoo City. "We were on the verge of finalizing the financial commitments to build

Newsprint South," Dunn recalled. "I was there with our banker, Jim Williams, from the Bank for Cooperatives." Hawkins got straight to the point: "You need to know Mississippi Chemical is about out of money, and I'm going to have to talk to the bank soon."

"It was the most desperate situation Mississippi Chemical ever faced," Hawkins later reflected. "We, along with the entire fertilizer industry, were losing money at a disastrous rate. We'd just lost $27 million. Our stock was at an all-time low of seven dollars per share, and there were no buyers." There seemed to be no end to the falling prices and mounting losses. The Bank for Cooperatives, which had been Mississippi Chemical's principal source of credit for four decades, had gone as far as it was willing to go. The bank finally drew the line and warned it would lend the company funds for only a six-month term—to March 1988. "It was dead serious," Hawkins recalled. "If things kept going as badly as they had, we might not have been able to meet our payroll come March. I think the bank's action shocked Tom Parry into seeing that drastic action was our only hope."

Desperate to save the company, in December of 1987 and January of 1988 Parry and the company took further extreme measures. To bring fertilizer sales under tighter control, Parry relieved the company's two chief sales executives; he asked his trusted financial vice president, Bill Hawkins, to assume responsibility for this critical task and named twenty-five-year veteran Billy Byrd to direct all day-to-day sales and marketing

matters. Soon after these management changes, the company began making even deeper slashes. In January 1988 ninety-two more members of its work force were released or took early retirement. "We had long since trimmed all the fat," Hawkins would recall. "This time we were cutting muscle and bone. It was very painful for everyone involved, but the company's immediate survival was in question."

In January 1988 Hawkins and Byrd insisted that firm prices be set and maintained at levels that would generate profits. Holding firm on prices took courage. "Initially, it made some folks mad as hornets," Byrd remembers, "because I called a halt to expensive and, in my opinion, unwise discount programs that were giving customers substantial discounts and costing us millions of dollars." For the first few months, Bill Hawkins and Byrd won no popularity contests among customers for steadfastly refusing to budge on the prices they set. In fact, one of Mississippi Chemical's district sales managers from Texas referred to Byrd as "'Just Say No' Byrd."

Mississippi Chemical's insistence on sound prices only slightly preceded the long overdue turnaround in the market. "We can't take credit for turning the market around," Hawkins would reflect. "Probably the time had finally come when it had to happen or everyone was going under. But we were sure elated when it did." So too were the company's bankers. When March arrived, with profits up and the outlook more optimistic, CoBank's loan was extended. The lowest point of the depression had been weathered,

In the spring of 1988 the fertilizer depression finally lifted, and MCC's sales and profits began a strong and long-awaited rebound.

and Mississippi Chemical had begun to rebound. The long slide had ended.

In addition to establishing firm prices, Billy Byrd guided the company in instituting a special contract sales program to facilitate sales both of fertilizer and of company stock to aggressive customers who wanted the right to larger fertilizer purchases. Over three years this program, in conjunction with rebounding agricultural and fertilizer profits, would lead these customers to purchase some 175,000 shares of company stock. As a result, the company's severely depressed stock price increased from $7.50 a share to $55 a share.

Senior vice president Robert Jones would later praise the manner in which Hawkins and Byrd had handled their pivotal assignment. "They were given the task of righting the ship at the most critical point in our company's history," Jones said. "They did an absolutely superb and courageous job of getting our sales policies and prices under control. They brought stability and firmness to our marketing. Bill Hawkins and Billy Byrd helped turn the company's tide."

Mississippi Chemical soon would have further good fortune. The persistent attempts by vice president Ed McCraw and engineer Kent Montgomery, to locate a buyer for the company's Pascagoula complex succeeded. "I talked to groups from China, India, and many other areas," McCraw said. Mississippi Chemical eventually began

lengthy negotiations with a group of American investors who owned Nu-West Industries. They wished to buy the Pascagoula plants and modify them to produce diammonium phosphates (DAP) for the world market. An agreement was subsequently reached, which salvaged for Mississippi Chemical a share of its investment in the thirty-one-year-old Pascagoula complex. On April 29, 1988, the company sold the facility to Nu-South Industries, a newly formed subsidiary of Nu-West, for $26.5 million, realizing a gain on the sale of some $7.6 million. Some of this gain was used to pay debt and retire bonds issued earlier in connection with the plants.

With the abrupt turnaround in both nitrogen prices and volume, the long-awaited recovery from the fertilizer depression arrived as forcefully as had the decline of six years earlier. In 1988 the company would have a profit of $18.2 million, a remarkable $45 million improvement over the loss of the prior year. And the following year, 1988–89, earnings would climb to $46.9 million. When Hawkins and Byrd were asked to take over responsibility for sales, the company had lost $46 million in thirty months. During the next forty months, Mississippi Chemical would achieve an astounding $157 million in fertilizer profits.

For nearly a decade, misfortune had seemed to beget more misfortune. Now prosperity came in waves. Just as the sharp rise in the American dollar had elicited the six-year agricultural depression, a marked softening in the dollar's international value helped spur recovery. Foreign markets again found American grains and fertilizers competitively priced, and export sales of these products began to skyrocket.

American potash prices rebounded following a U.S.–Canadian agreement that ended a heated dispute in which U.S. producers alleged that Canadian producers had unlawfully dumped potash on American markets. The recovery of potash prices made the reopening of the Carlsbad mine economically viable, and the company hastened to do so. "After five long years of waiting and watching the market, we were elated to have the opportunity to reopen our facility," Randy Foote, who had headed the Carlsbad caretaking force during the shutdown and was named general manager of start-up operations, would remember. "Fortunately we were able to recruit back a cadre of experienced mine and above-ground leaders who

had worked for the company in the early 1980s and had a warm feeling for the company."

In September 1988 Mississippi Chemical resumed the underground mining operations that had ceased in January 1983. By February 1989 the surface flotation, compaction, and granulation units were all running again, at an annual rate of three hundred thousand tons of potash each year. This sizeable output was made possible, in part, because the company had access to granulation facilities at the adjacent National Potash facility, which Mississippi Chemical had acquired in 1985 while its own mine and National's mine

were closed. To hold down costs and boost efficiency, the company took another bold step. It chose to operate with far fewer supervisors than other mines and to give its rank-and-file employees more responsibility and a larger role in decisions about their work. "Our people responded tremendously," Foote said. "They felt a higher degree of ownership and trust. They've done a super job of operating safely and efficiently." Most of the company's potash was to be sold in the Midwest or west of the Mississippi River to new but profitable markets for Mississippi Chemical, all easily accessible from Carlsbad.

At the same time, Mississippi Chemical

In 1988 rebounding American potash prices made it profitable for MCC to reopen its Carlsbad potash mining operations. At left, a mining crew—Timmy Walterscheid, Walter Bradley, Avery Williams, and Donald Louden—prepares to head underground, while, above, Viviano "Blackie" Trevino loads out a rail car of potash for shipment eastward.

was announcing important quality improvements for both its liquid nitrogen fertilizer, called N-Sol 32, and its ammonium nitrate. The company's research and development team had discovered ways to remove troublesome "free ammonia" from N-Sol. Continuing a thirty-five-year tradition of making substantial improvements in ammonium nitrate quality, MCC had developed a superior product that eliminated many of the storage and shipment problems incurred during hot, humid weather. To capitalize on this latest innovation, the company began selling its premium quality ammonium nitrate under the trade name AMTRATE, and this superior product nearly doubled MCC's share of the American ammonium nitrate market during the 1980s.

Mississippi Chemical's robust comeback was an appropriate finale to LeRoy Percy's four decades on the board and his twenty-nine year tenure as board chairman. When he retired on October 25, 1988, he was praised for the strong leadership he had given. "LeRoy Percy earned and commanded the respect, trust, and allegiance of every board member and company officer who served under him," Tom Parry would say. Robert Jones also spoke for many: "Mr. Percy is the wisest man I have ever met." Armstead Feland, who served as vice chair of the board under Percy for ten years, also paid tribute. "LeRoy Percy guided our board like a master symphony conductor in a bravo performance," he said. "With just a nod or word he'd halt our false moves. He was an absolute genius at building and holding consensus among the several different and

When Mississippi Chemical marked its fortieth birthday in October 1988, the company and president Tom Parry, right, honored LeRoy Percy upon completion of his twenty-nine-year term as the company's board chair and forty years of leadership to the board. As Percy stepped down, senior vice president Robert Jones spoke for many in calling him, "the wisest man I ever met."

With the addition of processing facilities purchased from National Potash and what Carlsbad general manager Randy Foote termed "the tremendous response of our people," production at Carlsbad soon topped 300,000 tons a year. A continuous mining machine's rapidly spinning bits dislodge the red potash ore from the mine face, hundreds of feet below the Carlsbad surface.

potentially contentious factions on this board. He was a man of few words, but immense wisdom."

The drama that would shape Mississippi Chemical's choice of Tom Parry's successor was then unfolding in a soybean field near Grenada, Mississippi. There, the company's subsidiary Newsprint South was building its world-class newsprint mill on the same site selected by Owen Cooper and an earlier group, who had considered such a venture in the early 1980s. And there Chuck Dunn was making his mark as he skillfully orchestrated this complex project.

If the technology used at other Mississippi Chemical facilities was state-of-the-art, that applied at Newsprint South represented state-of-the-future. The pulp mill utilized a "thermomechanical" technique for converting pine chips to pulp by crushing them mechanically under elevated temperature and pressure, thus avoiding the strong and constant odors caused by the typical chemical pulping process. After receipt of pulp, an enormous paper machine operated at a speed of 4,000 feet per minute, or 45 miles an hour, to produce rolls of newsprint 27.5 feet wide, ready to be cut to each publisher's specifications and shipped by truck or rail. However, the plant's design was not the project's only notable feature. Its complex financing arrangements and the construction contract itself were, on several counts, industry firsts.

The construction contract, ably negotiated for Newsprint South by a team headed by David Arnold and Jackson lawyer John

An aerial view of the sprawling $350 million Newsprint South mill just north of Grenada, Mississippi

Clark, proved to be a major factor not only in producing a fine pulp and paper mill but also in Newsprint South's ability to obtain financing for the mill. As the negotiations with the builder—RUST Construction Company of Birmingham, Alabama— neared an end in the late night in Birmingham, RUST's building lost electrical power. Undaunted, the group moved into the hallway and concluded the complex $300-plus million contract by the dim red glow of emergency lighting.

Even the electric power contract required complex negotiations. Because of the pulp mill's thermomechanical process, the facility required *100 megawatts* of electricity, an enormous load—equal to the power needed by a city of 100,000 people. The site chosen for the mill had the unique advantage of lying partly in the service area of Mississippi Power and Light Company and partly in the territory of the Tennessee Valley Authority (TVA). Both companies were obviously eager to supply this huge new customer with electricity. Company negotiators Robert Jones, Owen Cook, and Paul Lacy capitalized on this, coaxing the utilities into competitive bidding. Newsprint South ultimately chose TVA, because it believed that TVA would be the lower cost provider over the long-term.

Meanwhile Chuck Dunn, finance director

Tim Dawson, and attorney Ethel Truly spent much of the year in New York shaping a financing package. Ethel Truly recalls the challenges and the effort it required. "We had to arrange financing that was both a leveraged lease and a non-recourse project loan—that is, a loan payable only from the assets of Newsprint South and not guaranteed by Mississippi Chemical. We had to have the contractor guarantee the mill's performance over a start-up period of as long as four years and the lessor to agree to accept the mill whether or not it met operating specifications." All of these agreements were being negotiated simultaneously and all were intertwined. It was an assignment so unusual and so daunting that most observers predicted it could not be done. "We had to grit our teeth and refuse to give up on many occasions," Truly recalls.

They and their team of lawyers achieved success only through remaining in New York and enduring frequently acrimonious negotiating sessions that lasted from morning until late at night or into early the next morning, sometimes seven days a week. Truly would later recall receiving from one of the many attorneys involved in the project, Jackson's Jim Tohill, an invoice that reflected twenty-one hours of legal work in one day. "I would have questioned the bill," she said, "except that I was with him for every one of those twenty-one hours." When the marathon negotiations concluded, Newsprint South had the necessary $350 million in financing, while Mississippi Chemical had limited its investment to $22 million.

Various aspects of the project required

approvals from the U.S. Congress, the Mississippi legislature, the city and county of Grenada, the U.S. Department of Housing and Urban Development (HUD), and a host of regulatory agencies. First, the company had to obtain the approval of the U.S. Congress to preserve for the mill accelerated depreciation and certain other favorable tax provisions, slated to be eliminated by the Tax Reform Act of 1986. With the able guidance of Bill Simpson, a long-time aide of U.S. Senator Eastland, and the support of Senator John Stennis's able aide Guy Land, and Congressman Jamie Whitten, Newsprint South succeeded in doing so and therefore could qualify for less costly financing through a leveraged lease. As the mill became a reality, Gene Triggs, David Arnold, Ethel Truly, and others worked with the Federal Highway Administration, the Mississippi Department of Transportation, the state legislature, and the Department of Economic and Community Development to obtain permitting and funding for an exit off Interstate 55 North to serve the mill and the county's industrial park and to spare the city a steady stream of log trucks. Later Tommy McKiernon and Triggs worked closely with Grenada city and county officials who passed a $7.5 million bond issue to build a road from the Interstate 55 exit to the newsprint mill and beyond to the neighboring industrial park. Grenada Mayor L. D. Boone, city attorney Phil Embry, and consultant Woody Sample were successful in securing an $8.5 million grant from the U.S. Department of Housing and Urban Development to purchase major equipment for the mill. At the time it was

the largest grant of its type in HUD's history.

Soon the world's most advanced paper mill was taking shape in a field halfway between Memphis and Jackson. "It was an immense project—like building all our Yazoo City facilities from scratch at one time," engineer Rex Brown would recall. "We built roads, utilities, plants, offices, the whole works. We met all budgets, all timetables, and all operating specifications. We created, designed, and built a showplace paper mill for the world. It was my proudest moment in thirty-eight years at Mississippi Chemical." Brown was not alone in his enthusiasm. The Construction Institute of America honored the company by naming Newsprint South the nation's "Project of the Year." Observers cite the teamwork between Rex Brown and Paul Herbert, an Englishman who managed the construction for RUST, as instrumental to the giant project's success. "Paul and Rex were a superb team," Ethel Truly would recall. "When the inevitable differences arose, Rex and Paul would ask what was best for *the project*, rather than what was best for RUST or NSI. They were incredible leaders." Chester Grisham, Buddy Clark, Phil Gousset, Pat Brabston, and many others in Mississippi Chemical's engineering division also played key roles in NSI's construction success.

This achievement required rigorous adherence to high standards. A story often told at Mississippi Chemical exemplifies the expectations demanded by Pat Brabston, the hard-nosed MCC veteran who served as one of the project managers for Newsprint

A host of dignitaries rode a special train from Jackson to Grenada, Mississippi, to dedicate Newsprint South (NSI), described as a showplace paper mill for the world. Left: On the platform for dedication remarks were, from left, NSI board chair LeRoy Percy, MCC president Tom Parry, Governor Ray Mabus, U.S. Congressman Mike Espy, NSI mill vice president and general manager Rod Brown, MCC board chair Coley Bailey, and Grenada mayor L. D. Boone. Below left: Tom Parry and Mississippi Governor Ray Mabus enjoy the festivities. Below: NSI president Chuck Dunn and Newsprint South sales executive vice president Bob Reynolds inspect the giant mill's control panel.

South. As the story goes, when Brabston had some years earlier spotted a construction pipefitter not performing up to Brabston's exacting standards, Brabston jumped down in a ditch with the pipefitter and berated him for his inferior work. The men parted angrily. Later that day the pipefitter's supervisor stormed into a construction meeting to confront Brabston. "Did you call my pipefitter an SOB," the contractor demanded. "That depends," Brabston snapped back. "Are you calling that SOB a pipefitter?"

From the beginning the NSI undertaking was fraught with tight deadlines. The engineers assigned to select the most effective technology made an exhausting ten-day, six-nation tour to study the best and most modern paper mills. The trip was so grueling the MCC engineers called it "the death march." From England to Germany, Denmark to Norway, Sweden to Finland, the travelers searched for the most impressive design features. "Every morning we had to read the name on the money in our pockets to know what country we were in," Rex Brown recalled. "Some folks say sending a Cajun like me to look at paper mills is like sending a monkey to look at Rolex watches, but I'll stand by the job we did."

While construction was underway, Chuck Dunn and Lamar Peyton, a crusty former military man serving as MCC's personnel director, flew to Alpena, Michigan, to hire the first vice president and general manager of Newsprint South, Rod Brown, who was then working for pulp and paper manufacturer Abitibi-Price. Alpena was covered with snow and so cold that Peyton insisted that

Brown should accept the job upon nothing but the offer of a plane ticket out. Although he was able to get more than a plane ticket, Brown accepted the job and moved to Grenada. There he and Tommy McKiernon, soon to be joined by noted pulp mill "guru" Hitt Arnold, began the process of hiring an experienced group to supervise operation of the mill after construction, as well as a full cadre of mostly local employees without prior experience in the industry. They then faced the daunting task of training the inexperienced employees to run a mill they could not yet see. Rod Brown and his top team accomplished these tasks admirably, so well that the start up of the mill in 1989 was virtually flawless. In the early 1990s, a representative of General Electric Capital Corporation (GECC), which provided a significant portion of the mill's financing, told several of Newsprint South's officers that no one in General Electric had ever seen such a smooth start up. He added, "We have a lot of start ups for our own manufacturing facilities, and through GECC's investments, we see many others at close range. *Never* have we even heard of a start up this smooth." "I don't believe anyone could have done as fine a job as our people did in building and starting up that mill," Chuck Dunn said. "They overcame one huge obstacle after another. I just loved being around them; they were special people."

The Newsprint South enterprise required strict coordination from every aspect of the company: legal, finance, engineering, operations, distribution, personnel, and purchasing. Building and then operating this monu-

mental paper mill dominated the final years of Tom Parry's era as chief executive; it commanded *everyone's* attention. Those who had pursued the long struggle to realize the giant paper mill were justifiably proud. One of the most devoted, Ethel Truly, who served as general counsel for Newsprint South, said she would never forget riding the VIP train from Jackson to Grenada for the mill's dedication. "When our rail car entered Grenada, we passed an elementary school. Standing in the schoolyard were school children holding a banner that read 'Welcome Newsprint South.' I knew we would make a real difference."

While the ultra-modern mill met or exceeded all operating standards, its profitability was to be plagued by an unprecedented collapse in world newsprint prices. Inflation-adjusted newsprint prices had remained virtually level since the 1920s. When MCC considered the newsprint project in 1986–87, the prospect of steady prices for newsprint was extremely attractive to Mississippi Chemical as it struggled with the severe gyrations in fertilizer prices and profits. The company's board had approved construction of the mill, in large part, to counterbalance the cyclical nature of the fertilizer market. Consultants assisting MCC predicted a continuation of strong and stable newsprint prices and criticized the company for using "pessimistic" prices in deciding to invest.

Unfortunately, between the decision by Mississippi Chemical's board to build a newsprint mill in 1987 and its completion in 1989, the fundamentals of the newsprint market changed dramatically. For the first

time since the 1920s, real newsprint prices fell. And then they fell some more. Later, they would fall far below even the lowest prices anticipated in the company's conservative financial projections. Many factors coalesced to alter the North American newsprint market and send prices to unprecedented low levels, but the bottom line was that Newsprint South's profitability and MCC's return on investment in this giant project were never to materialize.

In spite of the slumping newsprint prices, the late 1980s to the early 1990s was an exceptional period for the company. "It was a most remarkable year," the fiscal 1991 annual report began. Nitrogen and potash demand, prices, and profits were healthy. The company was to receive back and reopen its Pascagoula complex. And Newsprint South continued to earn high marks by almost every measure but profitability.

Supported by its low-cost gas contracts, the company's nitrogen plants in Yazoo City and Donaldsonville recorded strong sales and led the U.S. fertilizer industry in nitrogen profits. In 1989 the company recorded earnings of $46.9 million. The following year patronage refunds dipped to $20.5 million but rebounded in 1991 to $46.1 million. Only a global drop in newsprint prices, which forced Newsprint South to take

Designing, building, and successfully starting up the Newsprint South paper mill was the most immense and complex construction project in MCC's history. For meeting all budgets, all timetables, and all operating specifications, the mill was named The Construction Institute of America's Project of the Year.

The Mississippi Chemical Snack Bar: Serving the World's Finest Tales

The center of social life in the Yazoo City offices is the company snack bar, where hot coffee, tall tales, and lively conversation are always on the menu.

"There is nothing in New York that can hold a candle to the Mississippi Chemical snack bar," says Chuck Dunn. "Where else on earth can you hear storytellers like Jerry Clower, Robert Jones, Owen Cook, Meadow Perry, and Harold Fisher spin one wonderful tale after another?" He will not get an argument from the generations of employees who have been grounded in the folklore of the company through the memorable stories embellished, savored, and passed down at the MCC snack bar.

In the early 1950s there was no snack bar, but employees would gather around a large urn where J. D. Cooper of the purchasing department brewed coffee and serve themselves. On the honor system, coffee drinkers were expected to donate a nickle. Then for many years Pete and Maude DeAngelo served coffee and assorted lunches at the MCC snack bar in a

Company employees Blanche Hester, left, and Francis Black Pierce straighten up the tiny corner of the Yazoo City plant office, in 1955, that served as the original MCC snack bar.

tiny corner of the plant office building. When inflation forced the DeAngelos to raise the price of coffee from a nickel to six cents, not everyone took this increase graciously. One who resented the increase was the frugal personnel manager Gene Turner. Turner, it seems, could never "remember" to bring an extra penny to the coffee bar and day after day asked his colleagues to "loan me a penny." One day Gene breezed into the coffee bar, ordered a cup, and made the usual request. No one responded, and finally accountant Jim Lane spoke for the assembled group, "Naw, Turner, I don't have a penny, but I've got change for a nickel."

Few have told and retold more stories in the snack bar than Harold Fisher. For forty years Fisher, the company's data processing specialist, was also the unofficial historian of company life, entertaining people on demand at coffee breaks with his boundless store of anecdotes about MCC's many colorful personalities. He delighted in educating the new generation to company lore, such as his accounts of John Bergman's terror of electric calculators. Bergman, MCC's first comptroller, was so frightened of electronic devices that he refused to enter "the machine room," which housed MCC's first giant computer. The only exception, according to Fisher, was one Friday when Frank Ellis, Jr., of the payroll department had sent not one but three consecutive sets of unsigned and unusuable payroll checks to Pascagoula. As pilot Jack Hawks waited to fly a final signed set to anxious Coastal employees, Bergman rushed into the usually intolerable machine room to see personally that the last batch of paychecks was signed; what he glimpsed instead was an oblivious Frank Ellis prancing around the room in an animated impersonation of the frustrated Bergman.

Fisher also tells of Hattie Murphy, the company's first nurse, who brought Prussian precision to the company's first-aid installation. Quick to cure any respiratory illness by swathing a throat with strong red antiseptic, she also believed that one or two painful blasts to the throat from her handheld immunizer could knock out treated polio germs. Once Murphy hastened to the rescue of a plant employee overcome with gas, forcefully strapped an oxygen mask to his face, and restrained his flailing arms. When her efforts failed to calm him, someone standing nearby exclaimed, "Murphy, for crying out loud, turn on the oxygen! The man's suffocating!"

Fisher loved to quote Truett Duncan, long-time plant employee who lived across the street from Owen Cooper. "When Owen Cooper interviewed me," Duncan had said, "he promised that if I came to work for Mississippi Chemical he'd put me in the biggest car in the country. He wasn't kidding. I accepted his offer, and before the day was over, he had me in the biggest car I'd ever seen—a forty-ton Illinois Central box car—with a broom sweeping it out for nitrate bags!"

J. D. Cooper, a company purchasing agent for many years, is another favorite subject of snack bar tales by Fisher and other company tale spinners. Known to his fellow employees as "Cool" Cooper, he never failed to further irritate already agitated co-workers inquiring about lost or late orders with his response: "It's rolling, man. It's rolling. You can count on it." "Cool" Cooper delighted in his attempts to share in some of Owen Cooper's fame by introducing himself to new vendors as "Mr. Cooper from Mississippi Chemical." Cooper was the first to greet Chuck Dunn when he came to work in Yazoo City in 1978 from Atlanta's pen-striped legal environs. "The first person I met was this guy decked out in crisp white yachting clothes," Dunn recalls. "I'll never forget it—I thought, what am I getting into?"

Almost all company veterans have stories to tell newcomers about the vicissitudes of flying with MCC's first pilot, Jack Hawks, in his corporate aircraft. Fellow employees dubbed Hawks "Commander of the Mississippi Chemical Air Force," because for a quarter-century he ran the corporate airplane as if he were General Patton, deferring to no higher authority. Any passenger who was late for takeoff or tried to board with items

For a quarter-century, a report on Al Allbritton's famous garden was a regular snack bar feature.

not approved by Hawks himself was in for a tough time. One corporate executive was ordered to leave a six-pack of Coors beer in Carlsbad because it would "overload the aircraft." "On my first flight after Hawks left," Harold Fisher recalls, "the new pilot asked me, 'What time would you like to return?' That was the first time I ever had a choice."

Al Allbritton, the company's persistent credit manager for more than thirty years, is remembered in company lore for knowing everything there was to know about every MCC customer across the South. One driving with him from Yazoo City to Clarksdale, for example, could learn the name of every farm, its owner, and how many or how few assets its owner could claim. Once Allbritton adamantly insisted that officers Tom Parry and Don McGraw refuse to sell a pound of fertilizer to a particular party he felt was a serious credit risk. "Don't sell to him, even if he offers to pay us cash in advance," Allbritton warned. When the man offered to do just that—pay cash in advance for three thousand tons—Parry overruled Allbritton and approved the sale. Months later the cantankerous customer filed complaints about the product he bought and took legal action against the company, eventually causing a loss of several thousand dollars on the sale.

The adventures of attorney Robert Jones's crisscrossing the world to conduct company business are the subject of countless snack bar tales. Lynn Montgomery, his assistant and a thirty-five-year veteran of the legal department, recounts the dozens of times Jones hurried from his fourth floor office to the airport without so much as a change of clothes. "They sell shirts and socks in New York," he would mutter over his shoulder. On his first trip to Manhattan, however, when he was broke and a fledgling junior attorney, he bought a new suit for the occasion. Preening in his new suit, he stepped out of his hotel and was promptly mugged by a street gang. They roughed him up and took his two-hundred-dollar cash travel advance, then declined to accept the VISA card Jones graciously offered them. When the discombobulated Jones returned to his hotel, he immediately telephoned his wife, Susan, in Yazoo City to report the attack. "Oh, Bobby," she exclaimed, "did they hurt your new suit?"

Co-workers avoid riding to the airport with Jones, who is notorious for boarding at the last second, if he boards at all. Once, determined not to miss a 7 a.m. flight in Jackson, an hour away from his home in Yazoo City, Jones elected to spend the night before at a hotel inside the Jackson terminal. "A fool-proof plan," Jones beamed smugly. But neither his alarm, his wake-up calls, nor the roar of jet engines aroused Jones until long after the 7 a.m. departure. Nevertheless, tardiness has had its advantages. Some co-workers insist that Jones's keen negotiating skills were honed persuading gate agents to hold planes or open aircraft doors to let him on board.

Jerry Clower may be Mississippi Chemical's most well known fertilizer salesman-humorist, but many fellow employees insist that diminutive Meadow Perry is the funniest person ever to walk and talk the halls of the sales division. One day during a coffee break, Meadow Perry turned from the *Clarion-Ledger* to muse to the group about some notable person's recent death from an apparent heart attack. "I hope the Lord never strikes me with an apparent heart attack," he declared. "I can handle a real heart attack with no problem, but I've never read of a single survivor of one of them apparent heart attacks."

When Jerry Clower was basking in his Grand Ole Opry fame and representing McCoullough chainsaws in national television commercials, Perry decided to saw Clower down a notch. Covering his receding hairline with an Elvis look-alike wig provided by traffic director Jim Pierce, Perry altered his voice to fit his hair style and strolled into Clower's MCC office. Introducing himself as the national sales manager of the Home-Lite chainsaw company, he asked Clower to represent his product with an offer that would have made Michael Jordan envious. Perry's performance was so convincing, company legend maintains, he nearly had to produce a contract for Clower to sign.

The price of a cup of coffee is no longer a nickel, but the snack bar tales are still free. In recounting and preserving bygone eras and the spirited personalities of company legend, the stories are a testimony to the corporate culture that is the vital heart of Mississippi Chemical.

Harold Fisher, computer guru and snack bar raconteur

J. D. "Cool" Cooper lets his hair down.

Key to the success of the company's Pascagoula complex, now operating as Mississippi Phosphates and devoted exclusively to producing DAP (18-46-0) for the world market, is an economical source of phosphate rock. The company found this critical source of phosphate rock and a long-term partner in Morocco. Inspecting OCP's massive Moroccan mine and huge mining dragline, above, are MCC and Mississippi Phosphates officials Ed McCraw, Jim Perkins, and Mack Barber. At left, the *Maritime Prosperity* unloads a shipment of Moroccan rock at Mississippi Phosphates's Pascagoula dock in March 1992.

significant initial losses, kept overall profits from going higher.

This period also included the return to Mississippi Chemical of its Pascagoula fertilizer facilities. In early 1990, two years after buying the Pascagoula complex and investing $12 million to convert it from mixed fertilizer (NPK) production to the manufacture of diammonium phosphate (DAP), Nu-South, Inc., filed for bankruptcy. According to MCC vice president, Ed McCraw, "The world DAP market had taken a nosedive, and Nu-South did not have the capital to absorb its losses." As a secured creditor, Mississippi Chemical received ownership of the Pascagoula plants on December 7, 1990, and

placed them in a new, wholly-owned subsidiary, Mississippi Phosphates Corporation. Now the company had to find a way to make good use of the facility.

That task fell to Ed McCraw, who two years earlier had made a worldwide search for an interested buyer of the Pascagoula plants. Now he and Robert Jones searched for a partner that wanted to collaborate with Mississippi Phosphates in producing DAP at Pascagoula. Ideally this ally would have a major phosphate rock mine from which to supply rock, the principal ingredient in DAP. Mississippi Phosphates would provide and operate the plant. The partner would provide phosphate rock at a price which

would fluctuate based on the financial performance of the business. McCraw conferred with groups in Russia, Morocco, and the Republic of Togo on the west coast of Africa. Each of these contenders controlled immense phosphate reserves and mines. Finally McCraw and Mississippi Phosphates found their partner in Casablanca, Morocco.

McCraw and Jones would not readily forget their sojourn in Casablanca to confer with officials of Office Chérifien des Phosphates (OCP), a Moroccan firm that is the world's largest miner of phosphate rock. "Casablanca is even more exotic and fascinating than you would imagine," Jones said. "You can walk out of a very cosmopolitan

During their trip to North Africa for contract negotiations with Office Chérifien des Phosphates (OCP), the national phosphate company of Morocco, MCC officials, at right, sightsee in the ancient city of Marrakech, Morocco. Standing, from left, Mack Barber, then general manager of Mississippi Phosphates, Jim Perkins, who would become general manager of Mississippi Phosphates, Chuck Dunn, Robert Jones, and their host from OCP. Above, Perkins, Dunn, Barber, and senior vice president Ed McCraw watch a reenactment of Arabian biblical scenes in Marrakech.

business meeting, where the OCP officials speak five or six languages, and step across an alley and feel as if you've gone back in time five hundred years. There's nothing in the United States as ancient as parts of Morocco." OCP was interested in Mississippi Phosphates's business plan and contract proposal, and soon an agreement was reached between the two firms from different continents and different cultures.

In December 1991 the company brought its Pascagoula plants back into full production using OCP's phosphate rock delivered by big ocean-going ships from Morocco. Ironically, the man chosen to guide this

comeback was Mack Barber, who had been the original Pascagoula general manager in 1957 and had returned to manage the plants for Nu-South in 1988. Barber made fertilizer history in 1954 by producing the first DAP ever made in the world.

By June 30, 1992, the Pascagoula operation, now devoted exclusively to producing DAP fertilizers, was operating at costs lower than projected. "Just when we had things running really well, the Russians dumped all their phosphate fertilizers on the world market and the price collapsed," Ed McCraw declared. "When that challenge came, we found out what fine partners we had in

OCP. To keep the plant running, both sides had to make concessions—and both were willing to do so. We felt we'd found a phosphate partner for the long haul."

To increase its ability to produce more nitrogen fertilizers even more efficiently, from 1991 through 1993 the company invested $34 million to add a new thousand-ton-a-day nitric acid plant and to increase its ammonium nitrate capacity at Yazoo City. It also completed an ambitious retrofit program to increase nitrogen output and to decrease the amount of natural gas and energy required for each ton.

This new nitric acid plant epitomized

Mississippi Chemical's leadership both in utilizing advanced technology and in leading the nation in operating efficiencies. This ultra-modern facility was completed on schedule and $2.5 million under budget. An independent survey of American nitric acid plants conducted by Competitive Dynamics, Inc., rated this new plant the nation's finest unit in efficiency, on-stream time, and hours of employee time required to produce each ton.

On March 31, 1993, Tom Parry completed his twenty-year term as president of Mississippi Chemical. Overall performance and profits during the two tumultuous decades he led the company were very solid. From 1973 to 1993, Mississippi Chemical generated $500 million in patronage refunds, despite the fact that six of those years were marred by the deepest fertilizer depression in history. Eighty-nine percent of that $500 million was

In March 1993 Tom Parry completed his twenty-year term as president of Mississippi Chemical Corporation. Above: As Dot and Tom Parry arrive for Parry's retirement festivities, corporate communications manager Melinda Hood pins a boutonnierre on Parry. On hand to pay tribute to Parry's accomplishments were the two men who served with him as board chairs, Coley Bailey, far left, and LeRoy Percy. During Parry's two decades as president, Mississippi Chemical earned cumulative profits of $500 million.

MCC president and CEO Tom C. Parry, left, discusses 1988 state trade mission to Japan with Gov. Ray Mabus, right

RETIRING

MCC's Parry is ready to travel, relax

At age 65, Tom Parry says he still has a lot to offer, but he's ready for retirement.

He's not so sure, however, that his wife Dot is.

"I heard her on the telephone the other day tell someone that she was going to have to make some major adjustments," he said. "She said 'I'm going to have twice the husband but half the money.'"

Parry is looking forward to a less regimented lifestyle and the opportunity to travel.

He's already bought a motor home with hopes of taking his first trip, maybe in late April, with Key West, Fla., as a possible destination.

"I've traveled a tremendous amount my entire life," he said recently. "But when you travel on business, most of the time all you get to do is go to meetings.

"Many conference rooms don't even have windows. A conference room pretty much looks the same whether you're in California, Mississippi, India or China."

Parry will concentrate on seeing the United States, but at his own pace. "I've always been on a schedule," he said. "I don't want a schedule.

"If I find a place I like and want to stay two or three days, or maybe a week, then I'll stay. If I find a place and don't like it and want to leave right away, then I'll go. I just want to be able to roll with the punches."

Parry is certain of one thing: He doesn't want any guided tours.

Continued on page 4B

Parry will miss visiting with his employees

"There should be an orderly time to retire so others can take over. I don't feel like I've slipped. I've got an awful lot of experience that would be valuable to a company. I've faced any type situation a company could face."

-- Tom C. Parry

Martha Stevens, right, and Sue Tatum, center, enjoy a laugh with the congenial Parry. At left, a special section in the March 20, 1993, *Yazoo Herald* recapped the accomplishments during Parry's era.

returned to shareholder-patrons in cash, a figure unmatched in the history of American cooperatives. Annual sales tripled during Parry's tenure, and company assets rose from $100 million to $330 million. Under his purview, the company acquired and now mines the nation's largest potash reserves in Carlsbad, completed the massive Newsprint South paper mill in Grenada, and installed environmental protection systems more sophisticated than anyone could have imagined when President Nixon and the Environmental Protection Agency issued the call for clean air and water for America in 1973.

As his leadership drew to a close, Parry summarized the state of the company he had led. "Our management staff is lean and efficient. Our plants are productive and economical. Our raw material supplies are reliable and cost efficient. Our employee team is the finest in the industry. We intend to remain a major force in the U.S. fertilizer business."

The World Beyond

It is 1998, and the world has taken more than a few turns. I live in Jackson now and often travel the forty or so miles north just to drive around my old town and absorb the memories and see for myself that it is still there. The Yazoo Motel and Stub's Restaurant, which used to greet one at the intersection of Highways 49E and 49W, have vanished from the landscape, replaced by a gargantuan K-Mart. Fast-food franchises dot the highways on the edge of the old town, and affluent subdivisions are tucked here and there. The streets in the black sections are all paved now, and a few of the fine old houses have been razed to make parking lots. There is a new federal penitentiary on the outskirts of town, an inspiration to the economy as MCC had been in 1948.

But, with these few exceptions, the town looks remarkably the same to me as it did in 1948. The old residential areas, with their secretive alleys, are still there. Main Street, my Main Street, has altered scarcely at all: only the names on the stores are different. The substantial edifice at Broadway and Main that housed the noble Dixie Theater is still there, but it is a mercantile establishment now. The Famous Store is still there and the Black and White Store. The Taylor-Roberts Feed and Seed Store in which radio station WAZF was quartered collapsed on its own in recent years and is now a vacant lot, as is Tommy Norman's Drug Store across the way. Main Street nonetheless has the patina of time. It seems just as I remember it in my childhood reveries. How can it be true that in 1996 there was a daytime murder on my Main Street?

The population has increased from 9,000 to 12,500. The pace of life seems still slow and easy, though fewer people are walking on the streets and almost none gather on front porches. I sense—or is this merely wishful thinking?—that Yazoo still has a certain supple inwardness: the mysterious whistles of the nighttime trains still beckon to the big world beyond. Its children still dream and imagine, I believe, and some of them still go to the Witch's Grave on Halloween to scare themselves. They still listen to the stories of their aging relatives, and the seductive Delta earth yet casts its spell. I pray that I am right.

Even so, when I talk to the young people there, I do not sense in them the isolation I felt. Inevitably shaped by the modern television culture, by the electronics and communications and computer revolutions, the young are not nearly so sequestered in Yazoo as in my day. The teenagers and younger children, too, are "on line" and using arcane computer rhetoric, which would have been enigmatic if not judged subversive in my day. And how can one calculate the difference Mississippi Chemical Corporation's presence has made on the town, its international connections bringing the distant horizons right to its door? My Yazoo City was the Gateway to the Delta, and now it's a gateway to the world. And this is good.

The six years leading to Mississippi Chemical's fiftieth anniversary in 1998 were vigorous and visionary ones for the company, reminiscent in many ways of its earliest years. After an extensive national search for a successor to Tom Parry as its third chief executive, MCC found the best man right at home: Charles O. (Chuck) Dunn. Under his purview the company engaged in an enormous expansion program to prepare for the increasingly international market. In June 1994, 99 percent of MCC's shareholders endorsed a plan to convert the company's operation from that of a cooperative to that of a publicly traded business. The battered survivors of the Great Fertilizer Depression of the previous decade proved they could go forward to Wall Street and finance innovative expansions around the world.

Two young Southern Baptists from Mississippi's adjoining states of Arkansas and Tennessee, Bill Clinton and Al Gore, were inaugurated as President and Vice President in 1993, and for a second term in 1997. They were the first Democrats elected to consecutive terms since Franklin Roosevelt, who died in office two years before Mississippi Chemical Corporation flickered in the imagination of Owen Cooper. Republicans formed the Contract with America and won control of both houses of Congress. Bill Clinton and Congress dueled over the budget, and the federal government was shut down twice because of inaction, but the U.S. national budget appeared headed toward balance, and the economy was healthier than it had been in years. The Clinton administration was plagued continuously with investigations into financial and ethical matters.

Three native Mississippians rose to national political prominence: Trent Lott of Pascagoula as majority leader of the U.S. Senate, and Yazoo natives Haley Barbour as chairman of the National Republican Party and Mike Espy as Secretary of Agriculture. Espy, before joining Clinton's cabinet, was the state's first black Congressman since Reconstruction. He would resign his cabinet post amid conflict-of-interest questions.

The Mississippi legislature passed a constitutional amendment allowing the governor to succeed himself, and Kirk Fordice became the first governor in Mississippi ever to serve back-to-back terms. When the governor vetoed the landmark Adequate Education Bill, which would establish a program of equitable funding for school children in property-poor districts, Mississippi Chemical led by CEO Chuck Dunn worked with the Public Education Forum of Mississippi, a coalition of state business people, to successfully convince the legislature to override Fordice's veto of the education bill.

Seventeen gambling casinos, several of them not far from the Yazoo City, Pascagoula, and Donaldsonville plants, opened in the state: on the Gulf Coast, in Natchez, Vicksburg, Greenville, Tunica County, and on the Choctaw Reservation in Neshoba County. In 1996 Attorney General Mike Moore took on the tobacco industry on behalf of the state and won. In 1994, thirty years after the crime, Byron De La Beckwith was tried and convicted by a biracial jury of assassinating Medgar Evers. The new Jackson post office was named after Evers. Yazoo City elected its first black mayor in history, Wardell Leach, in the spring of 1998. The city of Jackson, too, elected its first black mayor, Harvey Johnson, Jr., defeating a woman who, if elected, would have been the first woman mayor.

Violence, conflict, and crime took over many of the headlines in the state and nation. Jackson set frightening records for homicides as virulent, mindless crime swept the capital city. A shooting rampage at the Jackson fire department and the daytime murder in downtown Yazoo City epitomized the pattern of violence that was more than ever gripping the state and the nation. On the national scene, a standoff between the Branch Davidians cult and the federal authorities outside Waco, Texas, led to the burning of the compound. The World Trade Center in New York was bombed. The World Series was canceled in 1995 because of a players' strike. O. J. Simpson was charged in the murder of his ex-wife and a friend; he was acquitted of criminal charges, but a civil court jury found him liable for the deaths. The federal building in Oklahoma City was bombed and 168 persons killed; and Timothy McVeigh was found guilty of the bombing and sentenced to death. The Centennial Olympic Games in Atlanta in 1996 were marred by a bombing at Centennial Park.

In 1998 one man driving the largest, fastest mechanical cotton harvester could harvest 140,000 pounds of cotton a day, the equivalent of one hundred bales, by himself, a feat that would have required six hundred hand-pickers in the year of MCC's formation. The Delta and Pine Land Company at Scott, Mississippi, surprised everyone by developing an esoteric strand of cotton resistant to the despised and ubiquitous cousin to the boll weevil, the boll worm. In 1948 farmers were just beginning to experiment with exchanging their mules, hoes, and burlap cotton sacks

for tractors, weed-controlling chemicals, and mechanical cotton pickers. Anhydrous ammonia was new, as were entomologists, more generally called "insect scouts" or "bug doctors," working to control the boll weevil. Today Southern farmers and their MCC fertilizer dealers employ sophisticated satellite and computer-operated rigs to apply the precise amounts of plant food needed on every plot.

The history of Mississippi Chemical Corporation, like that of Southern agriculture, is a classic story of elemental dichotomies. The contrasts abound:

When MCC went public in August 1994, the $15 million in stock bought in the first ten minutes was four times the stock purchased in the company's first three years, 1948 to 1951. In those three earlier years MCC's people had confronted seemingly insurmountable odds to raise the $7.5 million in capital to begin operation. Yet in that first full day of public trading in 1994, the company sold $75 million in stocks, nearly ten times the entire 1950 figure.

In the company's maiden year of 1948, its founders walked the turn-rows of the Mississippi Delta cotton fields trying to convince farmers to invest in a risky new enterprise. Fifty years later the company managers, often traveling by jet across time zones, seek equity and debt financing in New York, Boston, Amsterdam, and other financial centers.

In its first quarter of a century MCC's sales were inexorably shaped by rains, droughts, and transformations in planting patterns across the South in response to national farm policy. In 1998 MCC is just as greatly influenced by how much fertilizer China, India, and the nations of South America are purchasing and by whether former Soviet Union states like Bulgaria are flooding the market with fertilizers to acquire hard currency for their struggling economies.

In 1950 MCC chose Yazoo City as its plant site because the town had two natural gas pipelines and two highways running into the Mississippi Delta. In contrast, forty-five years later, the company selected Trinidad as an ancillary locale because that island republic offered the most dependable and economical source of the same crucial natural gas and had oceanic ports allowing fertilizer deliveries to the whole world.

In the 1970s MCC struggled to locate sources of essential phosphate rock and potash for its plants and farmers. In 1998 the company is the largest potash producer in the United States. And it has created a partnership with the world's largest supplier of phosphate rock, located in Morocco.

In 1951 the company's original employees worked hard to produce the very first bags of ammonium nitrate at its crude and minuscule Yazoo City plant. Even then the technology utilized by Mississippi Chemical set the standard for the industry. Today the company remains the recognized leader in ammonium nitrate technology, its expertise studied and imitated and certain of its original technologies licensed to manufacturers in the four corners of the globe.

In MCC's callow days, skeptics everywhere scoffed at the notion of Mississippi farmers trying to operate complicated nitrogen fertilizer plants. Today foreign and domestic visitors flock to Yazoo City and Donaldsonville to study their techniques, and Mississippi Chemical is regarded as among the most efficient producers of fertilizer in the industry.

In 1952 MCC reported with immense pride that it had produced forty thousand tons of ammonium nitrate in Yazoo City. As the century ends, the company has the capacity to produce twenty-five times that amount—nearly one million tons each year in its Yazoo City facilities.

In 1951–52, MCC's first year of production, sales totaled $3.9 million. In 1998 the company's sales are nearing $2 million per day. That means that it currently requires the company forty- eight hours—just two days—to reach a sales total equal to its entire first year. Even after adjusting for inflation, the difference is astounding.

In 1948, my freshman year in Yazoo High School, and likewise the formative year of the Mississippi Chemical Corporation, the old section of the Yazoo City cemetery, a lovely bucolic expanse on the conclusive succession of hills swooping down to meet the peremptory Delta, had for all purposes reached its capacity. It was in that year that the "new section" as we called it, in much the local colloquial way we had called the new MCC the "chemical plant," was opened on vast adjoining hills separated from the old section by an emphatic little valley, the geologic divide between the two precise and recognizable.

Not long ago I was drawn there on a solitary visit. After fifty years the new section itself was running out of room. From its original perimeters to the farthest crest out at a verdant horizon of sweetgums, oaks, and cedars, these once untenanted hills were now crowded to filling with the tombstones of the older vanished generation I once knew, including many of the early MCC people. Half a century of Yazoo's citizens had passed along, and they were opening a newer section yet in some rises and descents to the south.

This landscape vista of the accumulating decades on this afternoon reminded me anew of how ineluctably linked were town and chemical plant in the irrevocable passing of time—and of how MCC and the long-ago dreams of Southern farmers were so intrinsically intertwined with the history of Yazoo itself. Mississippi Chemical had made a long and circuitous journey from the meeting in the modest and steamy boardroom at the Mississippi Farm Bureau office on President Street in Jackson in 1947 when Owen Cooper and a handful of visionary Mississippians had first discussed the possibilities of their chimerical scheme: if Mississippi farmers could not get fertilizer, then by God let's build a fertilizer plant for them.

From its first precarious beginnings in the muddy Delta cornfield abutting our small and sleepy river settlement, from its infant failures and dilemmas to its prominent position in the world itself fifty years later, our *little indigenous chemical plant had survived, overcome, and thrived through an era of thermonuclear terror, destructive warfare, and domestic turbulence while quietly pursuing those eternal things that matter: sustenance, life, human beings enduring on the Lord's good and equivocal earth.* Making things grow.

W. M.

CHAPTER EIGHT

Mississippi Chemical
goes to Wall Street

As the 1980s came to a close, Mississippi Chemical faced strategic decisions that would shape its destiny in the next century. It had now to answer three imperative questions: Who would succeed LeRoy Percy after three decades as board chair? Who would follow Tom Parry as president? And, perhaps the most complex question of its fifty-year history, should the company make the historic conversion from operating as an agricultural cooperative to operating as a regular and publicly traded business corporation?

Thirty-six-year-old Coley Bailey was worried. It was 1986, and he had just been elected vice chair of MCC's board and likely successor to LeRoy Percy, who would com-

Celebrating MCC's debut on the New York Stock Exchange, October 10, 1996, are, from left: Chuck Dunn, president; John Sharp Howie, board vice chair; William Johnston, New York Stock Exchange president; and Coley Bailey, board chair.

plete forty years of service and step down as board chair in just two years. Succeeding a man of Percy's obvious stature was reason enough to make a young man nervous. But Bailey had another concern. Tom Parry was scheduled to retire as company president shortly after Percy. "I didn't want my first job as board chair to be the crucial task of picking a new CEO. I wanted Mr. Percy's wisdom and guidance on that important choice," Bailey would explain. Bailey drove from his farm in Coffeeville, Mississippi, to Greenville to discuss his anxiety with Percy. "I asked Mr. Percy to go ahead and name a presidential search committee so we could make that choice before he left. Mr. Percy threw the ball right back in my lap and named me to chair the search committee. He always brought out the best in people by involving them in the process. He wanted us to pick the CEO and in so doing make us better."

Bailey had deep associations with the Mississippi Chemical board. His father, Joe Bailey of Coffeeville, and his father-in-law, Aven Whittington of Greenwood, spent a combined forty years on the company's board and executive committee. Bailey was elected to the board in 1978 when he was only twenty-eight. "My three life mentors—my dad, Aven Whittington, and LeRoy Percy—served over eighty years on the Mississippi Chemical board. And I met my wife because of their Mississippi Chemical affiliation." While he was a student at Millsaps, a liberal arts college in Jackson, his father and Aven Whittington drove to Yazoo City together every month to attend the company's executive committee meeting. Whittington's stepdaughter, Margaret Griffin, was also a student at Millsaps, and the two men kept encouraging Coley Bailey to meet Margaret. "I'm pretty hard-headed. So I resisted their advice for about a year. But finally I gave in, and I surely am grateful." Soon the Bailey-Whittington-Mississippi Chemical connection produced a matrimonial merger.

When he first joined the board, Bailey was articulate and confident; he favorably impressed his fellow directors, men between fifteen and thirty-five years his senior. The directors were just as impressed with the only other person elected at such a young age, John Sharp Howie of Yazoo City, whose grandfather, John Sharp Williams, had been the company's first board president in 1948. In 1988, with his retirement approaching, LeRoy Percy considered one of these two men, Bailey or Howie, as his likely successor. Bailey recalled that Howie, who was then involved in time-consuming business matters of his own, offered to defer to him, but Percy insisted both of them stand as candidates to take his place. Each represented generations of dedication to the company and were leaders in Southern agriculture. Each ran significant farming operations and had been seasoned for a decade in the company's board room, and each had years of service before him. The board could hardly go wrong with either of them. Finally it made its choice, electing the younger Bailey to succeed Percy. After Percy's retirement, the board elected Howie as vice chair.

In 1997 Bailey and Howie would reflect on how, a decade earlier, the board search committee had proceeded with the task of choosing the man to succeed Tom Parry as CEO. "We set out to get the very best man in America to lead Mississippi Chemical, and we believe we succeeded," Bailey remembered. Howie agreed. "We couldn't

have picked a better man," he said. The committee did not rush its decision. It summoned a well-known national search firm, selected forty candidates from across the nation and within the company, and gradually began reducing the roster. "We narrowed our list to about a dozen extremely qualified and proven leaders and then invited them to Yazoo City for three intense days of interviewing," Bailey remembered. "LeRoy Percy became seriously ill right at that juncture and was unable to take part in the interview process. So the job fell on our shoulders after all."

A 1996 study by the Stanford University Graduate Business School concluded that the world's thirty most visionary businesses all chose their chief executive officers from within their own ranks. Likewise, Mississippi

Chemical finally decided not to import an outsider, but instead to promote someone familiar and grounded in the company. In October 1988 Bailey, Howie, and the board selected forty-year-old Chuck Dunn to become, on Tom Parry's retirement in 1993, the third chief executive in the company's history.

"We selected Chuck Dunn to be our next chief executive officer because he was an exceptional talent and a proven quantity," Bailey reflected. "Our board had seen the incredible job he'd done managing Newsprint South, which was the largest project in Mississippi Chemical's history, and we didn't think anyone could match Chuck in leading our team to the next levels of achievement. He was a near-perfect balance of being a great manager and an entrepreneurial risk-

After being chosen to follow LeRoy Percy as company board chair, Coley Bailey, second from right, and Tom Parry, right, inspect Mississippi Chemical's potash mining facilities with Carlsbad employees, from left, Bob Dynan, Jill Farnsworth, and Randy Foote, plant manager.

taker." Howie noted that Dunn "can spot the opportunities and the torpedoes. Go for the former and dodge the latter."

Dunn was born and spent his early years in farming communities in Bolivar County and then in Greenwood, both in the Mississippi Delta. His family then moved to Mobile, Alabama, where he graduated from high school. He received an undergraduate degree at The Citadel, the venerable military college in Charleston, South Carolina, and, following a two-year stint in the army, got his law degree from the University of Alabama. After practicing tax and corporate law with an Atlanta firm for almost four years, Dunn became disaffected with Atlanta's fast-paced business world and joined Mississippi Chemical's legal department in 1978. "I'd grown increasingly tired of a culture in Atlanta that seemed to espouse shrewdness and cunning as its ultimate virtues, and I found the integrity and family values I saw at Mississippi Chemical and in Yazoo City extremely appealing," Dunn would recall.

MCC insiders were soon impressed with his level-headed savvy. "In addition to his obvious business skills," Ethel Truly observed, "one of Chuck's best features is his genuine caring about people—all kinds of people. But just as important for his success as Mississippi Chemical's president is his recognition that the company needs many different types of personalities and diverse skills to prosper. He knows that *each* employee is important." Holly Raney, who hired Dunn when he was corporate general counsel, remembered, "Chuck was born

In 1988 Mississippi Chemical chose Charles O. "Chuck" Dunn to become its next president and chief executive officer upon Tom Parry's retirement.

with the ability to size up a problem and give you a sound, sensible, workable solution." Dunn was the fourth ranking member of Mississippi Chemical's five-member legal department in 1984. Four years later he was picked as the next president. How does one account for this meteoric rise? Dunn, Bailey, and Howie were separately asked. Newsprint South was their unanimous answer.

As Newsprint South began the transformation from an idea to a reality, Mississippi Chemical needed a strong leader to bring it together. Dunn had recently moved from the legal department to the finance division and was working on Newsprint South's complicated financing, when Tom Parry appointed him to head the whole enterprise. Dunn suc-

cessfully oversaw the largest and most complex project in Mississippi Chemical's first forty years. Newsprint South capitalized on complex financing, a unique construction agreement, and the skills and experience in virtually every area in Mississippi Chemical, and it would eventually attract notice for its smooth start up, operating efficiency, and environmental sensitivity.

The Newsprint South project not only propelled Chuck Dunn into the Mississippi Chemical presidency, but developed inside the company a cadre of rising professionals with broad competence and experience. "When we took on the Newsprint South project, our staff and many of our board members were pretty demoralized by the lengthy fertilizer depression of the 1980s," Dunn would recall. "Designing, financing, building, and operating such a massive paper mill, which became a world showcase, proved to us that we had the intelligence and ability to play in the big leagues and compete with the best. It brought us out of the emotional and financial depression of the 1980s and into the 1990s with excitement about what Mississippi Chemical could do in the future."

Owen Cook, corporate director of planning, would credit Newsprint South with building competence and confidence within the company. Newsprint South, Cook would note, needed a number of high-performance teams composed from virtually every corner of the company: legal, finance, engineering, operations, distribution, purchasing, and personnel. These teams inspired self-confidence, pride, and a hard-earned belief that the company had the ability and the daring to do "whatever is necessary."

While Newsprint South required considerable contributions from every department of the company, Chuck Dunn orchestrated the manifold aspects of the undertaking. He was promoted to MCC vice president reporting directly to Parry and also selected to be president of Newsprint South. Ethel Truly and Tim Dawson, who had been involved in arranging the financing package to fund the paper mill, also became NSI officers: Dawson as vice president of finance and chief financial officer and Truly as general counsel.

In 1992 Dunn named Cook as MCC corporate director of planning and asked him to

The ultramodern $350 million newsprint mill, built by Mississippi Chemical's subsidiary Newsprint South, Inc. (NSI) at Grenada, Mississippi, is directed from control panels similar to the one pictured here. Chuck Dunn's success in coordinating this complex project, the largest of MCC's history, led to his selection as MCC president.

help organize and guide another substantial move that would radically alter Mississippi Chemical's direction. Dunn and Bailey chose a select group of board and staff members to make a probing examination of the company and set a strategic course for its future. "The company had sent me to the Harvard Business School for an intensive three-month program," Dunn would recall. "I came back convinced we had to conduct a comprehensive, no-holds-barred strategic analysis. We'd been so busy fighting fires during the fertilizer depression and building Newsprint South that we hadn't really taken a close look in years at where we stood and where we needed to go. While profits were rebounding, the company had to make a penetrating examination of our strengths, weaknesses, and needs to chart our own future."

What ensued was a two-year soul-searching study that was to transform Mississippi Chemical forever. In his charge to the committee Bailey urged its members to take an

incisive look into the company's capital, sales, stock, product, operations, and organizational structures and determine which should be part of the company's future. Bailey stressed that there were no "sacred cows."

While MCC's short-term sales and earnings were highly favorable, the planning committee uncovered several perplexing fissures in the company's foundations.

• Shareholders and customers were no longer the same people or entities.

• The company's financial strength had been eroded by the fertilizer depression, the return of almost all earnings to customers, and the losses of Newsprint South.

• Globalization and consolidation in the fertilizer industry would require the company to grow significantly if it wished to survive.

• Extreme fluctuations in farm ownership and fertilizer markets demanded considerable flexibility and independence in marketing, which were not possible for a cooperative.

• The company gravely needed to find significant new sources of capital if it were to grow and compete on a national and international scale.

• It would be difficult, if not impossible, to secure the requisite capital and market freedom within Mississippi Chemical's cooperative operation.

Fundamental changes had occurred in MCC's world, and the company had to make comparable responses in its operational methods.

When the company was founded, its shareholders and customers were Southern farmers or farm supply cooperatives anxious to have a faithful supply of scarce fertilizers. But forty-four years later, in 1992, more than half of MCC's fifteen thousand shareholders no longer purchased fertilizer from the company. In two generations nearly 50 percent of the shareholders, some seven thousand in all, had left the farming or fertilizer business but had retained their company stock. Mississippi Chemical had paid such lucrative patronage refunds throughout its history that even when farmers retired, died, or sold their farms, their families had held on to the company stock as a prized investment. This attitude, Chuck Dunn believed, underscored an elemental shift that had occurred. "Whereas the primary motivation for owning Mississippi Chemical stock when we began in the 1940s and 1950s was assurance of a reliable supply of scarce fertilizers," he would note, "in 1992 a high return on investment was the primary reason people gave for owning our stock. Fertilizers were available from many suppliers, and our customer base and ownership base were no longer coupled."

On the other hand, an increasingly higher share of the company's sales was to a few large fertilizer distributors and dealers. The twenty-five biggest customers purchased 69 percent of Mississippi Chemical's fertilizers, or nearly one million tons. Coley Bailey would touch on this rearrangement: "In the 1960s and 1970s we financed our growth and expansion by selling more and more stock to fertilizer distributors and dealers. This led to a fundamental change in our ownership and the composition of our customer base." The trend toward a more concentrated customer base was expected to continue as farms and fertilizer supply firms consolidated. Frequently these more substantial customers did not own sufficient stock to cover their full fertilizer needs, and they lacked either the capital or the desire to assume the risks associated with additional stock purchases or plant expansions. Thus, the company would inevitably face a dilemma in financing future growth by selling more stock: the few customers requiring more products lacked the money and/or desire to buy added stock, and the majority of shareholders no longer needed their current fertilizer allocation, much less additional products. How could the company obtain the equity capital it would need to remain competitive?

Compounding this quandary, the company's capital condition had taken a gradual but alarming turn for the worst. The amount of equity capital and reserves on hand (that is, all company assets minus all company debts) had deteriorated. First, as a cooperative, the company had traditionally returned almost 100 percent of its earnings to customers, and hence had failed to accumulate capital reserves as a regular corporation would. This absence of reserves was made emphatically apparent when the Newsprint South paper mill project incurred large deficits. Although the mill was exceeding operating expectations, a dramatic collapse in the worldwide price for newsprint had led to losses of nearly $60 million during its first four years. Additionally, the costs of new or replacement fertilizer plants had reached disturbing heights. Replacing an old plant with a modern one demanded seven to eight times as much money as the original. Clearly more capital would have to be raised. While a regular corporation might simply sell more stock to investors to build new plants, as a cooperative Mississippi Chemical could sell new stock only to new or old customers who wanted to buy more fertilizer. Just when the globalization of the fertilizer industry called for much more flexibility, the company's cooperative operational structure appeared to be acutely inhibiting it.

At a meeting of the committee in Gulf Shores, Alabama, in June of 1993, the directors considered an almost unthinkable option. "What would be the effect of converting Mississippi Chemical from a cooperative to a publicly owned corporation, with the freedom to sell stock and product to anyone interested in buying?" the directors asked.

Mississippi Chemical Corporation's headquarters and its board building (octagonal building at bottom left) were the site of two historic actions in 1994. In March the board of directors voted to ask its shareholders to approve converting the company from a cooperative to a regular business corporation. At a special stock-holders meeting in June more than 99 percent of all shareholders gave their approval. On July 1, 1994, the company began operations as a regular corporation. The Yazoo City production complex is shown at the top of the photograph, with the ammonium nitrate warehouses shown at left center.

Integrity and Trust: Cornerstones of the Company

A commitment to integrity guides the decision making at Mississippi Chemical and directs all its actions. "Integrity, honesty, fairness, and doing the right thing, the ethical thing, are the hallmarks of this company and lie at the core of its success," Chuck Dunn says. "These principles began with Owen Cooper and other early leaders and continue today. They define who we are and who we intend to be." Persons inside and outside MCC confirm the importance of this commitment.

Coley Bailey, who succeeded LeRoy Percy as board chair, feels deeply the influence of the company's principled leadership: "Although LeRoy Percy has retired after forty years on this board, his values are always with us," Bailey says. "We see those eyes staring down from his portrait in the board room and know we had better do the right thing."

Senior vice president of the company's technical group, David Arnold, recalls his first realization of the company's ethical standards. "In 1967, my first year here, MCC honored a contract with United Chemical Corporation that cost us a lot of money. That made a deep impression on me. The company could easily have broken that contract, but it didn't. It always tries to do the right thing."

Robert Jones, senior vice president of corporate development, emphasizes this, too: "Trust and integrity are our most valuable assets. Because of our reputation, we can do business on a handshake anywhere in the world. That's a big positive factor in negotiating."

According to Dunn, "When we were preparing to take Mississippi Chemical public in 1994, some advisors urged us to change our name to something flashy like Princeton Agri-Tech. But Mississippi Chemical has never and will never try to deceive people into thinking we're something we're not. Mississippi Chemical is a name people trust, and that trust is vital to us."

An integral part of corporate integrity at Mississippi Chemical has always been respect for its small and large shareholders and a responsibility to be wise with their resources. "From day one, Mr. Cooper insisted that the company keep faith with the hundreds of small investors who entrusted us with their savings," long-time corporate secretary Sue Tatum, now retired, remem-bers. "He was most proud that in our countless decisions and actions, we honored our faith to them." The board's decision to operate the company as a publicly owned corporation was grounded in the conviction that this course was the most responsive to the interest of the shareholders.

Bill Hawkins, retired senior vice president of finance, agrees: "Mississippi Chemical has always tried to be honest in its dealings with others, to be a responsible citizen, and to be fair with its employees as well." Mary Johnston, who has worked for more than half of her thirty-year career in the area of employee benefits, understands her role in fulfilling the trust of employees. "When I came to work here," Johnston recalls, "[vice president of sales] Charles Jackson said to me, 'Mary, you've been hired to do whatever it takes to be sure that the people in the plant get every single penny of the health benefits they're entitled to.' I have never forgotten Mr. Jackson's words, and whether I get a call from the president's office or the nitrate bagging line, my goal is to give the person who calls the best service and help I can."

The principled character of the company is well known by Griffin Norquist, Jr., president of the Bank of Yazoo City, who has observed the company closely for decades: "Over its fifty year history, Mississippi Chemical has had impeccable integrity from its leadership. I have never, ever known anyone to question the integrity of this company or of its leaders—Owen Cooper, LeRoy Percy, Charles Jackson, Harry Griffith [a vice president in the late 1960s], Tom Parry, Ed McCraw, Coley Bailey, Chuck Dunn, and others. Their actions are guided by the good of the company, the good of community, and the well-being of the farmers they serve—not by selfish personal motives."

Former Mississippi governor William Winter, whose half-century of service in the state parallels that of MCC, describes the impact Mississippi Chemical has had on the state: "The leadership of Mississippi Chemical, beginning with Owen Cooper, has set a standard of integrity for the rest of the businesses in the state. It has shown that a business can be profitable and successful and still maintain the highest ethical and civic standards. Mississippi Chemical has made a major contribution in calling our state and our business leaders to a higher ground."

"I could hardly believe my ears," Owen Cook would remember. "The staff had toyed with the idea of going public as a solution to the challenges we faced. But when we initially proposed it as an alternative, it had been quickly rejected by the strategic planning committee." Coley Bailey recalled, "Converting Mississippi Chemical to a public corporation was the farthest thing from our minds when we began this strategic study. We simply wanted to solve our problems, but the closer we looked the more complicated those problems and our cooperative status looked." John Sharp Howie would remember his own bewilderment about the proposal: "When the idea was mentioned, I remember thinking: abandon our cooperative roots? That's about like Aaron Burr forsaking his country."

Investment advisors were brought in to calculate the effect on the company of becoming a public corporation. Their figures were eye-opening. If Mississippi Chemical chose to go public, the experts predicted, its equity value could multiply fourfold to $300 million in contrast with the $75 million current value of its equity as a cooperative. This information was divulged to the strategic planning committee at a meeting in Grenada in August 1993.

On that momentous day, two staggering financial projections tested the committee's devotion to the company's forty-five year cooperative tradition. "The figures for going public were so overwhelmingly positive, it forced all of us to stretch our thinking and take a serious look at going public," Bailey recalled. Still, the board committee had pro-

found reservations about abandoning its cooperative status. The second set of financial projections also pushed them toward change. The committee had asked its staff to consider whether Mississippi Chemical, operating as a cooperative, would be able to make the substantial capital investments required to build expensive new plants in the years ahead. Analyses of several options indicated it would be nearly impossible for the company as a cooperative to come up with the huge investments of capital necessary to grow and survive. "The facts showed clearly and convincingly that Mississippi Chemical ran a high risk of *not* surviving if we remained a cooperative," Chuck Dunn would explain. "In the final analysis, I believe the danger and risk we faced if we failed to change had as much to do with the board's decision as the attractive gains to the company from going public."

At the end of that August 1993 meeting, the board committee made a far-reaching determination no less momentous than the one the company founders had made forty-six years earlier to begin their efforts to organize Mississippi Chemical. The five-member committee unanimously voted to recommend to the full board of directors that MCC relinquish its cooperative operation and re-organize itself as a regular publicly traded corporation as soon as practical. Their decision was subject only to additional work by management to ensure the feasibility of the company's metamorphosis.

"Their decision was the watershed event in our company's history," observed Robert Jones, senior vice president of corporate de-

velopment, who prior to his promotion from general counsel, had worked closely with the committee to make its choice and then to implement it. "If the board and shareholders adopted the recommendation, it would mean that Mississippi Chemical as we had known it for some forty-five years would cease to exist and would be superseded by a new corporate enterprise yet to be created."

Company officials were unanimous in their praise of the board committee and its chair, John Anderson, for inspiring a decision beneficial to all stockholders rather than any single shareholder group. During the August meeting Anderson, who was then president of Alabama Farmers Cooperative, stressed the obligation of directors. "Converting to a public company may not be in the best interest of Alabama Farmers Cooperative, but if it's in the best interest of Mississippi Chemical Corporation, I want to see it done." Also serving on the committee were Bob Dixon and Tom Gist, both closely allied with the company's largest shareholder, SF Services of Arkansas; John Sharp Howie; and Billy Percy, who had followed his father LeRoy onto the MCC board. The younger Percy was instrumental in shaping the committee's decision. "Billy Percy was the first member of that committee to grasp the huge advantages Mississippi Chemical stood to gain by going public, and his leadership guided others to that same conclusion," Owen Cook recalled. The new president Chuck Dunn also hailed the committee's work: "I can't say enough about the way all these men put aside their own private interests to genuinely seek the best solution for

Robert Perkins: Goodwill Ambassador

Robert Perkins accepts his retirement awards from Mary Johnston, right, as his wife Rosemary Perkins looks on.

For forty years as company courier and mailman, Robert Perkins was also a goodwill ambassador extraordinaire, exchanging as he did warm salutations with dozens of Yazoo City businessmen, citizens, and fellow employees in his rounds to the banks, post office, and company offices. He arrived at the Yazoo City post office at 6:00 a.m. every work day because he wanted to have the mail at the MCC offices before anyone else got to work. Perkins responded to fellow employees' greeting "How are you doing this morning, Robert?" with "I'm just glad to be alive and still kicking."

When his retirement drew near, Perkins did not want a retirement party calling attention to him or his work. But his many friends and well-wishers would not be denied. On his last day at work, Perkins was surprised not only by a going-away party: everywhere he looked, he saw red, his favorite color. Throughout the office building women wore red clothes and men wore red ties—all of them determined to make it a red-letter day for the man they so admired and appreciated. Local banker Miller Holmes said it well, "Robert Perkins was a fine citizen of this community."

Mississippi Chemical and its future. They refused to let forty-five years of history blind them from discerning and seizing the best long-term strategy for our owners, customers, and employees."

The committee's deliberations were kept in the strictest confidence. Now it was time to bring in the full board of directors. A two-day meeting was called for December 13–14, 1993, in Jackson to allow a full presentation and discussion of the committee's findings, the various options it had explored, and ultimately its recommendation.

As the meeting neared, the headquarters in Yazoo City became a frantic flurry of activity involving the crafting and rehearsing of the best conceivable presentation of the complex study and its implications. Robert Jones, Bill Hawkins, and Owen Cook worked closely with Chuck Dunn on this presentation. Dunn, just completing his first year as company president, recalls these preparations: "We honestly didn't know how the board would react to the recommendations. Management and the board committee had spent more than a year intensively scrutinizing the company and drawing various conclusions. Yet we were asking the full board to digest all this information in just two days and from that decide to fundamentally change the nature and course of the company. We certainly didn't want a failure on our part to make the facts crystal clear to sabotage the right decision."

Dunn and Coley Bailey sought the counsel of the retired board chair LeRoy Percy, then seventy-five years old. After being briefed in detail on the recommendations, Percy volunteered to come to the meeting and speak in favor of the conversion if that were needed. "I was 100 percent convinced that going public was the right thing for the company to do," Percy would remember, "but I'd repeatedly told Chuck I had serious doubts he could sell the board and shareholders on making such a monumental switch." The endorsement of Percy and his son Billy would certainly help. Then, days before the Jackson meeting, the elder Percy's wife Sarah became seriously ill and was hospitalized. It was doubtful that Percy could come to endorse the conversion.

"When the board got to the meeting, they had no idea what we were going to recom-

Clockwise from top left: In the four decades Dan "Ju-Ju" Russell has worked in the Yazoo City ammonium nitrate plant and warehouse, he has seen far-reaching changes in the way the company produces fertilizers and the way customers want it delivered. Company researcher Cori Ciaccio uses a supercritical fluid extractor to provide data for ongoing research projects that keep Mississippi Chemical on the leading edge of product improvement. Linard Anderson helps the Yazoo City ammonium nitrate plants run efficiently. Mississippi Chemical is the nation's largest producer of agricultural grade ammonium nitrate, and its **AMTRATE** brand-name is the highest quality product on the American fertilizer market.

mend to them," Coley Bailey would recall. "They just knew it was very important." For eight intense hours Chuck Dunn explained the findings of the committee and their implications for Mississippi Chemical's future. These points were made:

• The company's true equity capital position, after removing capital equity credits owed to shareholders and the Florida phosphate rock reserve, was nearly zero.

• Depreciation of current plants was falling far behind the replacement costs needed to purchase replacement plants. It was noted that the recently completed No. 9 nitric acid plant and related modifications had cost $32 million while the two units that were replaced had only cost $4 million.

• The continuing globalization of the fertilizer industry would require the company to expand toward a critical mass in

size needed to ensure modern plants and efficient raw material supplies and to sell on the world market. The company lacked the capital to meet these expansion needs, however, and the restrictions of operating as a cooperative made it virtually impossible to obtain access to this capital.

• The market was continuing to change dramatically, and the company could not enjoy the marketing flexibility

Clockwise, from top left: Shift supervisor Erie Daniels checks the controls of the Yazoo City ammonium nitrate plant, where he has worked for the last twenty-six years. Ammonia plant operator Rob Robinson changes a valve on top of a storage sphere. Senior research project leader Randy Weimer explores ways to improve product quality.

required as long as it was a cooperative. More than half the company's share-holders no longer purchased any fertilizer, and dealers who wanted more product would or could not invest the necessary dollars in additional company stock.

• The real market value of the company stock if it went public would be three times its current cooperative value.

• A ten-year projection compared the returns to average stockholders if the company remained a cooperative and paid patronage refunds, to returns to the same shareholders if MCC converted to a public company and paid dividends on stock. Going public offered a significantly greater return to the shareholders.

When Dunn finished, there was absolute silence in the room. The directors were jolted by the findings and the magnitude of the decision confronting them. Several directors then spoke in favor of the proposed conversion. No action would be taken until the next morning. "I was absolutely exhausted after presenting facts and answering questions for almost eight hours," Chuck Dunn would remember. "My voice was so weak I could hardly talk for days. But I felt great about the presentation and the directors' reception of the findings. I was optimistic we'd convinced them of the wisdom of the change. But we wouldn't know until the next day."

Billy Percy was more confident than Dunn that the board would adopt the changes. His father was waiting by the telephone in his wife's hospital room in Green-ville, ready to fly to Jackson if his support were needed. When Billy Percy phoned him, the elder Percy was relieved to hear his son's assessment: "Stay there with Mother. This thing is going to pass."

The next morning, December 14, 1993, the MCC board entered the crowded confer-ence room to make its decision. Chair Coley Bailey addressed the board: "You've heard all the findings and the recommendations. It's now time to vote. What is your pleasure?" Without any discussion or debate the board—without a single dissenting vote—authorized the conversion and instructed management to develop a complete and pre-

MCC's Miss Hospitality

When Porter Faye Vandevere completed thirty-two years of spirited service as Mississippi Chemical's public relations assistant in 1995, the crowd of well-wishers who gathered to bid her farewell could barely squeeze into the company's Yazoo City board room, which she had managed with grace and efficiency for three decades. It was a fitting tribute to the lively, red-headed woman whose kind, congenial presence had won countless friends for the company.

President Chuck Dunn described her contribution to the company: "I doubt if there is another employee who has represented the company to so many different publics, so well, for so long. Porter has dealt with presidents, governors, and ambassadors, temperamental customers, anxious fieldmen, upset dealers, inquisitive school children, and chagrined co-workers and left virtually every one of them with a

Porter Faye Vandevere

good feeling and fond memories of Mississippi Chemical. We all owe her a tremendous thanks for the thousands of friends she has made on our behalf."

Her last supervisor, Melinda Hood, said, "I've seen Porter confronted by some of the most demanding people and situations imaginable, and not once have I ever seen her lose her poise or her politeness. She is one of the warmest-hearted people on earth and the perfect person for the job she handled so well." In her thirty-two years of public relations and corporate communications work, Vandevere helped publish newsletters, annual reports, and sales promotional materials; organized tour groups, dealer meetings, and special events; and coordinated use of the company board room. She served all three company presidents and four public relations managers (Glen Jones, Jo G. Prichard, Tommy Thompson, and Melinda Hood) and made all of them look good.

In 1997, when the corporate public relations department faced an emergency need for extended staffing assistance, Hood telephoned Vandevere early one morning to ask whether she could come out of retirement on such short notice. "I'll be there at noon," Porter replied. Vandevere, loyal to Mississippi Chemical as always, reported for work shortly after lunch with a steno pad and pen in hand ready for that afternoon's staff meeting. However, her office in the corporate communications department was not her first stop in the building. Upon arriving, Vandevere went immediately to the snack bar to hug and kiss all the men she had not seen in two and a half years.

cise plan to transform Mississippi Chemical into a public corporation.

The die had been cast, but the enormous task of accomplishing the conversion had just begun. The work would continue nonstop from December 1993 to August 1994. MCC quickly summoned investment bankers, lawyers, and communications professionals from outside the company to work with their inhouse counterparts in preparing the necessary plans and documents. Making the largest single conversion of a cooperative to a for-profit company in American business history was an enormous task. It required legally "closing down" Mississippi Chemical and all its complicated assets, subsidiaries, agreements, and liabilities and transferring those to a newly created subsidiary, which would simultaneously take the name "Mississippi Chemical Corporation." The change would be invisible to customers, suppliers, and other parties. The new corporation would then go forward with an initial public offering of stock (IPO).

The single most complex and most significant step in preparing for a public offering was also the most painful: disposing of a majority of its interest in Newsprint South, Inc. (NSI). As the sole owner of the news-print company, Mississippi Chemical was required to consolidate its financial statement and balance sheet with those of Newsprint South. All involved understood that Mississippi Chemical could not hope to sell shares on Wall Street while burdened with NSI's still-increasing losses. But extricating Mississippi Chemical from the thicket

Triad Nitrogen's plants and people make it one of America's premiere nitrogen fertilizer complexes. Left: Dane Girouard monitors production in Triad's urea plant. Above: Kelly Carmouche checks the reformer in one of Triad's two Kellogg ammonia plants. Below, from left, Steve Nicholas compiles readings in the ammonia plant, urea operator Dudley LeBlanc records urea plant data, and Triad summer intern Heather Waquespack, left, daughter of Triad employee Steve Waquespack, and Triad safety analyst Glenda Shaheen, right, get a first-hand view of a urea barge on the Mississippi River.

Sanford Searcy stands in front of a mound of red potash produced at Mississippi Potash in Carlsbad. Chief mine engineer Jill Farnsworth waits to go 1,500 feet underground to her job in Mississippi Potash's Carlsbad mine. The special light mounted on her hard hat is standard equipment for every member of the Carlsbad underground team.

of newsprint losses required sacrificing the largest project in the company's history and one to which many MCC employees from all departments had strong emotional bonds. The construction of Newsprint South's mill and the operation of the new company had required the determination, persistence, creativity, and endurance of many people in Yazoo City who were proud of their contributions.

Informing the staff that the company's involvement in Newsprint South was going to be terminated—after they had invested so much into it against tough odds—was one

of the most onerous things he ever had to do, Dunn would say. "When I explained that giving up NSI was essential, and we would proceed with it," he remembered, "I looked around at several people who had performed so magnificently—heroically, if you will—and I suddenly choked up and couldn't speak. You could just feel the sadness and sense of loss in that room. It was the right decision, but abandoning that project was like giving up a child for adoption."

Divesting itself of Newsprint South was a complicated process, again requiring a team of professionals from inside and outside the

company and members of management traveling to New York on a regular basis. Mississippi Chemical conveyed 70 percent of its ownership of Newsprint South to NSI officers selected by General Electric Capital Corporation, a major party in NSI's financing; ceased to provide management services to NSI; and settled all outstanding business with NSI and its lenders. This divestiture of ownership of NSI allowed MCC, and ultimately those who would consider purchasing its publicly traded stock, to focus on the company's core business of producing fertilizer.

On March 22, 1994, the company's conversion blueprint passed its first hurdle. Meeting in Yazoo City, MCC's board of directors heard the meticulous plans for changing to a publicly traded company. After Dunn had made his presentation on these matters, Wayne Thames of Evergreen, Alabama, a long-time member of the board, asked what Bill Hawkins thought about the idea. Hawkins, the corporation's conservative and highly trusted financial vice president for thirty years, walked to the podium. "I have no doubt this is the best thing Mississippi Chemical could do," he said simply, "and I recommend you vote for it." Hawkins had added the exclamation point to a convincing presentation, and that provided added comfort for the board. The motion was made, seconded, and unanimously adopted to call a special shareholders meeting for June 28 and to recommend that all stockholders approve the plan and conversion. Dr. Rodney Foil, land-grant director from Mississippi State University, warned the board, "The major opposition will come from stockholders who remember MCC as it never was and want it to stay that way!"

The board's unanimous endorsement was particularly impressive in that, among the many steps they approved, they had voted to reduce the size of the board from twenty-four to twelve members effective *that day*. The directors, in effect, were voting themselves out of a job. Historically, the company's sizeable board had allowed maximum representation from its owner-customers across the South. Over the prior four decades the directors had been farmers or fertilizer dealers like the shareholders they represented, and most had been chosen in district caucuses in which shareholders convened to cast their ballots. More than a few of these democratic nomination caucuses had been hotly contested. Serving on Mississippi Chemical's board had always been perceived as a coveted honor. "The time had come to move toward a smaller working board that not only represented our historic owners but also involved some skilled outsiders whose advice we would need," Billy Percy, who proposed the reduction, would explain. Coley Bailey would observe, "We reduced the number of board members from twenty-four to twelve. Nine of these were selected from the previous board that very day. We used the same rules they use in electing a Pope." There were no nominations, no speeches, and no politicking, and ballots were written in secret. It took three rounds of confidential balloting for the board to narrow its number to nine. The remaining three directors would be enticed

The phosphoric acid plant helps convert phosphate rock from Morocco into concentrated phosphate fertilizers for farmers across the South and the world. John Copeland, phosphoric acid operator, Mississippi Phosphates, Pascagoula, is an integral part of the process.

From 1996 to 1998 Mississippi Phosphates invested $25 million to expand its capacity to produce DAP fertilizers at Pascagoula by 25 percent. Earl Martin, standing, and John Chisholm are sulfuric acid operators at Mississippi Phosphates, Pascagoula.

from outside the industry, an advantage not available to a cooperative.

A notice and lengthy prospectus were prepared to inform every shareholder of the June 28 meeting and of the decision they faced. These documents were forwarded to fifteen thousand stockholders on May 27. The company would also carry its message to shareholders in person. In a succession of meetings throughout the South, Chuck

Dunn discussed the proposed changes with more than a thousand shareholders. Many of them at first disagreed with the changes, but after listening to Dunn's explanations, they almost universally agreed it was the proper thing to do.

Coley Bailey also conferred with many of the shareholders. "Only two or three isolated shareholders who were taking advantage of our current system really criticized our pro-

President Chuck Dunn, left, and Ronnie Curtis, principal trading officer for Wertheim Schroder, the Wall Street investment banking firm that handled the company's initial public offering, celebrate the debut of Mississippi Chemical's stock on the NASDAQ National Market, August 18, 1994. A million shares of MCC stock were sold in the first ten minutes, and the five million shares offered brought $75 million in capital to the company.

To secure investors for its initial public stock offering in August 1994, Mississippi Chemical officials embarked on a seventeen-day, whirlwind "Road Show" to sixteen American cities and London. Above from left, David Faris of Wertheim Schroder investment banking firm, senior vice president Ed McCraw, and president Chuck Dunn virtually lived in the rented jet, traveling 20,000 miles in seventeen days. Right: Preparing to embark on this odyssey are, from left: Ed McCraw; Chuck Dunn; Peter Bacon, investment banker; Tim Dawson, vice president of finance; and David Faris and Steve Silver, from Wertheim Schroder.

posals," he would recall, "—mostly those who had been allowed to purchase substantial fertilizer without purchasing an equivalent amount of stock. Almost everyone else could see it was the right thing to do." Bailey quoted LeRoy Percy in these meetings. "Mr. Percy told me one day: never forget that Mississippi Chemical was formed to benefit its shareholders. The cooperative operation

was chosen in 1948 because at the time it was the best way to benefit our owners. But now that operating as a co-op has ceased to be the best way to serve our stockholders, it behooves us to change. I also believe Owen Cooper, once he looked at the tremendous economic benefits it offers shareholders, would have been the first to recommend the conversion."

The corporate bylaws specified that approval of the conversion would require not just a majority vote of all stockholders, but a majority vote in *each class* of corporate stock, the three classes being nitrogen, mixed fertilizer, and potash customers. The identity and location of the mixed fertilizer shareholders were uncertain, because their stock had lain dormant since the company halted production of NPK fertilizers in the early 1980s, and the company had not heard from many of these stockholders in well over a decade. Owen Cook would recall the campaign to locate and persuade each NPK shareholder of the benefits of the conversion and to keep a running tally to ensure that a majority had been reached. "As June 28th came closer," he remembered, "we added the names of each NPK shareholder we reached and confirmed to support the conversion. It was like getting those last few votes in a presidential primary. I'll never forget reaching an elderly lady who didn't even realize she owned a substantial amount of our NPK stock. Rather than thanking me, she was upset I had bothered her."

The day of the vote arrived. The company's boardroom in Yazoo City was packed with shareholders and company employees. Thousands of shareholders had mailed in their votes. Others came to vote in person. The ballots were cast and tallied, and the results announced. Only the margin of victory itself was surprising. The owners of over 99 percent of the outstanding stock, some 3,191,321 shares, had approved the reorganization plan. Only 47,471 shares, less than 1 percent, had voted nay. As required, each class of shareholders had voted yea overwhelmingly.

The last necessary approval had been obtained, but there was hardly time to celebrate. Two days later, precisely at midnight on June 30, 1994, the forty-six-year-old Mississippi Chemical Corporation ended its operations, and a new legal entity bearing the same name came into being. Immediately

the company turned its attention to Wall Street and the final challenge.

In six brief weeks, MCC would make its debut on the NASDAQ National Market. (Two years later the company would move the listing of its stock to the New York Stock Exchange.) Five million shares of Mississippi Chemical stock—some 25 percent of the company—would be offered to investors from around the world in hopes of raising millions of dollars to fund the company's future growth and to establish a solid, public market for its stock. But the impending appearance on the national stock exchange posed more questions than answers.

How would a small Southern company be received by investors from Los Angeles to London, who knew little of fertilizers and farming? Would hardnosed mutual fund managers be disposed to invest their millions in Yazoo City, Pascagoula, Carlsbad, and Donaldsonville? What would the world's most sophisticated investors be willing to pay for Mississippi Chemical stock? The answers to these questions would have enormous impact on the company.

Mississippi Chemical's finance department and the company's internal and external auditors worked long hours to produce the year-end financial facts necessary to educate potential investors. These figures were decidedly impressive. Profits in every category—nitrogen, phosphates and potash—had increased over the previous year. Total earnings were up 19 percent to $26.9 million. Fertilizer sales totaled $309 million, exceeding the $300 million mark for the first time since 1985. Bolstered by record produc-

tion at the new nitric acid plant in Yazoo City, the annual output of ammonium nitrate synthesis had surpassed one million tons, twenty-five times the ammonium nitrate produced in the original Yazoo City facility during its first year of production. At Carlsbad, Mississippi Potash had procured new mining and compaction equipment, enabling potash output to soar from 300,000 to 420,000 tons a year; at Donaldsonville, Triad Chemical had responded to a worldwide ammonia shortage by producing its largest quantity in history. But Mississippi Phosphates achieved the most significant advance, since the world price for DAP had jumped 40 percent. The prospects for 1995 appeared even brighter. The timing was perfect for introducing the nation's financial markets to Mississippi Chemical.

"Road Show" is what institutional investors and stock analysts call the grueling odysseys made by a company's officials to woo potential buyers as the company stock is about to be offered publicly for the first time. President Chuck Dunn, senior vice president Ed McCraw, finance director Tim Dawson, and investment advisers Peter Bacon and David Faris hit the road. In the eleven work days between August 3 and August 18, the five men traversed the nation and the Atlantic on a seventeen-city blitz, making forty-four presentations to some of the world's most important investors and securities analysts. "Over and over and over we'd introduce Mississippi Chemical to these major money managers and try our best to convince them we were a good investment, and then invite them to become company

On October 10, 1996, Mississippi Chemical Corporation stock made its debut on the New York Stock Exchange, under the big-board symbol, "GRO."

Above: Chuck Dunn is interviewed by the New York Stock Exchange Network on the exchange floor as MCC's stock makes it first appearance on the exchange October 10, 1996.

Top left: MCC officials, from left: Chuck Dunn, Tim Dawson, Ethel Truly, Keith Johnson, and Robert Jones. Left: Chuck Dunn; Frank Murphey, MCC's specialist at the stock exchange; and Coley Bailey, MCC board chair.

Right: Celebrating the historic event are MCC president Chuck Dunn, right, and William Johnston, president of the exchange. In the background are MCC board vice chair John Sharp Howie (left) and Stan Froelich of Morgen-Walke & Associates, MCC's investor relations agency in New York.

MCC board vice chair John Sharp Howie, vice president Ethel Truly, and William Johnston, exchange president.

MCC senior vice president Robert Jones, left, and Stan Froelich of Morgen-Walke.

Alice Patz of the stock exchange, right, and Melinda Hood, the company's corporate communications manager, watch Mississippi Chemical's "GRO" listing flash across "the Big Board" for the first time in history.

shareholders when our stock went public," Dunn would remember.

The Mississippi Chemical men tackled hundreds of questions and encouraged the interest of potential investors, but did not sleep, rest, or eat regularly during the marathon. Forty-six years earlier the company's founders had traveled miles of rural roads to sell the company's original stock. In 1994 its new leaders took to the airways for that same purpose. The five men squeezed into a tiny Lear jet with little breathing room and no bathroom. They met audiences in New York on Wednesday, Atlanta and Nashville on Thursday, Kansas City on Friday, London on Monday, Memphis and Jackson on Tuesday, and Minneapolis, Chicago, and Milwaukee on Wednesday. They were on to Denver and San Francisco on Thursday, and Portland and Los Angeles on Friday. At dawn on Monday, they were speaking in Philadelphia, then flew to Boston for seven presentations on Tuesday, followed by five more in New York the following, final day.

"We flew to so many cities and made so many talks, we just never had time to sit down and eat," Dunn would remember. "We just grabbed a bite off the closest person's plate and kept on running. I got so tired of making my speech and hearing Ed McCraw make his that somewhere along the way—I think it was on the West Coast—I turned to Ed and said, 'How would you like to be Chuck Dunn today and give my talk, and I'll be Ed McCraw and give yours?' It was becoming surrealistic." Peter Bacon, the company's investment banker, gave Dunn,

McCraw, and Dawson credit for the job they did in winning the trust of the international investors: "These money mangers are used to hearing slick, glib presentations," Bacon would say. "It was very refreshing for them to meet and hear people as direct, honest, and knowledgeable as Chuck, Ed, and Tim."

The tour concluded with a tense meeting in the Wall Street offices of the investment underwriters Wertheim Schroder and Company late Wednesday afternoon, August 17, just hours before Mississippi Chemical's stock would be offered to the public the next morning. The underwriters gathered the tentative orders and expressions of interest produced by the "Road Show" and closeted themselves in what Wall Streeters call "the boiler room." This was the last meeting at which the underwriting firm would set the price for which it would offer Mississippi Chemical's stock the next morning. Dunn would recall that the air was heavy with anticipation and uncertainty about the offering price. "I told Peter Bacon if he returned with a price of fifteen dollars a share or higher, we could go have a good dinner. But if he came back with a lower price, he was in for a long meeting."

Throughout all the presentations to shareholders about taking the company public, the company's leaders had hoped for a stock price of fifteen dollars a share, which would be three times the going price of the company's stock as an agricultural cooperative. "Our investment advisers had their necks on the line," Dunn said. "They had to use their savvy to determine what the world market would actually pay." The underwriters met

for only thirty minutes. When the doors opened, the price had been set—fifteen dollars a share. The only question left unanswered was whether the world's investors would actually buy Mississippi Chemical stock at that price.

The answer came at 9:30 the next morning. For Dunn it was one of the most exciting days he had ever experienced. During the thirty minutes before the market opened, Schroder's principal trader, Ronnie Curtis, was talking on three or four telephones at once, checking with every financial market in America, counting the advance orders for Mississippi Chemical's stock. As the minute hand closed in on 9:30, Dunn, Dawson, and Robert Jones nervously waited for the market to open. They believed the fifteen-dollar price was a good one, but no one could be sure what would happen.

A split second before trading began, the lead trader turned to Dunn, winked, and gave him a thumbs up signal. When the bell sounded, Mississippi Chemical's stock skyrocketed. A million shares were sold in the first ten minutes. In the first hour two million shares were sold for over $30 million. That day the company sold its five million shares of stock for $75 million, ten times the total raised so painstakingly from 1948 to 1951 to launch the company. Equally important, going public at fifteen dollars a share tripled the value of the stock owned by Mississippi Chemical's shareholders across the South. One year after its board committee had decided to recommend that the company "go public" if management could confirm the plan's feasibility over the next

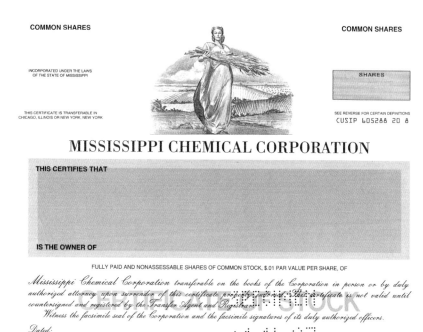

47150

COMMON SHARES

COMMON SHARES

INCORPORATED UNDER THE LAWS
OF THE STATE OF MISSISSIPPI

NUMBER

C

SHARES

THIS CERTIFICATE IS TRANSFERABLE IN
CHICAGO, ILLINOIS OR NEW YORK, NEW YORK

SEE REVERSE FOR CERTAIN DEFINITIONS
CUSIP 605288 20 8

Mississippi Chemical
Corporation

MISSISSIPPI CHEMICAL CORPORATION

THIS CERTIFIES THAT

IS THE OWNER OF

FULLY PAID AND NONASSESSABLE SHARES OF COMMON STOCK, $.01 PAR VALUE PER SHARE, OF

Mississippi Chemical Corporation transferable on the books of the Corporation in person or by duly authorized attorney upon surrender of this certificate properly endorsed. This certificate is not valid until countersigned and registered by the Transfer Agent and Registrar.

Witness the facsimile seal of the Corporation and the facsimile signatures of its duly authorized officers.

Dated:

1·14·97

COUNTERSIGNED AND REGISTERED:
HARRIS TRUST AND SAVINGS BANK
(CHICAGO)

BY

TRANSFER AGENT
AND REGISTRAR,

AUTHORIZED SIGNATURE

SECRETARY

PRESIDENT

SEAL
1948

American Bank Note Company

A Mississippi Chemical Corporation stock certificate, now traded on the New York Stock Exchange.

few months, the new company was sitting squarely and successfully on the NASDAQ National Market.

Those who took it there, in one short year, collapsed in exhaustion. "I've never been so completely spent in my life," Dunn would remember. He, McCraw, and Dawson had traveled nearly twenty thousand miles in two weeks, after an exacting six-month campaign to convert Mississippi Chemical to a public company, and dozens of dedicated employees back at the home office had worked just as hard. When he fell in bed that night, Dunn slept for almost forty hours. Hundreds of shareholders and employees could now sleep better, too. Mississippi Chemical had access to the world's

capital market so essential to its survival and success in the 1990s and the next century.

On October 10, 1996, two years and two months after its introduction on the NASDAQ National Market, Mississippi Chemical would switch to the New York Stock Exchange. That morning the president of the venerable financial center, situated among the stone canyons of Wall Street, opened its doors to greet Mississippi Chemical officials. Some forty-nine years earlier, John Sharp Williams had made the motion that Mississippi farmers take up the daunting task of selling stock to form the company. On this day his grandson, John Sharp Howie, the company's vice chair, would witness Missis-

sippi Chemical's stock being listed and traded on the New York Stock Exchange for the first time ever. Appropriate for both the farmers who use its products and the investors who buy its stock, the symbol used to designate Mississippi Chemical on the New York Stock Exchange that day and today is "GRO."

CHAPTER NINE

Into the Twenty-first Century

In the concluding years of its first half-century, 1993 to 1998, Mississippi Chemical implemented a five-phased expansion intended to position it for the future. When completed and operational in the company's fiftieth year, 1998, these strategic additions almost tripled the company's assets and sales in only five years. In rapid succession the company constructed the world's largest single train ammonia plant in The Republic of Trinidad and Tobago, purchased First Mississippi Corporation's fertilizer business, expanded its Yazoo City nitrogen facilities, acquired two new potash mines near Carlsbad, New Mexico, and signed a new sixteen-year agreement with its Moroccan partner, Office Chérifien des Phosphates

Mississippi Chemical nearly tripled its production capacity during the 1990s, by completing major expansions at Yazoo City, left, Pascagoula, Carlsbad, and Trinidad, and by acquiring all of the fertilizer operations of First Mississippi Corporation.

(OCP), to expand Mississippi Phosphates's Pascagoula complex and increase its DAP production by 25 percent.

Swift change characterizes most aspects of modern-day Mississippi Chemical and the environment in which it operates. New undertakings and increasing exports have connected the company to the economies and agricultural markets in China, India, and South America. Developments in Beijing, Bombay, or Rio de Janeiro demand attention in Yazoo City, Pascagoula, or Carlsbad.

During this expansionary period Mississippi Chemical registered strong increases in sales and profits every year from 1994 to 1997. Because of surging world demand and successful additions in plant capacity, the company in these years reached records in production, sales and earnings. The period opened with the company's completing its newest and largest nitric acid plant, making

possible increased nitrogen production *and* the further lessening of emissions. Utilizing the French Grande Paroisse process, this ultramodern plant was constructed for $2.5 million under budget and has operated above design capacity from inception—"a splendid example of our technical staff's ability to supervise and manage the design and construction of a leading edge, economical, and environmentally advanced plant—a tribute to the skill and teamwork of our people," MCC president Chuck Dunn would call it. The new nitric acid plant allowed Mississippi Chemical's ammonium nitrate synthesis to surpass one million tons a year.

Among the numerous elements impacting the world fertilizer market in the late 1980s through the late 1990s had been the role of the former Soviet Union in marketing its fertilizer. For decades the Soviets had been augmenting their nitrogen and potash capac-

Cottruel Generette: Mover and Shaker for Five Decades

Cottruel Generette has been a positive presence in the Yazoo City plant services department for forty-six of the company's fifty years. Having grown up in the hills just north of the plant, he likely knows the MCC environs better than anyone. As a teenager, he watched the original site being prepared: "I can see them now building the first levees around the property and then straightening out the creek that runs back to the nitrate plant." A year later Generette was baling hay in the meadow now filled by the ammonium nitrate warehouses, when Mike Ellison offered him a job at MCC. "I already got a job," he replied. But when Ellison offered him seventy-five cents an hour, double his hay baling pay, he cast his lot with the brand new chemical plant.

Cottruel Generette (right) and Nate Lee Blount salt the road to the administration building after the January 1971 snow.

Known for his enormous physical strength and ever-present broad smile and friendly disposition, Generette is undoubtedly one of the most beloved and respected figures in the company's history. His work ethic and feats of strength are legendary and seemingly at odds with his warm, soft-spoken demeanor.

One summer day when temperatures soared into the high 90s, Chuck Dunn, president of the company, walked into the administration building and saw Generette and four members of his crew casually moving some furniture. Dunn said, "Cottruel, I don't think it takes five men to move a table." Generette paused for just a moment and displaying his famous smile, replied, "Yes sir. But let's just keep that between us boys." Dunn looked out at the blazing sun and walked away, chuckling, "That's probably the best thing to do, just keep it between us boys."

In addition to his company job, Generette has operated a moonlighting moving service for fellow employees, transporting furniture and appliances into hundreds of new homes. He estimates he has moved every Yazoo City employee once and some two and three times. Melinda Hood vows that, while in his sixties and without help from anyone else, he picked up her piano and moved it across her house, asking her to leave so she would not worry about anything.

Longtime MCC employee Jerry Clower speaks for many MCC employees when he says, "If everyone on earth had Cottruel's attitude, you would swear you were in heaven."

ities. Throughout the Cold War, the United States had been exceedingly wary, of course, of the Soviet Union and the threat it posed to international peace and stability. But following Gorbachev's *perestroika* the Soviet Union quietly began a chaotic market assault that perplexed the world fertilizer industry during the late 1980s. During the Great Fertilizer Depression from 1981 to 1987 virtually no new plants had been built anywhere in the world. Then when demand caught up with the oversupply, the dissolution of the Soviet Union caused its agricultural sector to fall into a tailspin, thereby substantially reducing fertilizer consumption. The governments of the former Soviet Union began diverting almost all their fertilizer production from their own farmers to the world market to obtain the hard currency they needed to stay afloat. Information from the former Soviet governments was so unorganized and unavailable, however, that the world fertilizer industry did not immediately realize what they were doing. For several years the abundance of Russian fertilizers on the market masked the growing world demand and the pointed need for new plants to meet that demand. By the mid-1990s plants around the world were running at full capacity. More capacity would be required to fill the future growth in demand. Mississippi Chemical and its new management team led by its new president Chuck Dunn moved boldly to expand its participation in meeting this growing world requirement for plant food. After converting the company from a cooperative to a public company, giving MCC more flexible access to capital and fertilizer markets, Mississippi Chemical's management team carefully laid its expansion plans.

MCC had three choices in multiplying its nitrogen outputs: buying existing facilities from other producers, building additional plants at its Yazoo City complex, or constructing an entirely new nitrogen facility at some location with an economical source of readily available natural gas. Ultimately, although no one surmised it in 1993, the company would choose to use all three of these options.

Because natural gas amounted to nearly three-fourths of the cost of ammonia, the most basic nitrogen product, locating a reliable source of natural gas was of the highest priority. MCC's search for this gas, and the solution it finally devised, would illustrate how international and globally-connected the fertilizer business had become in these waning days of the century. Company executives were to travel to four continents seeking supplies of gas and the capital to construct the ammonia plant which would convert that gas to fertilizer. Senior vice president Ed McCraw, who led this important search, was an experienced international negotiator for MCC. In the 1970s his first important assignment had taken him to Algeria in North Africa to try to sell an expensive ammonia plant the company did not need. McCraw recalls his Algerian venture: "Apparently they didn't trust Americans, because everywhere we went there were soldiers with sub-machine guns. It was hard to relax looking down the barrels of their guns. They put us up in a brand new, ultra-

At Clancy's, a Yazoo City restaurant, Mississippi Chemical's president Chuck Dunn, center, and board vice chair John Sharp Howie, left, discuss activities around town with Griffin Norquist, Jr., president of the Bank of Yazoo City.

modern hotel, but we were the only guests in the huge building. There were new TVs in every room, but they came on only four or five times a day, and that was for televised Islamic prayers." Then, in the late 1980s, McCraw was instrumental in forging an alliance with the world's most substantial phosphate rock mining concern, Morocco's Office Chérifien des Phosphates (OCP). This trans-Atlantic partnership would enable Mississippi Phosphates to return its Pascagoula complex to full operation and to make large export shipments of DAP fertilizers to India, China, and South America.

Now the soft-spoken, savvy McCraw traveled to three continents in search of a stable

nation with surplus gas to sell. His quest led him into unusual places and tight situations. He made numerous trips to Venezuela, the site of South America's richest gas reserves, and sojourned in several countries of the Far East and in the Republic of the Ivory Coast in western Africa. "In Africa," McCraw recalls, "they took me to meet the president at his impressive state residence, surrounded by a moat filled with hungry crocodiles. After I watched a man feed those crocodiles, I felt sure the president was safe." The company considered the natural gas sources in South America and Africa. "While all these places could offer us natural gas at excellent prices," McCraw would later reflect, "we

While Mississippi Chemical now operates in a global environment, the company is still characterized by a family atmosphere where employees and their families picnic together. Left: Enjoying the 1997 employee picnic in Yazoo City are, from left, Sheila Holley and Larry Holley, vice president of nitrogen products; Jan McCraw and Ed McCraw, senior vice president of operations; and Bill Smith, general counsel. Above, from left: John Holt, retired plant supervisor, visits with Chuck Dunn, as Jim Golden, manager of human resources and compensation, (holding his son James Peyton Golden) and Elizabeth Golden look on.

could never get comfortable with the political stability of those nations. In our view and others', it was simply too risky to make a massive investment in those volatile nations."

Eventually McCraw's hunt for a place with political stability and abundant natural gas led him far down the Caribbean to the exotic Republic of Trinidad and Tobago. Located less than ten miles off the northeast coast of Venezuela, this tiny nation comprises two separate islands. The island of Tobago is a lush tropical paradise, in which tourism is a major industry. More heavily developed, Trinidad is a gas-rich island forty miles wide and eighty miles long. Because of its stable and progressive government, Trinidad had attracted a number of major

petrochemical plants and companies over the years. In the 1970s a Mississippi Chemical team had explored building a nitrogen plant there but at that time was not comfortable with any foreign investment. In 1994 a new company delegation composed of McCraw, Dunn, and Robert Jones liked what they saw and heard in Trinidad. When they discussed with government and business officials the likelihood of producing ammonia there, a fascinating possibility unfolded. The Trinidad government had decided to sell its own nitrogen plants to interested private firms. Here was a chance for Mississippi Chemical to augment its ammonia capacity immediately by acquiring an extant ammonia complex with a solid and economical supply of natural gas. This approach would

avoid the long delay of designing and constructing its own facilities. But was the company really prepared to invest in an unfamiliar land beyond the laws and regulations of the United States?

Yes was Chuck Dunn's emphatic answer: "Certainly there are major political risks to be assessed before you invest in a foreign nation—any nation. But after careful discussions with our State Department and international bankers and the business and government leaders of Trinidad, we concluded that an investment in Trinidad, as a partner with their government, was a sound and wise risk to take." However, the capacity of the complex was more than MCC wanted, and so they began to look for a partner.

Farmland Industries, the Midwest's

largest cooperative distributor of fertilizers and farm supplies, was also interested in off-shore ammonia facilities in Trinidad. Perhaps MCC could join Farmland Industries, and together they could buy the Trinidad ammonia complex. When Mississippi Chemical approached Farmland about such a joint venture, they found the Midwesterners highly receptive. Both companies had a long history of designing, constructing, and operating state-of-the-art nitrogen plants and had similar operating philosophies. Only ten days later, after round-the-clock drafting sessions, the two companies presented the Trinidad government what they considered an excellent proposal. Unfortunately the Arcadian Corporation was willing to pay the same amount for the complex and agreed to assume certain financial risks requested by the seller which MCC and Farmland had found unacceptable. MCC failed to get the plant it wanted, but it found something perhaps more important for the long-run—a compatible partner in Farmland Industries.

During the course of these discussions, Farmland representatives made several visits to Yazoo City. On their first visit Farmland's president Harry Cleberg and its executive vice president Bob Honse received an unusual introduction to the amiable small-town environment of MCC's headquarters. Because of confusion regarding their scheduling, the Farmland executives arrived in their company plane at Yazoo County's new but sequestered airport (six miles west of Yazoo City on the road to the hamlet of Carter) several hours before their hosts expected them. No one met them, nor was

anyone at the airport to help them get to the MCC offices in Yazoo City. As far as they could see were expansive cotton fields, but not a solitary sign of human life. Cleberg, who had visited Mississippi Chemical several years before, recalled that the distance to town was only a few miles, and he suggested that they hitchhike. The two men—executives of a $10 billion corporation, one of America's hundred largest—found themselves standing on the side of the Carter road in the broiling Mississippi heat. Before long a woman driving a battered Oldsmobile stopped and offered them a ride. The travelers sank into the worn back seat for an un-air-conditioned ride to the company's offices. Only with considerable difficulty did the Oldsmobile negotiate the steep drive up the bluff to the headquarters. When the two men were deposited in front of the building, Cleberg thanked the Yazoo woman and slipped a twenty dollar bill into her hand.

Glancing at the bill, she raised her eyebrows and quickly inquired, "When are y'all heading back to the airport?"

Some eighteen months later, Farmland and MCC were once again allies in an initiative to obtain ammonia production in Trinidad. During the early phases of this project, the Farmland/Mississippi Chemical team had extensive contacts with Dr. Ken Julien, chairman of The National Gas Company of Trinidad and Tobago Limited (NGC) and Malcolm Jones, president of NGC, concerning the infrastructure and gas supply needed to construct the world's largest single train ammonia plant in the jointly owned affiliate, to be known as Farmland MissChem Limited. Dunn was very impressed by the intelligent, personable, and down-to-earth Julien, who had been instrumental in developing the natural gas industry in Trinidad and Tobago. It was Julien who had devised the strategy of joining with

After a worldwide search for the most economical and reliable source of natural gas to fuel a new ammonia complex, Mississippi Chemical and Farmland Industries teamed to launch Farmland MissChem Limited and build the world's largest single train Kellogg ammonia plant in Trinidad. Announcing the kickoff in October 1995 were, from left: Dr. Ken Julien, chairman of the National Gas Company of Trinidad and Tobago (NGC); Malcolm Jones, president of NGC; Bob Honse, executive vice president of Farmland Industries; Chuck Dunn, MCC president; and John Prijatel, president of Farmland MissChem Limited.

companies willing to build plants in his nation, thereby converting Trinidad's gas to fertilizers.

Eager to develop a part of its island that had no industrial jobs, the Trinidadian officials persuaded Mississippi Chemical and Farmland to select a site at La Brea, a small isolated village on the coast of Trinidad, miles away from the established industrial estate. A site closer to the industrial base of the island would offer significant advantages, but the government offered substantial additional incentives for an agreement to help develop this remote region. Mississippi Chemical, Farmland, and Trinidad ultimately reached an agreement. The price

Farmland and MCC agreed to pay for the Trinidad gas would fluctuate in correlation with the price of ammonia in the Caribbean. If ammonia prices increased, so would the price of the gas; if ammonia prices slumped, the price of the gas would drop also. In other words, they established a sliding scale that protects the ammonia producer in difficult times and rewards the nation of Trinidad in good times. Farmland and MCC would each be required to use or dispose of half of the output of Farmland MissChem. For Mississippi Chemical, this agreement meant price protection on nearly 30 percent of the amount of natural gas the company then used in all its ammonia plants.

Then came the first of two shocks that threatened to derail the project. The M. W. Kellogg Company dismayed Mississippi Chemical with the price it submitted to build the two-thousand-ton-a-day ammonia plant at the Trinidad site. The bid far exceeded what MCC had anticipated. After extensive negotiations, Mississippi Chemical and Farmland were ultimately able to negotiate a lump sum contract price with Kellogg with performance standards and schedule guarantees acceptable to the partners.

For the first time in its history MCC sought large-scale lenders on the world financial markets. They found international banks eager for such an extensive undertaking. After discussions with numerous banks from several nations, Mississippi Chemical and Farmland settled on ABN AMRO, N.V., a Netherlands bank, as the lead lender. Farmland MissChem arranged to borrow 65 percent of the $330 million project total from a syndicate including ABN AMRO, The ExIm Bank of the United States, and others. Each partner contributed 50 percent of the equity. (In 1948 no commercial lender anywhere had so much as considered Mississippi Chemical's request for a $3.4 million loan to build its first plants. Forty-five years later, Farmland MissChem was an attractive borrower to a number of banks which competed to secure this $200 million loan.) The decision was made to obtain project financing for the ammonia plant; that is, all loans were to be repaid only from revenues generated by Farmland MissChem's Trinidad ammonia plant, without access to the assets or guarantees from the parent corporations.

Farmland MissChem's Trinidad ammonia plant at the Point Lisas Industrial Estate, 1997. Located on the island's west coast, the $330 million complex overlooks the Gulf of Paria.

Such transactions are very complex, and negotiating the terms of the construction and long-term loans was an agonizing process that required many months.

Soon the prodigious project in Trinidad gathered speed. Chester Grisham, an MCC project manager for twenty-five years, went to Kellogg's Houston offices to supervise the design of the $330 million job. All was progressing smoothly, and nearly $10 million had been spent, when Kellogg delivered a shocking conclusion. Contending that the soil at the selected site was not solid enough to support the enormous plant, in early 1995 Kellogg refused to proceed with the project at that location. Mississippi Chemical and

Kellogg had discussed the shortcomings of the La Brea site many times, and Kellogg had specifically committed to building the plant there and had declared the site acceptable for construction. La Brea is located in an area of Trinidad well known for its deposits of pitch, or tar. For a century or more ships had anchored at Trinidad to coat

Officials from Trinidad welcome representatives of Mississippi Chemical and Farmland Industries at the groundbreaking ceremonies of Farmland MissChem. Top: Trinidad's prime minister Basdeo Panday greets MCC senior vice president Ed McCraw, left, and Farmland vice president Stan Riemann, center. Above: Sharon Christopher, board member of the National Gas Company of Trinidad and Tobago Limited (NGC); MCC president Chuck Dunn; and NGC president Malcolm Jones enjoy the occasion. Left: To support its neighboring Trinidad schools, Farmland MissChem donated computers for use in classrooms.

Trinidad Offers Caribbean Culture to MCC

The company's newest production site, a huge ammonia production complex constructed by Farmland MissChem at the Point Lisas Industrial Estate, lies far across the Caribbean Sea, on the tropical and gas-rich island of Trinidad in The Republic of Trinidad and Tobago, just ten miles from the coast of South America. A British colony until 1962, Trinidad has a festive, multiracial culture shaped by its tropical climate and an ethnic blend of Africans, Indians, Asians, and a sprinkling of Europeans, each of whom brought diverse foods, religions, customs, and languages to their adopted island homeland. The Republic's island of Tobago is a tourist haven, but Trinidad is a "blue collar" island dotted with major petrochemical industries which have come to capitalize on the island's rich oil and natural gas reserves, stable government, and productive work force.

Trinidadian student performs for Farmland MissChem groundbreaking ceremonies.

Farmland MissChem's facility was carved from the sugar cane fields that overlook the Gulf of Paria on the island's west coast, near the town of Couva. Coconut trees and bamboo thickets abound there, and ninety minutes north, tropical rain forests with exotic flowers are a haven for spectacular birds. On this warm, frequently muggy island, temperatures never climb as high or dip as low as at Mississippi Chemical's southern U.S. plant sites.

Trinidadians are highly literate (ninety-nine percent read and write) and speak a clipped version of English, a carryover from generations of British rule. "We are excited to find our new Trinidadian co-workers to be extremely capable, diligent, hard-working folks," David Arnold, senior vice president of the technical group says. "In many ways they are like Triad co-workers in Louisiana. They are warm and friendly; they work hard and then they play hard." Trinidadians particularly love their holidays, and with various ethnic and religious groups on the island, they celebrate many. On the same day Cajuns celebrate Mardi Gras, Trinidadians celebrate Carnival with steel bands and calypso music (both of which originated in Trinidad), flamboyant costumes, limbo dancing, and much revelry.

Though the culture of Trinidad differs markedly from that of Yazoo City, Pascagoula, Donaldsonville, and Carlsbad, the operation there features the same characteristics as its U.S. counterparts: modern, state-of-the-art production facilities and skilled, highly-trained employees collaborating in a friendly, family-like atmosphere to operate efficiently, productively, and safely. "As we grow and expand in Trinidad and other cultures and communities, our greatest challenge will be to maintain the values and principles that define Mississippi Chemical and make us successful, while respecting their cultural traditions. I am very pleased at how this is occurring in Trinidad," Chuck Dunn said.

their hulls with La Brea pitch. To this day the spacious thoroughfares surrounding London's Buckingham Palace are coated with La Brea pitch. Now Mississippi Chemical pitched a La Brea fit.

McCraw was at the doorway of Kellogg's offices in Houston when they opened the next morning. He demanded answers. Kellogg maintained its position that the La Brea site was unsuitable. "At that point I wouldn't have given the project a 5 percent chance of ever becoming a reality," McCraw recalled. Not only had Kellogg suspended work, Trinidad had elected a new prime minister, and all the cabinet officials who had worked with Mississippi Chemical and Farmland were now gone. "We had negotiated in good faith with one set of government officials. Now we'd have to tell a completely new group of Trinidad officials that it wouldn't work and try to get them to give us a new site and new gas contracts. It was an absolute nightmare."

McCraw and general counsel Robert Jones, along with Stan Riemann and Randy Sims of Farmland, flew to Trinidad determined to resolve the debacle one way or another. They faced formidable odds. "We looked at dozens of sites, but nothing would work," McCraw remembered later. Ultimately they succeeded in persuading the government of Trinidad to drop the La Brea locale. The project was finally relocated to the industrial area of the island at Port Lisas. It took nearly six months to renegotiate the intricate contracts with both Kellogg and the Trinidad officials. However, at long last the Trinidad undertaking could go forward in earnest. Completed in 1998, the plant is capable of producing seven hundred thousand tons a year of ammonia. Mississippi Chemical's share of its output totals 350,000 tons annually.

Back in Mississippi the company was in the midst of negotiations just as crucial as those it had just concluded with Trinidad and Kellogg. Several times during the previous twenty-five years, MCC had explored the prospect of buying First Mississippi Corporation's one-half interest in the Triad Chemical nitrogen complex at Donaldsonville. Shortly after joining the company in 1978, one of Chuck Dunn's assignments had been to prepare documents to purchase First Mississippi's half of Triad. The deal did not come to fruition, and similar subsequent efforts were unsuccessful. But over the years, Mississippi Chemical's acquisition of First Mississippi's half of Triad, or even all of First Mississippi's fertilizer assets, made more and more sense.

Buying First Mississippi's nitrogen facilities fit neatly into the company's strategy for future growth. In the spring of 1994 Dunn approached First Mississippi's president Kelley Williams and discussed the mergers and consolidations then occurring in the American fertilizer industry. Both men agreed that, as separate fertilizer-makers, Mississippi Chemical and First Mississippi might eventually be too small to compete with the enlarging competition. First Mississippi owned not only half of Triad Chemical but also a sizeable ammonia plant in Donaldsonville adjacent to Triad Chemical in a sub-

sidiary called AMPRO. MCC was pointedly interested in both the Triad and AMPRO facilities.

After the company's public stock offering in August 1994, Chuck Dunn stayed in contact with Kelley Williams about buying his fertilizer properties. But the timing did not fit First Mississippi's plans, and Dunn and Williams agreed to a hiatus in the discussions. Mississippi Chemical believed it had a contractual right of first refusal to buy First Mississippi's half of Triad should First Mississippi receive an otherwise acceptable offer from another company.

Then, in early 1996, Dunn was surprised to learn from Williams that First Mississippi had retained a well-known investment banking firm to find the highest bidder for the First Mississippi nitrogen facilities. Dunn had no interest in fueling a bidding war for First Mississippi's plants and informed Williams that MCC would abstain from any auction process. The Mississippi Chemical president then wrote Williams and First Mississippi stressing that the Triad joint venture agreement gave MCC a right of first refusal should First Mississippi decide to sell its half of Triad. Williams firmly disputed MCC's claim and urged Dunn to submit an offer. However, Williams told Dunn that he had been advised by investment bankers that $375 million would be an appropriate price for the fertilizer assets. Dunn was adamant that MCC would not pay such a price. Negotiations came to a standstill and remained stalemated for weeks. First Mississippi continued to seek other purchase offers.

Finally the MCC team working on the project decided that the timing was right to see whether the stalemate could be broken. Dunn called Williams prepared to submit a bid of $280 million for just the nitrogen fertilizer facilities and asked Williams whether he would give such a proposal reasonable consideration. Williams said First Mississippi was talking to another party, but encouraged Dunn to submit a bid. Williams committed to submitting the proposal to the First Mississippi board of directors for consideration but told Dunn the price still seemed low. "Based on that conversation, we decided to make our best offer for the First Mississippi properties," Dunn recalls, "one that was good for them and good for us, submit the proposal, and then stick with it." MCC formulated a proposal which added the purchase of First Mississippi's ammonia barge company and its half of a Pasadena, Texas, ammonia terminal. MCC offered to purchase all First Mississippi's fertilizer assets by assuming $150 million of First Mississippi's debt and conveying 6.8 million shares of MCC stock, a total purchase price of some $296 million based on the value of MCC's stock at that time.* Dunn went to First Mississippi's headquarters and reviewed the proposed offer with Mike Summerford, First

* MCC's offer was complicated by First Mississippi's tax structure, which required that all of First Mississippi's non-fertilizer business be spun off to a subsidiary (ChemFirst) through a "Morris Trust" procedure, leaving only fertilizer assets in First Mississippi. Then, Mississippi Chemical would purchase the stock of First Mississippi in exchange for MCC stock and the assumption of fertilizer-related debt.

Mississippi's CFO, and later that day Robert Jones delivered a firm offer to First Mississippi. First Mississippi had scheduled a board of directors meeting within the next few days at which time Mississippi Chemical's offer would be considered. All Mississippi Chemical could do now was wait.

By coincidence, Dunn had committed to make several presentations regarding Mississippi Chemical's future to a number of large investors in Boston and New York on August 26 and 27. The regulations of the Securities and Exchange Commission prohibited Dunn from disclosing the offer Mississippi Chemical had made.

Without so much as hinting of a possible arrangement, Dunn made his rounds in Boston and then flew to New York on the 26th for his afternoon conferences on Wall Street. After each meeting he telephoned Robert Jones in Yazoo City for any word of First Mississippi's response. There was nothing to report. During his last appointment of the day with Chris Willis of Schroder and Wertheim, Robert Jones called. "I'm standing here at the FAX machine," he said, "and the signed papers are coming through. We've got a deal."

The exhilarated Mississippi Chemical people worked late into the night preparing an announcement for a breakfast meeting scheduled the next day with two dozen prominent securities analysts. When the guests arrived, the news release describing the purchase of First Mississippi's fertilizer operations was waiting for them. "The timing of that meeting couldn't have been better," Dunn would recall. After explaining

In December 1996 Mississippi Chemical acquired sole ownership of the Triad Nitrogen production facilities, above, at Donaldsonville, Louisiana, purchasing from First Mississippi its portion of this modern nitrogen complex. Triad Nitrogen's state-of-the-art ammonia and urea plants and its location on the Mississippi River make it one of America's premiere nitrogen fertilizer complexes.

Triad Storytellers Make Work Fun

Triad Nitrogen's gregarious employees, like their Mississippi counterparts, enjoy reminiscing about beloved co-workers, past and present. Lee Dowdy, Houston Holland, and Buddy Ball are three names that come up often in the conversations of long-time employees. Stories about these three men epitomize the special character of the people and the place.

Lee Dowdy, maintenance manager of the Donaldsonville complex from 1969 to 1975 and then general manager until his retirement in 1977, was universally admired as a hardworking "hands-on guy." Pam Gregoire, Triad's longest service employee and self-appointed company historian, recalls: "Mr. Dowdy never liked being in an office. He loved being out in the plant among the workers and the machinery. He could just walk up to a piece of equipment, put his hands on it, and tell you what was wrong in a minute—a mechanical wizard. But he

Houston Holland

also loved people. He and Mrs. Dowdy took a special interest not only in every employee but in all their family members."

Retired ammonia manager Houston Holland is legendary for his dramatic methods of ensuring that everyone at Triad did his or her work correctly. To make an impression on company maintenance crews who had left tools and used supplies in his plant vicinity, Holland arrived at the plant at 4:00 one morning. He gathered up all the tools, barrels, and other debris the men had abandoned and used them to block the road to the maintenance building. When the maintenance workers came in at 7:00 a.m., they became so enraged the general manager had to arbitrate the fracas. Holland claims he made his point. On another occasion Holland removed a pistol from a dozing plant security guard and delivered it to the Jackson office of Triad partner First Mississippi with a terse note suggesting that security needed tightening.

During his thirty years in Triad's urea production facility, from 1967 to 1997, Buddy Ball entertained and perplexed company employees with incessant pranks. For instance, Ball heard environmental engineer James Patterson boasting about the fantastic gas mileage his new Ford pickup was getting. The

minute Patterson left the control room, Ball said to his co-workers, "Boys, we've got to buy that guy some gasoline." For the next month, Ball and his cohorts would secretly slip gasoline into Patterson's new truck. Every week the unsuspecting victim would return to the control room bragging about his continually improving mileage—21, then 23, 26, on up to 32 miles a gallon. Then Ball abruptly stopped supplementing Patterson's fuel. Patterson became so puzzled and worried about his truck's declining performance he took it back to the dealer for a complete overhaul.

At Triad, not only do the employees work hard and play hard, they work hard at play and play hard at work.

Standing left to right: Ricky Gautreau, Kenneth Gomez, Rocky Hood, and seated at control board, Lloyd Giroir

Triad's Buddy Ball

the transaction to the analysts present, he quickly called those with whom he had met the previous day to explain the transaction and his necessary silence about it. A general conference call with more than one hundred analysts and investors was held later that morning.

Dunn got yet another call from Mississippi. It was from LeRoy Percy, seventy-nine years old then, retired as board chairman of both Mississippi Chemical and First Mississippi. "I can't tell you how grateful I am that Mississippi Chemical finally bought those Donaldsonville plants," Percy told Dunn. "If you hadn't, when I got to heaven I'm afraid Owen [Cooper] would have never forgiven me."

Percy was not the only one who approved of the transaction. Later that day, August 27, 1996, as news of the transaction circulated, the value of both Mississippi Chemical and First Mississippi's stock increased significantly. This increase, signaling that the nation's investors believed the deal was a sound one for both parties, was critical to ensuring that the transaction would go forward.

First Mississippi benefited from the transaction because it removed the cyclical fertilizer business from its portfolio of specialty chemicals. The acquisition increased MCC's nitrogen capacity by 750,000 tons a year, doubling the company's urea sales to 560,000 tons annually and providing 625,000 tons a year of ammonia from AMPRO's plant.

Along with additional quantities of ammonia came a fleet of eleven ammonia barges, each with the capability of transporting twenty-five hundred tons of ammonia on

America's inland waterways and intercoastal canals. Gary Elliott, marketing director for ammonia and phosphates, explained the significance of this acquisition: "These eleven barges represent roughly one-third of the U.S. ammonia barge capacity and are extremely important to us in selling and shipping ammonia across the Gulf Coastal area and the Midwest. Our ability to make water deliveries frequently determines whether we make the sale or not, so these barges are a strategic asset."

While the intricate negotiations for the First Mississippi acquisition and the new Trinidad plant were taking form, Mississippi Chemical was proceeding with a third considerable addition to its nitrogen production. On April 19, 1996, the company announced it would invest $130 million to make substantial increases in the nitrogen capacity of its original Yazoo City plant site. This expansion would feature a 500-ton-a-day ammonia plant of British design, an advanced 650-ton-a-day nitric acid plant, and modifications to increase the company's ammonium nitrate capacity from 750,000 tons to 900,000 tons a year.

The modification of Yazoo City's nitrogen complex continued the company's long practice of utilizing the latest and most advanced technology available in order to maintain its efficiency and cost competitiveness. The new ammonia plant, the first of its kind to be built in the United States, employed a new technology perfected by I.C.I. at Severnside, England. A small 500-ton-a-day ammonia plant constructed with this new technology could now be competitive with much larger plants. Thus, Mississippi Chemical was able to construct a plant to provide only the amount of ammonia it expected to consume in Yazoo City. In the past, the industry could increase ammonia production efficiently only by the construction of large plants, which might well produce far more ammonia than the market could absorb.

The new nitric acid plant was identical to the unit completed in Yazoo City three years earlier with the French Grande Paroisse design. The Yazoo City expansions used a process air compressor from Switzerland, an ammonia compressor from Italy, and a prodigious absorption tower from France. The 180-ton absorption tower was much too enormous and too heavy to be transported on highways. Like the earlier tower, it came across the Atlantic by ship, then was dispatched up the Mississippi and Yazoo Rivers from New Orleans on two barges, and finally was "crawled" up the steep Yazoo

Carlsbad's Old Faithful

Kenny Willis

While Mississippi Chemical or its subsidiary Mississippi Potash has owned the historic "U.S. Potash mine" since 1974, seventy-eight-year-old Kenny Willis has been a presence at the property for fifty-two years. Affectionately called "Grumpy" as a counterpoint to his endearing personality, Willis went to work at U.S. Potash, the first potash mine in the United States, in 1946 as engineer on the sixteen-mile company railroad shuttling ore from the present mine shaft to the original potash refinery on the Pecos River, which closed decades ago. "U.S. Potash brought that narrow-gaged train in here from their Death Valley borax mine," Grumpy remembers. "We made four round trips a day, carrying up to two thousand tons of that rich 26 to 28 percent potash ore each trip. We carried our shotguns on the train, and when I spotted a covey of quails along the route, I'd stop the train and we'd hop off and shoot a few quail."

Today, Willis has officially retired but nevertheless works as needed and oversees the company's eleven water wells in the Caprock mountain area and the sixteen-inch pipeline that transports the water across the sixty miles of desert to the mine and to other customers who purchase it from Mississippi Potash. "Grumpy watches that water flow like a hawk," maintenance foreman Donnie Cantrell says. "He inspects the wells Monday, Wednesday, and Friday, and if the pressure drops unexpectedly or a meter shows excess flow, Grumpy hops in his four-wheel-drive pickup to run down the leak or find out who is using too much water and why. You'd better not mess with Willis's water." Skip Shafer, another maintenance foreman and admirer of Willis, says, "Grumpy has forgotten more about this property than the rest of us will ever know. He's incredibly valuable in chasing down spare parts and helping us in the shop when he's not tending that water line."

When asked how long he intends to work, Willis's eyes twinkle. "Well, when I got my new heart six years ago [he had open-heart surgery], Randy Foote told me I'd have to work until I reached a hundred. But I might just retire at ninety so I can have more time to hunt and fish."

River levee on the back of a monstrous centipede-like vehicle, three-hundred-feet long with one hundred wheels spaced in close intervals, and transported to the Mississippi Chemical plant six miles away. When this behemoth finally arrived in the Yazoo City plant in the summer of 1997, the eight-hundred-ton construction crane that

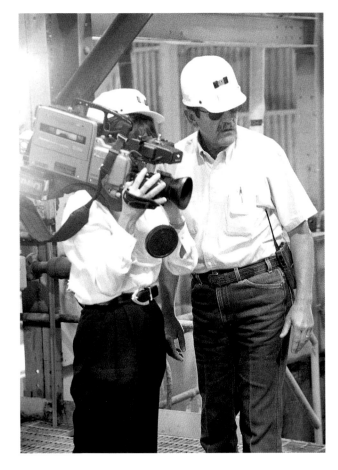

With the acquisition of two adjacent Carlsbad mining operations in 1996, Mississippi Potash became America's largest producer of potash. Left: Ralph Griffin, who managed Mississippi Potash's surface operations, takes Suzanne Hurst of KOTK-TV of Roswell, New Mexico, on a tour of the potash facility. Above: Manager of mines Kent Aveson, left, and Bart Frintz.

would hoist it into place was so enormous it required twenty-seven transport trucks to move it from Baton Rouge to Yazoo City.

To ensure favorable access to natural gas reserves to supply the expanding Yazoo City complex, Mississippi Chemical acquired the Mustang natural gas pipeline, a sixty-mile, twelve-inch diameter pipeline built in the 1970s to deliver gas from the Thomasville, Mississippi, gas fields. Explaining this strategic acquisition, vice president of nitrogen production Larry Holley said, "Owning the Mustang pipeline not only gives us favored access to the gas reserve at Thomasville; it also provides access to the largest intrastate

gas system and two major interstate gas systems not previously available to us. Owning the Mustang pipeline significantly multiplies our natural gas purchase options and makes us more competitive and flexible in our gas acquisition."

At Carlsbad, halfway across America from Yazoo City, MCC's subsidiary, Mississippi Potash, made another enhancement that would increase its capacity to mine, process, and market potash. On August 19, 1996, Mississippi Chemical announced the purchase of two additional potash mines and above-ground processing facilities from Trans-Resources, Inc., at a price of $45 mil-

lion plus the cost of working capital; the two mines had operated as New Mexico Potash Corporation (NMPC) and Eddy Potash, Inc. When combined with the company's existing Carlsbad mine, they would make Mississippi Potash, which had become very "bullish" on the potash market, the nation's largest potash producer with the capability of producing 1.3 million tons of potash annually.

"This clearly positions us as the leader in the southwest U.S. potash industry," Mississippi Potash vice president of operations Randy Foote would say. "When we reopened in 1988, some people saw us as a flash in the

Above: An aerial view of the Pascagoula complex, Mississippi Phosphates, on Bayou Casotte. (In the background, the Chevron USA oil refinery, on land initially purchased by Mississippi Chemical.) Mississippi Phosphates invested $25 million between 1996 and 1998 to expand by 25 percent the capacity of its Pascagoula complex to produce DAP fertilizer. Left: A huge ocean-going vessel offloads phosphate rock from Morocco, which is stored outside, above left, until converted to phosphoric acid.

pan, but with this expansion and the innovations we employ—such as using fewer supervisors and counting on line employees to handle more responsibility—we intend to be the most efficient operator in the basin for years to come."

The former NMPC mine was the asset Mississippi Potash actually sought because it would offer significant synergies and reserves for the next two decades. "This mine is located very close to our existing mine and close to our richest ore reserves," Foote would emphasize. "We expect to have it eventually tunnel into our best reserves, giving us two mines drawing ore from our most valuable deposits." The NMPC mine also broadened the company's products, providing for the first time the technologies to produce and market industrial and specialty grades of potash. The Eddy mine, however, was known to be mining the last of its desirable reserves when Mississippi Potash purchased it. After utilizing the mine as long as was economically feasible, Mississippi Potash closed that mine in December 1997. The company then expanded production at its other two mines and related facilities to offset most of the three hundred thousand potash tons lost when the Eddy mine ceased operations.

Mississippi Phosphates also had expansion plans for its Pascagoula complex. Inextricably connected to the international market, Pascagoula's phosphate rock supply comes from Morocco, and the majority of its output is sold to foreign customers, primarily in China, India, and Latin America. First, the

Mack Barber

The Father of DAP

Mack Barber, Mississippi Phosphates's seventy-one-year-old fertilizer guru, is known across the world fertilizer industry as the man who first produced diammonium phosphate (DAP). Since its creation in 1954, DAP has become the prevailing phosphate fertilizer in the world: 90 percent of the phosphate fertilizers used today—some twelve million tons each year—are diammonium phosphate. Barber recalls making the first DAP, which is 18 percent nitrogen and 46 percent phosphate (specified 18-46-0): "I had no idea I was inventing what would become the world's dominant phosphate product. The truth is, I was simply trying to make 13-39-0, but the gypsum filler I added kept making my slurry gum up like Jell-O. When I took the filler out, I had produced 18-46-0." And the rest is fertilizer history.

Over the next four decades, the pioneering Barber helped build and then operate more than a dozen major phosphate fertilizer complexes around the world, beginning with Mississippi Chemical's Coastal plant in Pascagoula. After serving as Coastal's first general manager for two years (1957–59), Barber made a thirty-year odyssey that took him to Louisiana, then the Philippines, India, Venezuela, Germany, Brazil, England, France, the Canary Islands, Idaho, and finally back to Pascagoula in 1987.

When Nu-South, Inc., purchased the Pascagoula complex from MCC, Barber returned to reopen it and convert it to DAP production exclusively. After Nu-South went bankrupt in 1990, Mississippi Phosphates received the plant and hired Barber as general manager; he held this position until 1997, when Jim Perkins succeeded him. Today Barber is a special consultant advising both Mississippi Phosphates and its Moroccan partner OCP on DAP production. Under Barber's guidance Mississippi Phosphates's annual DAP output has grown to 720,000 tons per year, with its current expansions projected to boost DAP capacity to 900,000 tons annually. Both MCC's and OCP's leaders credit Barber with Mississippi Phosphates success since it returned the plant to full operation. Barber, however, says, "Our production efficiency over the last decade is a tribute to the entire Pascagoula team; dozens of people deserve a salute for returning this complex to profitability," Barber says.

"I've worked for many companies in many countries, and Mississippi Phosphates is the best employer I've ever had," Barber says. "This company treats employees more fairly than any other, and it maintains the most friendly, family-like atmosphere I've ever experienced anywhere. As an example, when the wife of our administrative manager died last year, a group of his fellow employees attended her funeral. The priest told me he'd never seen so many co-workers turn out to comfort a fellow employee. That's just the way the Mississippi Chemical family works."

Members of Mississippi Chemical's political action committee met with U.S. Senate majority leader Trent Lott in 1997 at the nation's Capitol. Standing, from left, Larry Savell (Triad), Senator Lott, Tim Fleming (Mississippi Phosphates), Donnie Jay Gosset (Mississippi Potash), and company lobbyist Bill Simpson. Seated, from left, Wendy Weathersby, Glenda Smith, and Trudy Allen from MCC's Yazoo City headquarters.

the company's exports of DAP. Vice president of marketing and distribution John Duffy would note that Mississippi Potash utilizes a similar group, PCS Sales Corporation, to market its potash in the international market and the UAN Solutions Export Association to enable the company to sell its nitrogen solutions to international customers. "These international marketing affiliations give us worldwide representation in the major fertilizer consuming regions of the world and a cost-effective means of exporting our products," Duffy explained. He noted that MCC is also an active participant in the International Fertilizer Association and other trade groups, and in 1997 sent company delegations to meetings in Beijing, China; Warsaw, Poland; the Netherlands; and Great Britain.

"The fertilizer market is truly a global one and growing more so every day," said Duffy. "When the fertilizer people in China, India, or the former Soviet Union cough, it can shake our world here in Yazoo City, Pascagoula, Carlsbad, and Donaldsonville." Events in China during 1997 and 1998 bore out Duffy's words: China suddenly ceased buying urea, and almost overnight world nitrogen prices and profits declined steeply. Chuck Dunn explained, "China recently completed major new fertilizer plants capable of producing over three million tons of urea a year and needed to assimilate this new output before importing more product." Toward that end, in mid-1997 China placed an embargo on urea imports and sent the prices for urea, ammonium nitrate, and N-Sol spiraling downward.

company negotiated during 1997 an extension of its partnership agreement with OCP, the Moroccan national phosphate company—a contract that would run until the year 2016. Then, on July 21, 1997, the company announced it was investing $10.5 million to augment Pascagoula's ability to produce diammonium phosphates (DAP) from 720,000 to 900,000 tons a year, in addition to $16 million already spent to enlarge its gypsum storage capacity. These expansions, as described by Jim Perkins, Pascagoula's general manager, would increase both the capacity of the phosphoric acid plant and

the company's ability to load large ocean-going vessels for China and India. The Pascagoula plant would then be able to load twelve thousand tons a day, a capacity important in filling the Panamax ships that hold fifty to sixty thousand tons. (These ships are the largest that can traverse the Panama Canal, hence their name: Panamax.)

To enhance its ability to market products to its worldwide customer base, Mississippi Phosphates joined PhosChem, a U.S. phosphate industry export consortium. On October 1, 1997, PhosChem, an important presence in the world market, began handling all

Dunn continued:

This is the latest of the inevitable downturns in the cycles that the world fertilizer industry and every other commodity go through. These cycles are a function of world supply and demand, and the timing of these dips is not very predictable. We do not, however, expect this trough to resemble the one in the mid-1980s. Nevertheless, the worldwide demand for food is strong and growing. Meeting that demand will require the use of more fertilizers. For the long-term, I remain optimistic about agriculture and the fertilizer industry. The world's population is predicted to double (to ten billion people) in just forty-five years. Doubling food production is going to be very difficult because virtually every acre of suitable land is already in cultivation. The *only* way the world can produce the food our surging population will need is increased yields, including the use of fertilizers.

Mississippi Chemical is committed to providing employees the tools and knowledge necessary for the company to be successful in the world fertilizer industry. "We have a dedicated and talented work force and we pledge to give them ongoing access to the technology and training they need to ensure we remain a competitive fertilizer manufacturer," MCC president Chuck Dunn emphasized. Keeping up with the computer revolution is one way the company honors this commitment to top technology. From 1992 to 1997 MCC's information and technology task force guided the company and its office work force to a new level of computer efficiency: new systems

Mississippi Chemical engineers, from left, Don Meyer, Dan Kilpatrick, and Danny Hood. The company's in-house engineering staff has a combined total of more than 450 years experience in the fertilizer business and makes MCC the industry leader in technical expertise.

were installed corporate-wide, and comprehensive computer training and support services were offered to employees.

Advanced new computer systems are also at work in Mississippi Chemical's fertilizer plants, greatly enhancing the ability of the company's production personnel to control, monitor, and adjust the operations of its nitrogen plants in Donaldsonville, Yazoo City, and Trinidad. This new generation of plant computer systems, called "distributive control systems," has reduced much of the manual labor and some of the risks of plant start ups, shutdowns, and adjustments. In

earlier days, when critical adjustments had to be made, operators had no choice but to adjust by hand and "feel."

Throughout its history, Mississippi Chemical's benefit programs have been among the most egalitarian in the nation. In 1991 Mississippi Chemical added an employee profit sharing plan that is unusual in providing *every* employee with an additional payment of up to 10 percent of his or her base compensation when certain profit levels are reached. This profit sharing plan quickly took its place alongside the company's thrift

Company employees and family members celebrate Christmas with parades and parties. Readying Mississippi Phosphates's float for the 1997 Pascagoula/Moss Point Christmas parade are, from left, Dennis Reid, Robin Higginbothan, Anthony Young, Derrick Reddix, and John Paul Hardy.

Annual company picnics for employees and their family members are eagerly awaited events. Above left: Randall Woods and Truett Duncan (with ears) cook over a thousand hot dogs each year for the Yazoo Easter Egg Hunt. Left: Robert Jones resting during the Easter Egg Hunt. Above: Glen Moore, right, dishes out barbecue to Carlsbad employees in 1995 to celebrate winning the nation's highest mine safety award, the Sentinels of Safety.

Employees and their families joining in the fun at the Mississippi Chemical picnic in Yazoo City include hula-hooping children, top photo; retiree Porter Faye Vandevere, far left; and William "Duke" Williams from maintenance and Linda Patterson, above right. Panel at left: Instrument mechanic Kathy Walker, top, prepares MCC's annual Santa Claus float for the parade; center, corporate communications manager Melinda Hood and Debbie Ewing, wife of Joe Ewing, watch the parade with apparent delight; below, riding the float are, from left, D. L. Ashley (son of David Ashley of information services), manager of accounting Ginger Roark, and her daughter Morgan Roark.

plan and defined benefit pension plan in popularity with employees.

As Mississippi Chemical concluded its first fifty years, the company implemented award-winning programs in environmental education and protection as well as in employee health and safety. It likewise heightened its campaign to fortify public education, encourage the arts, and strengthen social services in those communities where its plants are located.

The company's actions in environmental education and protection have made it a recognized example in this field. In 1993 the board of directors formalized the company's longstanding commitment to environmental protection and to the well-being of its workers. The board characterized Mississippi Chemical's environmental responsibilities as going beyond full compliance with all federal and state guidelines. The company pledged itself to help guard and wisely use the air, water, and land resources of its home communities.

The executive committee of the board agreed in 1995 to invest a fixed percentage of the company's annual income in environmental education and protection. From 1995 to 1998 some of these corporate funds were used to buy, restore, and preserve threatened wetlands and forest lands, the largest such investment being the purchase of a 3,900-acre tract of land on the Mississippi River just north of Vicksburg, Mississippi. The company's conservation program calls for the replanting of native hardwoods, preservation of wetlands, and restoration of some barren areas. The property will be maintained as a

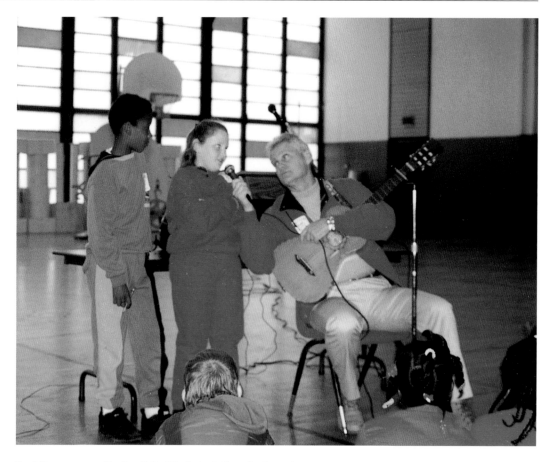

Paul Ott presents *Seeds of Life*, **Mississippi Chemical's environmental education program, to elementary students. This program, featuring singing conservationist Ott, has won regional and national awards and the acclaim of teachers and students across the South and Southwest.**

wildlife preserve and made available for research and promotion of wildlife management. MCC is also working closely with the U.S. Bureau of Land Management and The Nature Conservancy on similar programs for setting aside lands on the Pecos River near Carlsbad, and with the government of Trinidad on protecting environmentally endangered areas of that island. For these pioneering activities the company was cited as Corporate Volunteer of the Year in 1996 by The Nature Conservancy.

MCC is also a pioneer in environmental education. It funded and helped develop a national environmental education program for the Future Farmers of America (FFA), now used by teenagers in every corner of the United States. Perhaps the company's most successful education project has been *Seeds of Life*, featuring Paul Ott, the company's singing environmental conservationist. Designed especially for elementary students, *Seeds of Life* has won a national Take Pride in America award, several regional awards, and the acclaim of thousands of teachers and students across the South and Southwest. It is performed each month for elementary students in those communities with company plants and in other schools across the region. A third environmental education agenda is being offered to elementary school science students in New Mexico through the state mining association, of which Mississippi Potash is an active member. Mississippi Potash distributes educational materials and provides speakers for science classes to instruct students on the scientific principles used in potash mining and the impact of potash on the world food cycle.

The company is further involved in environmental education and conservation undertakings for farmers, ranchers, and agricultural organizations. Mississippi Chemical actively works with the Natural Resources Conservation Service, an arm of the federal government and successor to the Soil Conservation Service, which has programs in almost every county in the United States. The company's field sales representatives and the company's agronomist Bob Thompson work with its farmer-customers on Best Management Practices intended to maximize farm production while minimizing farm costs and environmental disturbances. The company is a major sponsor of the 4-H Clubs and the widespread services they provide to rural youth across America.

For its environmental achievements, MCC has received considerable attention. The company earned the first Betz Industrial Return on Environment Award for successes in its reduction of water consumption and its sound wastewater treatment practices. Innovations perfected by Mississippi Chemical's technical staff are used to protect the environment not just in its own plants but in facilities all over the world. The company's ammonium nitrate neutralizer process, for example, is now used as far away as Egypt to reduce emissions and prevent runoff problems that threatened the Nile River.

Nearly five decades ago Mississippi Chemical's Yazoo City plant—under its first safety director, Mike Ellison—won a national safety citation for operating throughout its entire first year without a single accident. The safety tradition has continued. Twice in the 1990s Mississippi Potash won the nation's most prestigious mine safety award, The Sentinels of Safety, presented by the U.S. government's Mine Safety and Health Administration, for operating the safest mine in the country. The company has also been named Operator of the Year by the New Mexico Mining Association on five different occasions since the mine's reopening in 1988. "While we must make a profit to survive," vice president Randy Foote would say, "we make it crystal clear to our employees that their safety is more important to Mississippi Potash than one extra ton of potash. That is the foundation of all our safety records—we put people and their safety first."

At Triad Nitrogen in Donaldsonville the company's workers in 1997 recorded their ninth straight year of accident-free operation, a performance that has brought Triad numerous tributes from the National Safety Council and the Louisiana Workman's Compensation Administration. "When I arrived in 1967, we had a heck of a time convincing these Cajun guys to wear hard hats and safety glasses," general manager Bobby Shackelford, who transferred to Triad from Coastal Chemical in Pascagoula, remembers. "Today safety is a way of life with our people—and not just with our staff, but with our contract labor people and our suppliers and vendors as well."

Continuing its long history of responsible corporate citizenship, Mississippi Chemical has worked to foster improvements in the public schools in those locales where it has plants by offering leadership and funding selected programs. Especially notable is the company's initiative in the Public Education Forum of Mississippi, a coalition of the state's industries that has challenged the Mississippi legislature and department of education to break new ground in reforms and funding. Both Tom Parry and Chuck Dunn served two-year terms as president of the Forum while Gene Triggs, retired vice president of governmental affairs, provided—at company expense—considerable time and behind-the-scenes expertise, both before and after he retired from the company. With funding furnished in part by Mississippi Phosphates, consultants are assisting the public schools in Moss Point in delineating strategies to guide their educational commitments into the next century. Mississippi Chemical is funding the same strategic planning program for the Yazoo City schools. For more than a decade David Arnold, vice

In 1997 Triad Nitrogen completed nine consecutive years of operation without a lost-time accident. Among its many awards is a commendation from the Louisiana Workers Compensation Corporation (LWCC). Pictured, from left, are Harold Capello, safety and security coordinator; Steve Mistretta, safety and security manager; Hardy Ziegler, a former Triad employee now on the staff of the LWCC; Bobby Shackelford, general manager; and Tom Torr, administrative manager. Right: Paul Bollich, left, lowers Bobby Cedotal to safety during a training exercise of the Triad rescue team.

president of Mississippi Chemical's technical group, has led campaigns to reverse the trend of declining test scores in mathematics among students across the state. In 1986 Dr. Arnold was asked to chair a statewide mathematics improvement task force, which developed sweeping recommendations for strengthening the math skills of students. Two years later he directed a symposium that brought together leaders from the state's

senior colleges, community colleges, and elementary and secondary schools to address the recommendations for improving math education and to devise ways to boost mathematics scores of students. Arnold also chaired the math and science task force of the state's Public Education Forum, which continued the drive for stronger science and mathematics education.

Corporate secretary Rosalyn Glascoe

serves on the Mississippi Department of Education accreditation commission, as well as the Yazoo City Municipal School board, the Yazoo City high school vocational advisory council, and the school-to-work partnership council. While the company has contributed some of her time to these projects, Glascoe has devoted much of her personal time and energy to these and other community improvement efforts, including

Spanning the Generations

MCC's ranks are filled with talented local men and women who have chosen careers with MCC and are continuing to expand their skills and responsibilities as the company and the fertilizer industry have grown progressively more complex and international. Many corporate officers and senior managers grew up in the tiny hamlets and small towns of Mississippi, but increasingly they must travel to Wall Street, Poland, China, Morocco, the Netherlands, and South America to find customers, suppliers, and capital.

Joe Ewing, who directs the sale of nearly two million tons of ammonium nitrate, urea, and N-Sol each year, is typical of the company's gifted homegrown staff. The son of Andrew Ewing, a respected member of the company's Yazoo City maintenance and operations work force from 1955 to 1976, Joe was born the same year the company's original plants were built in Yazoo City. He grew up swimming and fishing at Hilltop, then the company's employee recreation complex, and enjoying the annual employee picnics with his dad and his younger brother Bill, who works in the ammonia plant. "I can still remember Charles Jackson's famous Brunswick stew and the delight of having all the free ice cream you wanted," Ewing recalls. Joe was born and reared in rural Vaughn, Mississippi, three miles from the site of Casey Jones's fatal train crash, and twenty miles east of the company's Yazoo City headquarters. After graduating as valedictorian of Benton High School in 1969, Ewing used the company's "Dollars for Scholars" college assistance program to earn a mechanical engineering degree from Mississippi State University. After a four-year stint in the space industry at Huntsville, Alabama, he was called by Mississippi Chemical, "and they were doing so many exciting things that I was delighted to come home in 1981," Ewing says.

For seventeen years he has served successfully in a variety of increasingly challenging positions, first in engineering, then in the purchasing department, and then in the personnel department, where he succeeded Lamar Peyton as

Bobby Perkins and Joe Ewing, second generation employees

director of personnel and services in 1991. Ewing was asked to direct all company procurement and distribution activities in 1994 and two years later was promoted to director of converted nitrogen sales, with responsibility for marketing the company's "bread-and-butter products"—AMTRATE, urea, N-Sol, and nitric acid. "I appreciate the opportunity the company has given me to take on varied and exciting challenges and to participate in the Millsaps MBA program and the Stanford Executive Program," said Ewing. "We have the best of both worlds right here at Mississippi Chemical—a warm, friendly, small-town atmosphere and exciting international challenges. I wouldn't trade it for any place on earth."

Bobby Perkins, enterprising manager of the company's headquarters and plant office facilities, is another second-generation employee, who grew up riding in the company van with his dad, Robert Perkins, for four decades the company's courier. "Dad would leave home in the MCC mail truck at 5:00 every morning and often not return home until late in the evening. On Saturdays and school holidays, I was thrilled to get to accompany my dad and assist him with his company duties," Perkins remembers.

After getting his college degree at Chicago City College and working in Chicago with the U.S. Postal Service for thirteen years, Perkins returned to Yazoo City and Mississippi Chemical in 1985. His first job at MCC was as a temporary employee at the Yazoo port facility. "I am very grateful for the opportunity, the trust, and the responsibility this company has given me," says Perkins, an employee who has come up through the ranks to supervise the office security forces and coordinate a wide range of office services. "At Mississippi Chemical, there are tremendous opportunities for people who want to achieve the excellence the company asks of all its staff. If you're qualified, you get the job; and if you work hard, you have a chance to grow with the company. I am excited to be here," Perkins says.

the repair of homes for Yazoo County's elderly, handicapped, and disadvantaged.

Mississippi Chemical each year invests a portion of its earnings to support charitable causes and community projects. Many of its workers also donate a day's pay through the company's Community Charity Fund. In 1997, when the state of Mississippi did not have funds for medicine for AIDS patients, Ethel Truly proposed that the company contribute twenty-five thousand dollars to help patients survive until federal funds were forthcoming. This was reminiscent of the company's advocacy of Mississippi's and the nation's first Head Start kindergartens three decades earlier. Neither was popular with critics, but Owen Cooper in 1967 and Chuck Dunn in 1997 believed these were the right things to do.

"I'm especially proud of our new and expanded support of the arts," Melinda Hood, manager of corporate communications, said. The company has an expanding collection of paintings and photographs from Southern artists on display throughout its offices, including the painting the distinguished Mississippi artist Bill Dunlap was commissioned to create for this fiftieth anniversary history. Included in the collection are striking black and white photographs by Marion Brown, a retired MCC vice president, whose photographs enhance corporate and museum collections across America and Europe. Wildlife scenes, made by his son, noted wildlife photographer Paul Brown, also hang at the company's Yazoo City headquarters. Grants from Mississippi Chemical help to make possible a rich range

Since its founding fifty years ago, Mississippi Chemical Corporation has grown from the aspirations of a few imaginative Mississippi farmers to become a successful publicly traded corporation, with plants, partners, and markets around the world. Steadfast in its original purpose of providing farmers with low cost fertilizer, to feed a hungry world, the company is poised to begin a second prosperous half century of making things grow.

of musical, artistic, cultural, and special events in the communities where it operates. The company will also continue to help with various projects and exhibits in the public schools ranging from Shakespearean drama to choirs, youth symphonies, art, music, and dance.

A Half Century of Service

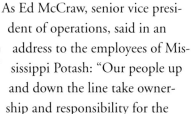

I n its first half century MCC has emerged from the aspirations of a few Mississippi farmers to become a player on the world stage—transforming itself from a struggling enterprise located where two highways converge at the gateway to the Mississippi Delta to a New York Stock Exchange corporation with plants, partners, and markets around the globe.

Why has Mississippi Chemical succeeded for fifty years when 90 percent of its competitors in the U.S. fertilizer industry have gone out of business? It has survived largely because of its commitment to being an efficient, cost-competitive producer of fertilizer. "Mississippi Chemical is a survivor. We have always found a way to remain competitive," senior vice president Robert Jones reflects. For most of its fifty years, comparative figures from the fertilizer industry show Mississippi Chemical at or near the top of the list of the nation's lowest cost and most efficient producers.

Four factors undergird the company's cost-competitiveness:

1. Mississippi Chemical has consistently invested in advanced technology—both in large scale, technologically advanced plants and in a skilled technical staff. The company's pioneering role in applying modern fertilizer technology and investing in technical expertise is distinctive and possibly unsurpassed in the industry.

2. Mississippi Chemical has continually made aggressive moves to obtain dependable, low cost supplies of essential raw materials such as natural gas, phosphate rock, and potash, which represent major elements of fertilizer costs.

3. Mississippi Chemical has developed efficient means of storing, shipping, and delivering millions of tons of fertilizers to its customers, when and where they need it.

4. Mississippi Chemical has maintained an employee team whose technical knowledge and *esprit de corps* are second to none.

"It all begins and ends with our people," Chuck Dunn explains. "The employees of this company consistently find ways to make our products at lower costs. To use football terms, our people are masters at blocking and tackling—the basics. We may not be flashy, but no one beats us at executing these basics."

As Ed McCraw, senior vice president of operations, said in an address to the employees of Mississippi Potash: "Our people up and down the line take ownership and responsibility for the success of this company. We operate very efficiently because our employee team is encouraged, inspired, and required to take responsibility for efficiency and success. And they welcome that opportunity and challenge."

Combining these aspects—people, plants, raw materials, technology, and delivery systems—has produced one of the most successful fertilizer-makers in America. "And we fully intend to continue that record in our second fifty years," Jones emphatically declares.

Despite the myriad technical and physical changes that have occurred during Mississippi Chemical's first half century, the original culture of the company has endured. The work ethic, integrity, concern for people, and determination that characterized MCC employees in the company's earliest days remain guiding values today, passed down from the company's first employees to succeeding generations. Ethel Truly, vice president of administration, says, "From the day I was hired, I was impressed by the strong ethical mores and work ethic that permeated this company. But until I learned more about Mississippi Chemical's history, I did not realize the debt that I and other current employees owe to those who went before us. We certainly didn't invent this company's incredible culture; they did."

Throughout five decades the company has held true to the fundamental values that have made it a successful business, an exceptional work place, and a responsible civic leader. As Wall Street investment banker Peter Bacon succinctly puts it, "Mississippi Chemical is not just a profit-making concern, it's an institution. I sense that those who work there view it as a sacred trust that they must safeguard for future generations."

∽

People Who Served

BOARD OF DIRECTORS

John W. Anderson (Destin, FL)

Coley Bailey (Coffeeville, MS) *Chairman*

Haley Barbour (Yazoo City, MS)

Frank R. Burnside, Jr. (Newellton, LA)

Robert P. Dixon (North Little Rock, AR)

Charles O. Dunn (Yazoo City, MS)

W. R. Dyess (Ennis, TX)

Woods Eastland (Greenwood, MS)

John Sharp Howie (Yazoo City, MS)
Vice Chairman

George Penick (Flora, MS)

W. A. Percy II (Arcola, MS)

David M. Ratcliffe (Atlanta, GA)

Wayne Thames (Evergreen, AL)

Tom C. Parry (Madison, MS)
Director Emeritus

OFFICERS

Charles O. Dunn, *President & Chief Executive Officer*

David W. Arnold, *Senior Vice President–Technical Group*

Robert E. Jones, *Senior Vice President–Corporate Development*

C. E. McCraw, *Senior Vice President–Operations*

Timothy A. Dawson, *Vice President–Finance & Chief Financial Officer*

John J. Duffy, *Vice President–Marketing & Distribution*

Larry W. Holley, *Vice President–Nitrogen Production*

William L. Smith, *General Counsel*

Ethel Truly, *Vice President–Administration*

Rosalyn B. Glascoe, *Corporate Secretary*

FORMER BOARD MEMBERS

R. H. Abbey (Webb, MS)

Ransome E. Aldrich (Michigan City, MS)

Frank E. Allen (Canton, MS)

W. H. (Bill) Allen (Belzoni, MS)

W. H. (Bill) Allen, Jr. (Belzoni, MS)

F. A. Anderson, Sr. (Gloster, MS)

F. A. Anderson, Jr. (Gloster, MS) *Vice President***

Fred A. Anderson, III (Gloster, MS)

W. B. Andrews (State College, MS)

Joe N. Bailey, Jr. (Coffeeville, MS)

George Baird (Inverness, MS)

William L. Ballew (Columbia, MO)

A. E. Beall (Jackson, MS) *Vice Chairman*

Arnold A. Berner (Little Rock, AR)

U. Owen Bibb, Jr. (Tunica, MS)

W. E. Blackmur (Water Valley, MS)

George B. Blair (Lake Charles, LA)

Jasper Blount (Hickory, MS)

F. Neal Bolton (St. James, LA)

Paul E. Bounds (Picayune, MS)

Randon D. Bounds (Picayune, MS)

Hilton Bracey (Portageville, MO)

Anthony L. Brady (Lula, MS)

Bruce J. Brumfield (Inverness, MS)

Frank T. Brumfield (Inverness, MS)

Frank R. Burnside (Newellton, LA)

Harry Campbell (Section, AL)

Robert A. Carson (Lambert, MS)

R. E. Chapman (Lambert, MS)

W. M. Clingan (Florence, AL)

Julian E. Cobb (York, AL)

Oscar Cobb (Uniontown, AL)

Owen Cooper (Yazoo City, MS)

G. C. Cortright, Jr. (Rolling Fork, MS)

George Crawford (Madison, MS)

J. B. Cunningham (Brooksville, MS)

Homer Darby (Columbia, MO)

W. E. Deer (Claiborne, AL)

C. D. (Dave) Denton (Shelby, MS)

C. E. Denton (Shelby, MS)

John A. Denton (Shelby, MS)

W. M. Duncan (Inverness, MS)

Julian E. Elgin, (Montgomery, AL)

A. T. (Gus) Evans (Shuqualak, MS)

Carl S. Farmer (Abbeville, AL)

A. M. Feland, III (N. Little Rock, AR) *Vice Chairman*

Eugene Fisackerly (Sunflower, MS)

Joe Fleming (Huntsville, AL)

R. Rodney Foil (Mississippi State, MS)

Waldo Fraiser (Little Rock, AR)

Thurman O. Fulton, Sr. (Clarksdale MS)

John Garmon (Clarksdale, MS)

Edmon P. Garrett (Decatur, AL)

John A. Gaston (Madison, MS)

Dr. William L. Giles (State College, MS)

Thomas H. Gist, Jr. (Marianna, AR)

F. A. Graugnard, Jr. (St. James, LA)

R. L. Griffin, (Montgomery, AL)

Robert P. Guyton (Jackson, MS)

Carroll F. Harpole (Albany, GA)

Jerry L. Harpole, Sr. (Madison, MS)

Council B. Hightower, Jr. (York, AL)

E. B. Hill (Merigold, MS)

J. L. Hill, Jr. (Webb, MS)

Charles T. Hull (Winona, MS)

G. L. Jackson (Laurel, MS)

G. David Jobe (Columbia, MO)

Ernest B. Johnston (Selma, AL)

Tom C. Jones (Amarillo, TX)

E. C. Kahl (Egypt, MS)

Russell G. Kahl (Okolona, MS)

Charles Bobo (Bo) Keeler (Clarksdale, MS)

D. M. Kell (Tallulah, LA)

Donald Kirkpatrick (Compass Lake, FL)

S. H. Kyle (Clarksdale, MS)

Henry H. Leveck (State College, MS)

H. R. McIntosh (Picayune, MS)

C. L. McNeil (Jackson, MS) *Vice President***

Loryn E. McQuerter, (Mount Vernon, MO)

C. D. Maddox (Kosciusko, MS)

R. C. Malone (Pace, MS)

John H. Mathews (Decatur, AL)

D. Mercier (Corinth, MS)

John D. Mercier (Corinth, MS)

Glenn U. Miller (Marianna, AR)

Ernest N. (Bo) Minor (Paulette, MS)

Wayne Mixson (Marianna, FL)

R. D. Morrow (Brandon, MS)

A. N. Nichols (Vaughan, MS)

L. A. Olson (Carrollton, MS)

J. P. Overstreet (DeKalb, MS)

LeRoy P. Percy (Greenville, MS) *Chairman*

W. A. (Billy) Percy, II (Arcola, MS)

Clyde J. Perry (Tunica, MS)

George D. Perry, Jr. (Tunica, MS)

Frank J. Phariss (Amarillo, TX)

Gene C. Pickens (Mt. Hope, AL)

Troy Pitts, Jr. (Jackson, MS)

George L. Polley (Columbia, MO)

William Hunter Pratt (Inverness, MS)

Walter Randolph (Montgomery, AL)

H. L. Rankin (Columbia, MS)

J. Riley Rankin (Poplarville, MS)

Maurice T. Reed (Jackson, MS)

Thomas L. Reed, III (Belzoni, MS)

Nathaniel S. Rogers (Jackson, MS)

R. J. Rosier (Columbia, MO)

E. C. A. Runge (College Station, TX)

L. C. Salter (Sheffield, AL)

William R. (Bob) Sharman (Madison, MS)

W. L. Smith (Cleveland, MS)

E. G. Spivey (Jackson, MS) *Vice Chairman*

Stuart L. Spradling (Columbia, MO)

L. D. (Pete) Stacks (Lake Charles, LA)

Boswell Stevens (Macon, MS)

Morel Stientjes (Ft. Dodge, IA)

J. Russell Summers (Nesbit, MS)

H. P. Sullivan (Walls, MS)

Walter Swoope (Columbus, MS)

John Tabor (Winona, MS)

John W. Taylor (Sunflower, MS)

George Theriot, Jr. (Fenton, LA)

Adolph W. Treppendahl (Woodville, MS)

Irby Turner (Belzoni, MS)

F. M. Vaughn (Columbus, MS)

Dr. Irvin Woodrow Wander (Winter Haven, FL)

Aven Whittington (Greenwood, MS)

Charles S. Whittington (Greenwood, MS) *President**

James C. Williams (Lake Charles, LA)

John Sharp Williams (Yazoo City, MS) *President**

P. C. Williams (Yazoo City, MS)

Dr. Louis N. Wise (State College, MS)

Oscar Wolfe (Duncan, MS)

R. A. Young (Columbia, MO)

C. L. Youngblood (Rosehill, MS)

*The position of President of the Board of Directors held the same responsibilities as the position of Chairman of the Board of Directors.

**The position of Vice President of the Board of Directors held the same responsibilities as the position of Vice Chairman of the Board of Directors.

FORMER OFFICERS

Marion L. Brown, *Vice President–Research & Development*

Owen Cooper, *President*

W. B. Dunwoody, *Vice President–Operations*

R. H. Fisackerly, *Vice President–Sales*

James M. Gambrell, *Vice President–Operations*

Harry C. Griffith, *Vice President–Administration*

William F. Hawkins, *Senior Vice President–Finance & Administration*

Esma A. Hawks, *Treasurer*

Charles J. Jackson, *Executive Vice President*

Paul Lacy, *Vice President–Operations*

Don A. McGraw, *Senior Vice President–Sales & Distribution*

Mamie F. Marshall, *Acting Secretary/Treasurer*

Tom C. Parry, *President*

John R. Phillips, *Senior Vice President–Operations*

Jo G. Prichard, III, *Vice President–Corporate Services*

Hollaman Raney, *Vice President & General Counsel*

Donald B. Roark, *Vice President–Corporate Services*

John C. Satterfield, *General Counsel*

A. B. Sherling, *Vice President and General Manager of the Yazoo City Plant*

Sue Tatum, *Corporate Secretary*

H. Leroy Thompson, *Vice President & Technical Director*

Tom K. Tisdale, *Vice President–Corporate Services*

Gene A. Triggs, *Vice President–Governmental Affairs*

EMPLOYEES OF LONG SERVICE

45 YEARS

Cottruel Generette
Blanche H. Hester

40 YEARS

Bobby P. Barrington
Leon C. Brown
James A. Cox
Patricia H. Davis
Emery A. Gregory
James G. Hicks
Earnest E. Jackson
Allen F. Johnston
Joseph E. Martin, Jr.
Billy C. Mashburn
Robert Perkins
Bonnie Ruschewski
Barbara H. Standley

35 YEARS

Hugh W. Adams
Benford F. Adcock
S. D. Allen
Sam Allen, Jr.
James Edward Bell
Eddie M. Berry
W. P. Brabston, Jr.
Rex Brown
Billy Thomas Bruce
Charlie W. Burns
J. D. Clark
Jerry Clower
Robert E. Cotton
Patricia D. Cranston
DeWitt A. Dixon
Charles Eldridge
Margaret A. Ferguson
David W. Gairhan
Jane C. Gordon

Doyle W. Green
Elbert H. Guthrie
Frank J. Harper
Wilbur W. Harpole
Freddie Ray Harvey
John L. Harvey
Carl J. Hicks, Sr.
Ruby W. Hinkle
Davis G. Irwin
Mona S. Ketchum
Lawrence W. Long, III
Jimmy D. Mauney
Bobby Gene Martin
Lynn McCallister
Winnie B. McMaster
Joseph C. Milner
Lynn D. Montgomery
James Irvin Mood
Travis E. Moore
Thomas C. Parry, Jr.
Floyd E. Penton

James A. Pierce
Walton E. Plunkett
Phil Reeves
Joe H. Regan
Alton O. Rivers
Dan Arthur Russell
Larry W. Savell
Bobby K. Shackelford
Charles Shannon
A. B. Sherling
Leora Lee Smith
W. J. Smithhart, Jr.
James E. Steen
Inez Straughter
Herbert Suttlar
Sue Tatum
Luther E. Vandygriff
Robert E. Wentworth
Edward L. Williams
James E. Williams
John G. Williams, Jr.

Ronny W. Williams
Thos S. Williamson

3 0   Y E A R S

Otis C. Addison
Robert E. Allen
David W. Arnold
Thomas S. Backstrom
Lea Clark Black
Travis Bland
Nate Lee Blunt
Bobbie Ray Bond
Curtis Dale Bowman
Arthur E. Boyanton
James L. Brannon
Marilyn J. Brown
Marion L. Brown, Jr.
William E. Byrd
Betty G. Cargil
Cheryl D. Carver
Steve S. Cheatham
Frank Clifton
Charles M. Coker
W. Owen Cook, Jr.
John R. Copeland
John M. Crothers
John Hubert Crow
G. W. Cummings, Jr.
Charles E. Daniels
Aubrey J. Dearman
John W. Deaton
Bobby Kenneth Deer
Phillip N. Dixon
S. J. Dixon, Jr.
William B. Dunwoody
James Allen Edwards
Ollie G. Elkins, Jr.

Gary C. Elliott
Billy Wayne Ellis
James C. Epperson
Irvin Evans
Lina M. Farrish
Paul G. Ferriss
Harold C. Fisher
Henry L. Fisher
Robert W. Fisher, Jr.
Walter D. Fisher
Larry Max Fort
Paul D. Fraiser
James M. Gambrell
Jack Goodwin
David W. Green
Pamela P. Gregoire
Robert Lee Griffin
Leon Grimes
William A. Grimes
Wanda H. Grubbs
Robert J. Guion
Reuben D. Hall
Ollie Hampton, Jr.
Dorothy R. Hatchett
Philip Hathaway, Jr.
William F. Hawkins
Benton Hayman
Clinton Hayman
Patrick X. Hearst
Sidney Henderson
James M. Holland
Richard Guy Holland
John B. Holt
Dwight E. Hulgan
Gloria J. Humphries
Jerry W. Irwin
Thomas D. Irwin
Charles J. Jackson

George M. Jefcoat
John H. Jefferson
Howard Jiles
Bernard Johnson
Mary B. Johnston
Wesley Earl Kaho
Harold M. Keith
J. T. Ketchum, Jr.
Kenneth D. Ketchum
Billy Joe Kettleman
Omer Kettleman
Bessie B. King
Hugh Dendy King
Robert Wayne Kirk
Paul E. Lacy
John W. Lampley
Leo Newton Lewis
Sam Henry Lofton
Priscilla O. Martin
Robert Ross Martin
C. R. McCormack
Donald A. McGraw
L. C. McKennon
Birdon Mitchell
James Ivan Moore
James O. Moore
Ruby J. Moore
B. B. Neely
Bobby L. Neely
James C. Nerren
Charles D. O'Brien
Willie C. Parker
Meadow Perry, Jr.
John R. Phillips
Calvin M. Pierce
Glyn D. Pittman
Lannis F. Plummer
Dallas E. Powell, Jr.

Irvin Harry Puckett
Walter Richardson
Charles R. Roark
Wiley N. Saxton
Dow Scarborough
Roy Lamar Self, Jr.
George F. Sigrest
Paul L. Speaks
Patrick C. Spiars
William M. Stampley
Robert Stevens, Jr.
G. Ray Stokes
Chester C. Stovall
Holly Ray Stovall
W. C. Strickland
Fred P. Sullivan
David Summerlin
W. N. Sutherland
Wesley Taylor, Jr.
Roger G. Threet
Gerald L. Tucker
Eugene H. Turner
Porter F. Vandevere
Thomas H. Vice
Bernard Warren
Willie Warren
Roosevelt Washington
Amos B. Wigginton
Posey T. Wilburn
J. P. Williams
H. Walker Williamson
Inez Williamson
Joe Frank Wilson
Willie E. Wilson
Allen J. Winters
Wilma V. Young

Melvin E. Ables

A. J. Adams

Rodney P. Adams

Lanson J. Albarado

A. L. Allbritton

Larry A. Allen

William E. Allgood

Major Lee Anderson

Dale C. Andrews

Robert D. Appleton

John Clarence Autry

Arthur C. Ball

Walter J. Ballard

Elmo L. Barber

C. G. Barlow, Jr.

Johnnie L. Bennett

Tolbert F. Bennett

Willie L. Blackmon

Harvey Lee Blowe

Glen Boler

Robert J. Boudreaux

Willard J. Bourg

Riley G. Bowman

Tillman Branch, Jr.

John T. Brannon

Frank J. Broocks

Willard Broom

Earl Brown, II

Jack Louel Brown

Fay A. Burns

Johnnie E. Burns

J. W. Burwell, Jr.

Charles Bush

C. W. Butler

Robert Butler

Dennis A. Callihan

Harold E. Capello

Robert L. Cawthon

Charles A. Chambers

Ben Avery Chapman

Harold J. Chiquet, Jr.

Jack Clark

Charles Clayton

David Clement

Burvon T. Clyburn

Roy Glen Coats

Helen Coker

Peggy M. Coleman

Luther Q. Compton

Robert D. Conerly

J. D. Cooper, Jr.

William T. Cottom

Raymond K. Cowart

John Ralph Cox

Murray C. Criswell

Thomas Erie Daniels

Charles P. Davis, Jr.

Harrison Davis

Norman H. Davis

Rayford Glyn Davis

Sarah P. Deal

O. D. Dearmon

Pamela Ann Deer

R. B. Donnell

Viven James Douglas

Albert G. Draughn

George T. Duncan

Frank W. Ellis, Jr.

Beja R. Everett

Philip R. Ferriss

John W. Fife

R. Wiley Fisher

Archie Lee Flowers

Louis W. Fortenberry

Moses Fox

Henry Franklin

James R. Frans

Quinton Gammill

Thomas J. Garner

Allen Gauthreaux

Robert C. Gearhart

Monroe Gentry

Leslie Gibson

James Bondy Glisson

John Gary Golden

Kenneth J. Gomez

Roger Allen Goodin

Diane S. Gordon

Paul Green, Jr.

Robert R. Guardia

Hayzell Hall

Royal C. Harrelson

Ford Harrington

Henry Coble Harris

Nick W. Harris, Jr.

Fred W. Harrod

Milton Harry

Esma Hawks

Helen Henderson

Charles C. Herrin

Gary C. Hidalgo

Lucian O. Hill

Oscar J. Himel, Jr.

Harold Hinkle, Jr.

Olen C. Hinton

James Holmes

Dennis Marvin Hood

Mack M. Hood

R. T. Huxtable, Jr.

John W. Ingram

Donis O. Jefcoat

B. J. Jefferson

Fearon H. Jenne, Jr.

Mark O. Joachim, Jr.

Marion R. Johnson

Wellington C. Johnson

Willie Johnson

James E. Johnston

Lou C. Johnston

R. C. Jones

Georgia Mae Jones

Morgan E. Jones

Richard T. Jones

Richard H. Kelly

James L. Kennedy

Carolyn Dell Kern

Lonnie Kight

Vincent R. Knaps

Ronald R. Kuntz

Albert J. Landry

Kenneth L. Landry

Leon G. Landry

Nelson J. Landry

Stephen Landry

Gerald J. Lasseigne

Miguel Lawrence

Fred G. Lawson, Jr.

Donald G. Leblanc

Dudley P. Leblanc

James T. Leboeuf

David William Ledbetter

Herman M. Leister

John L. Limerick

Charlie G. Linton

Robert Lee Long

Alvin Love

John A. Lyles

Billy W. Martin

Jerry D. Martin

Weldon E. Martin

Roy J. Martinez

Plum M. Mathis, Jr.

Randy Matthews

William M. McCrary

Joseph F. McGee, Jr.

Sylvia McGraw

Horace H. McIntosh

Robert F. McKee

John W. McLellan, Jr.

L. C. McWilliams

Harold E. Merritt

Robert J. Miglicco

Robert Lee Miles

James H. Mills

Edy Lee Mitchell

James F. Moffatt

Lanelle Montgomery

Larry Kent Montgomery

Jimmie Garland Moore

William T. Moore

Herbert L. Moorehead

Homer C. Morgan

Edgar Allen Muse

John W. Neal

Edgar J. Nelson, Jr.

Luther L. Netherland

Steve E. Nicholas

Ollie O'Connor

Calvin S. O'Reilly

Carlton W. Parker

Robert A. Parker

Peyton Pell

Jed T. Pepper

Wilson Perry

Dwight A. Phillips

James R. Picou

Elizabeth Pitterle

Jimme C. Pizzolato

R. L. Plunkett

E. F. Poindexter

Billy Poore

Joseph V. Porto, Jr.

William T. Potter

John E. Rednour

John S. Richard

Andrew Richardson

Harold H. Riggan

Charles A. Riley

Garry Bon Roark

Charles E. Roberts

Spencer Roberts

Charles J. Robinson

Carl D. Robison

Robert M. Rodgers

Ronald M. Rome

Walter James Ross

Thomas Milton Rush

James C. Sauceman, Jr.

John Thomas Saxton

Peggy Sue Saxton

H. L. Scarborough

Louis L. Schexnayder

Robert D. Schutt

A. B. Shelton

George E. Shelton

Ralph W. Shirling

Sam M. Simmons

Johnnie Simpson

Bonney Eurias Smith

Eddie C. Smith

Ephraim M. Smith, II

Kenneth T. Smith

Marjorie R. Smith

Thomas W. Smith

Willie James Smith

Albert Jay Soday

Vincent Sotile, Jr.

Shirley R. Speights

C. A. Stancill, Jr.

Richard E. Steele

R. Darryl Stewart

Martha M. Street

Clyde Strickland

Willis N. Sutherland

Timothy A. Templet

Ronald A. Terrell

Donald P. Tiblier

Dan W. Tolar, Jr.

Gene A. Triggs, Sr.

J. R. Turner

Ralph B. Tutterrow

Max I. Twiner

Willis E. Van Sickel

Albert Veal, Jr.

Patrick Vernon

Alfred O. Walters

Nat Walton

James L. Ware

Ronnie Warren

M. L. Washington

Thester Washington

Norris W. Wheeler, Jr.

Barbara C. White

Donnie Ray Wilburn

J. W. Wilkinson

Ronald Edward Wilkinson

Julius A. Willis

Zoe Y. Woodruff

Victor L. Wren

Bobby Wright

Walter S. Wright

Robert J. Young

20 YEARS

Hugh W. Adams, Jr.

Thomas C. Adams

Chris Addison

Judy A. Addison

Michael Alexander

Herbert J. Alleman

William J. Allen

F. Bradford Allgood

Donald L. Allison

Arthur Anderson

John R. Anderson

Linard Anderson

David Lewis Ashley, Jr.

Blane P. Babin

Warren J. Baldwin

Dennis Beasley

Stafford L. Beaubouef

Chet Beaumont

Dan Allen Bell

Linda G. Bentley

John Bergman

Burkett Berry

Gerald J. Blanchard

Ronnie R. Blanchard

Ladell Blanton

Walter R. Bliss

Patrick T. Blunt

Leroy Bonner

Gilbert Bosarge

Della M. Bowman

Marian C. Brewer

Benjamin F. Bridges

Delma Bridges

Frank L. Brister

Majure Steve Brister

Clarence Brooks

Douglas Brooks

Noble Brooks

Robert Broughton

John Morris Brown

Obie Brown

Otto Browning

Leo Buford

William D. Burge

Charlie Wade Burns, Jr.

Robert G. Cader

A. B. Campbell

Gale Campbell

Eric R. Carbo

John Carley

David Carter

Michael F. Cascio

Danny P. Castro

Sammy Chapman

Michael J. Chifici

Bob F. Chisholm

John M. Chun

Richard J. Clark

Thomas J. Coburn

John Henry Coleman

Regina T. Coleman

Thermon Dwight Coleman

Clarence T. Collins

Darryel Comeaux, Sr.

Toby Marlar Cook

Morris L. Cooper, Jr.

Owen Cooper

Ottie S. Corder

Maxine J. Corson

Michael Ray Coutch

Carl Cowan

Raymond Keith Cowart

Edward James Cox

Lee Arthur Cox

Johnny B. Creer

Robert A. Crow

James D. Crowson

Cecil G. Cummings

Barry P. Daigle

Larry G. Dale

Sherman Davenport

Andrew M. Davis

Ann D. Davis

Carl I. Davis

Gillie E. Davis

James G. Davis, Jr.

James W. Davis

Michael K. Davis

Pearl F. Davis

Richard Paul Davis

Leonard A. Dearman

Peter Delatte, III

Shirley Annette Dixon

Gregory Dortch

Jimmy Douglas

Julian D. Drake

James M. Drennan, III

William H. Duck

Truett Duncan, Jr.

Charles O. Dunn

Robert W. Dunwoody

Clyde M. Edwards

John Clark Edwards

Paul Davis Elkin

Phillip Ellis

Mike C. Ellison

James L. Eubanks

Bill D. Evans

James A. Evans

Perkins Evans

Charles T. Everett

Andrew A. Ewing

William E. Ewing

Hardie Lee Ezell

Willie Ezell

Richard A. Fisher

Gaston Cassel Fletcher

Gladys L. Foster

Howard E. Fox

Moses Fox, Jr.

Roy Franklin Fox

Reginald L. Francis

Willie J. Garvis

Ricky J. Gautreau

Arthur N. Gentry

Marlin George

Claude D. Gibson

Joe Gibson, Jr.

Bea Gilliland

Benny G. Gore

Becky Graves

Willie G. Grayer, Jr.

Albert W. Green

Jerry Green

Richard C. Green

Zebedee Greer

Chester A. Grisham

Robert Guardia, Jr.

John J. Hall, III

Emmett C. Hamilton

Leeanna Hampton

Tommie Hankins

Robert L. Harden

Frank Harper

James R. Harrelson

George A. Harris

Albert Lee Harrison, Jr.

Wilson H. Harvey

Roosevelt Hatchett

Charles Havis

Jack Hawks

Philip Hebert

Robert M. Heidel

John Earl Hewitt

Michael A. Hidalgo

Norman W. Higgins

Henry Frank Higgs

Danny Paul Hill

Henry B. Hitt

James A. Hoffman

Jake Bryant Hogue

Major Gene Holland

Larry W. Holley

Stan R. Hollowell

Thomas C. Holt

Albert H. Hood

Joyce H. Hood

Lawrence Daniel Hood

Charles T. Hoof

Calvin M. Howard, Jr.

Ralph G. Hunt

Henry O. Hurd

Dennis S. Hutchinson

James R. Hutchinson

B. J. Ivers

Hilary T. Ivers

ONeil Jackson, Jr.

Thomas W. Jackson

Jerald L. Jarrard

Londell Jefferson

Richard Clifton Jennings

Kenneth J. Joffrion

Floyd E. Johnson

Thomas A. Johnson

Charles J. Jones

George Jones

Lawrence J. Jones

Robert Eugene Jones

Ross Jones
Sammy B. Jones
Sidney A. Joseph
Hannah P. Kelly
Emmett L. Kight
Beverly Jean King
Judith Ann Kinnison
Perrin R. Kirk
Dwan H. Ladner
Jewel A. Lambert
Carmen M. Landry
Dale Landry
Lester P. Landry
Stephen P. Landry
Robert N. Lane
Bernice Langford
Dennis Lavender
H. Lamont Lavender
John Bonner Lee, Jr.
Roosevelt Lett
Wilburn Little
Wilburn Lofton
J. Robert Lott
Robert A. Lungrin
Robert E. Manning
Hollis Franklin Martin
Hugh Garnett Martin
Roy Glenn Martin, Sr.
Brett A. Martinez
Ruth P. Mason
Joann B. Massey
Richard Massey
Samuel Lee Matthews
William A. Mathis
Harold G. McAnally
David Lee McBride
Donald B. McCormick
Charlie Eddie McCraw

F. A. McDonald
Zegory A. McGalliard
Swain J. McLeod
Gladys McMaster
Melvin L. McVey
Steven E. Melton
George Donnell Meyer, Jr.
James R. Miles
Steven J. Mistretta
Doyle J. Mitchell
John Monroe
William J. Montgomery
Lowell B. Mood
Horace L. Moore
Percy Lee Moore
Walter L. Moore
Wesley B. Moore
John Mullins
David M. Nance
Eugene Garland Neely, Jr.
Clifford G. Nelson
Karl M. Nelson
Printess Earl Nelson
Donna L. Nesbit
Ann Scott Lacy Nestelroad
William O. Nettles
Tommy J. Newchurch
Roosevelt W. Newton
Michael H. Norman
Barbara O'Mary
David M. Oubre
Kenneth J. Oubre
Vester L. Padgett
Robert G. Parker
John A. Parks
Mamie W. Passons
James Pearley
Marvin H. Pearson

James Gordon Perkins
Lamar Peyton
Margaret J. Pickett
Jimmy Dale Pinter
Calvin Clay Polk
Glynn Dale Porter
Nicholas J. Porto
Candace M. Potter
John Luther Potter
Wilson Carl Potter
J. Barney Potts
William K. Pregeant
William E. Prejean
Jimmy J. Ramagost
Wyeth T. Ramsay
Hollaman M. Raney
Jeremiah H. Reeves
Carlton Renfrow
Cecil O. Richards
Robert L. Robinson
Sam D. Roby
Jack Rodenbaugh
James A. Rome
Raynard Rose
A. Buford Rowland
E. A. Ruppert
Sara Sue Rush
Sandra M. Russell
Warren W. Russum
Charles E. Ryan
Frank Lee Sadler
Malcolm L. Sawyer
Howard A. Saxton
Ivy McGinty Saxton
Larry S. Saxton
Francis J. Schexnayder, Jr.
Larry Earl Scott
Sheila M. Scott

Sidney Sebren
Mance Sellers
Glenda D. Shaheen
David E. Sharp
H. B. Shaw
James E. Shirley
Shelby S. Shows
Fred Shurley
Daniel Small, Jr.
Arbey Lee Smith
Jimmie F. Smith
J. Wesley Smith
Leona E. Smith
Percy Calvin Smith
Perry Edward Smith
Philip R. Smith
Sherman Smith, Jr.
Wallace Smithhart
Pratess P. Snow
Rufus Lee Stamps
William T. Stanford
Randy Dale Stephenson
Jerry L. Stevens
C. L. Stewart
Monroe Stewart
Lucy H. Sutterfield
James V. Tait
Charles H. Taite
Merilon Taite
Robert E. Taylor
Opal E. Terrell
Harry J. Thibodaux
Frank Thomas
Tommy Thompson
Irby S. Toombs, Jr.
Herman F. Torres, Jr.
Vincent D. Tripp
Albert L. Turner

James Turner

Robert Tyrone

Vincent Vincent

Lewis S. Von Kanel

Kathy Waguespack

Kenneth Charles Walker

Malcolm Wascom

Ezzard J. Washington

George M. Washington

Gene Raymond Watson

James V. Whitaker, Jr.

Pamela M. White

Fleming Whitney, Jr.

Darnell Williams

Mark Williams

Robert Lee Williams

Hattie S. Wilson

Issac Wilson, Jr.

Ed Windham

William T. Young

James E. Zeigler

Harold Zumalt

EDITOR'S NOTE: *The previous list-ing represents the company's best efforts to recognize all those who served the company for twenty or more years. If any employees of long service were omitted, the company sincerely regrets the error.*

REFERENCES

PUBLISHED SOURCES

"Ammonia as Fertilizer." *Fortune Magazine,*
　August 1948.

Andrews, W. B., F. E. Edwards, and J. G.
　Hammons. *Ammonia as A Source of
　Nitrogen.* Bulletin 448. State College,
　Miss: Mississippi State College
　Agricultural Experiment Station, June
　1947.

Blake, Ed. *Farm Bureau in Mississippi.*
　Jackson, Miss.: Mississippi Farm Bureau
　Federation, 1971.

Delta Farm Press (Farm Press Publications,
　Clarksdale, Miss). Golden Anniversary
　Edition. 29 January 1993.

*First Mississippi Corporation: The First
　Twenty-five Years.* New York, Exton,
　Princeton, and Portland: Neucomen
　Society in North America, 1982.

Hand, Robert S. *Report on a Mississippi
　Fixed Nitrogen Fertilizer Plant.* Jackson:
　Mississippi Agricultural & Industrial
　Board. December 1947.

Jackson Clarion-Ledger (Miss.). Special edi-
　tion commemorating Owen Cooper's
　retirement and Mississippi Chemical
Corporation's first quarter century. 3 June
　1973.

McCandliss, D. A. *Base Book of Mississippi
　Agriculture 1866–1953.* Jackson, Miss.:
　U.S. Department of Agriculture and the
　Mississippi Department of Agriculture,
　1955.

McGregor, Don, *The Thought Occurred to
　Me: A Book About Owen Cooper.*
　Nashville: Field Communications &
　Publishing, 1992.

McLemore, Richard Aubrey, ed. *A History of
　Mississippi.* Vol. 2. Jackson: University
　and College Press of Mississippi, 1973.

Morris, Willie. *Yazoo: Integration in a Deep-
　Southern Town.* New York: Harper's
　Magazine Press, 1971.

New Mexico Potash. Carlsbad: Carlsbad,
　New Mexico, Potash Producers, 1980.

Pittman, Bob. *First Mississippi Corporation:
　A Twenty-five Year History.* Jackson, Miss.:
　Franklin Printers, Inc. 1982.

U.S. Department of Agriculture. *Farm
　Employment and Wage Rates 1910–1990.*
　Statistical Bulletin No. 822. Washington,
　D.C.: National Agricultural Statistics
　Service, 1991.

Yazoo City Herald (Miss.). Special edition
　commemorating Mississippi Chemical
　Corporation's first ten years of operation
　in Yazoo City. 19 June 1961.

———. Special edition commemorating
　President Jimmy Carter's visit. 21 July
　1977.

Workman, Noel, *Staplcotn, The First 75
　Years.* Greenwood, Miss.: Staplcotn, Inc.,
　1996.

ARCHIVED SOURCES

THE CATFISH INSTITUTE, BEL-
ZONI, MISS.
Miscellaneous documents.

MISSISSIPPI CHEMICAL CORPO-
RATION, CORPORATE
ARCHIVES, YAZOO CITY, MISS.
DeCell, Harriet. Unpublished transcriptions
　of interviews conducted for the corpora-
　tion in 1980 with corporate officers Owen
　Cooper, LeRoy Percy, Armstead Feland,
　Charles Jackson, and Tom C. Parry.

Gilbert, A. S., III. *Mississippi Chemical
　Corporation Documentary.* 1965. An

unpublished, eight-volume collection of newspaper clippings, correspondence, brochures, and other materials describing the early history of Mississippi Chemical Corporation or actually used in its founding. The eight volumes are titled "Background: Development of Anhydrous Ammonia Fertilizer Technology, 1947 and Before"; "In the Beginning: The Farm Bureau, June 1947–December 1947"; "Senate Bill No. 1, January 1948"; "Organization of Committee on Nitrogen Plant for Mississippi, Inc., February-March 1948"; "Initial Stock Campaign, March-September 1948"; "Creation of Mississippi Chemical Corporation, September-December 1948"; "Orignial Application to RFC and SEC, 1949"; "1949"; and "1950–51."

Mississippi Chemical Corporation employee newspapers, photography collections and files, newspaper clippings, minutes of board meetings, personnel records, corporate files, and published corporate brochures.

Mississippi Chemical Corporation's Annual Reports to Stockholders, 1951–1997.

Nichols, Norwood. Unpublished speech delivered at dedication of Mississippi Chemical Corporation headquarters building, 1968.

Preliminary Report of Prospective Fertilizer Plant, Pascagoula, Mississippi. Prepared and published by Mississippi Chemical Corporation. 23 February 1956.

Prichard, Jo G. Tape recordings and notes from interviews conducted from May 1997 to February 1998 with seventy current and former employees, officers, and directors of the corporation and with community leaders.

MISSISSIPPI DEPARTMENT OF ARCHIVES AND HISTORY, JACKSON, MISS.
Owen Cooper Collection.

MISSISSIPPI STATE UNIVERSITY
Research statistics on farm-related employment. Compiled by U.S. Department of Agriculture and provided by the university's Agriculture Economics Department.

SOUTHEASTERN OIL REVIEW, JACKSON, MISS.
Information on gas fields located near Piney Woods.

INDEX

Reagan, Ronald, 171, 174
Recession, 105, 109, 111
Reconstruction, 23
Reconstruction Finance Corporation, 35, 37-39, 42-45
Reddix, Derrick, 246
Rednour, John, 80, 82, 83, 84, 85-87, 160, 172
Reed, M. T., 30, 73-75
Reeves, Phyllis, 65
Regan, Joe, 97, 106
Reid, Dennis, 246
Republic of Trinidad and Tobago, The, 227, 230, 235. *See also* Trinidad
Retirement program, 59
Reynolds, Bob, 188
Richards, C. O., 53
Richardson, Walter, 152
Rickover, Hyman, 148
Riemann, Stan, 234, 235
Rio Hondo, Tex., 111
"Road Show," 220, 221, 224
Roark, Ginger, 247
Roark, Morgan, 247
Roberts, Charlie, 152
Roberts, Spencer, 157, 158, 160
Robinson, Rob, 215
Rogers, Julian, 50, 91
Rogers, Nat, 90
Roosevelt, Franklin D., 24
Ross, Aline, 61
Ross, Jim Buck, 181
Ross, Vincent, 156
Rush, Sabin, 63
Rush, Sara Sue, 61, 63
Russell, Dan "Ju-Ju," 164, 214
Russum, Julia, 61
Russum, Warren, 79
RUST Construction Company, 181, 186, 187

S

SF Services, 212
Safety records, 46, 52, 178, 246, 249, 250
St. Gobain Company, 77
Salazar, Ezequiel "Sonny," 153
Sales and delivery staff, 98-99
Sample, Woody, 187
Sanders, Ralph, 53
Satterfield, John, 29, 32, 38, 39, 40, 45, 90, 93, 94, 95,

105, 116, 146, 176
Savell, Larry, 178, 244
Schroder and Wertheim, 237. *See also* Wertheim Schroder and Company
Screws, Jim, 163
Searcy, Sanford, 218
Seat, Ward F., 29, 38, 39, 40, 142
Securities and Exchange Commission, 75, 90, 237
Seeds of Life, 248-49
Sentinels of Safety, 246, 249
Shackelford, Bobby, 249, 250
Shackelford, Dave, 37
Shafer, Skip, 240
Shaheen, Glenda, 217
Shannon, Alta, 63
Shell Oil Company, 143-45, 149, 168, 174, 175-76, 180
Sherling, Bob, 49-50, 51, 97
Shift workers, 164
Shipley, Bill, 50
Shows, Shelby S., 29, 38, 40, 55
Shuman, Charles, 46
Shurley, Fred, 79
Sillers, Walter, 26, 27
Silver, Steve, 220
Simoneaux, A. J., 101
Simpson, Bill, 148, 187, 244
Sims, Randy, 235
Singh, Sohan, 131
Smith, Bill, 230
Smith, Ephraim, 22
Smith, Glenda, 22, 244
Smith, Henry, 79
Smith, J. O., 22
Smith, Jim, 47
Smith, M. L., 76
Smith, Marjorie, 63
Smith, R. L. T., 126
Smith, Wesley, 79
Snack bar, 191-93
Soday, Al, 81, 128-29
Southern Farmers Association, 97
Southern Natural Gas Company, 111, 176
Soviet Union, 147-49, 227-28; embargo, 167, 172; grain shipments, 166
Speights, Durwood, 83
Speights, Shirley, 83, 84-85, 86, 113, 118, 173
Spencer Chemical, 36

Spivey, E. G., 95
Standley, Barbara, 98
Stanford, William T., 146
Staplcotn (Staple Cotton Cooperative), 24, 29
Starkville, Miss., 49
Start ups: of Newsprint South, 189; of Pascagoula complex, 78-81; of Triad, 102; of Yazoo City's initial complex, 16, 48-50
Stennis, John C., 43, 45, 94, 95, 125-26, 149, 187
Stevens, Boswell, 30, 94, 117
Stevens, Martha, 197
Stewart, Ernest, 38, 39, 40
Stock sales, 25, 26, 27, 28-32, 53, 55, 59, 75, 77, 90, 154, 159
Stoneville, Miss., 22
Strickland, Clyde, 79
"Stuck nut," 50-51, 58
Sulfuric acid plants, Pascagoula, 75, 76, 78, 81, 111, 133, 150, 161
Sullins, Fred, 28
Sullivan, Fred, 63, 98-99, 154
Sullivan, H. P., 30, 42
Summerford, Mike, 236-37
Sunflower County, 28
Superphosphate plant, 111

T

Tatum, Sue, 23, 30, 40-41, 43, 45, 51, 55, 61, 63, 100, 107, 113, 116, 118, 121, 124-25, 142, 144, 175, 197, 211
Tax code, 116
Tax Reform Act, 187
Taylor, John W., 30
Teledyne, Inc., 150
Tennessee Valley Authority, 35, 48, 81, 82, 186
Terrell, Opal, 61
Texaco, 101, 104-05, 116, 168, 174, 175, 176
Thames, Tom, 87
Thames, Wayne, 218
Thomas, Don, 128, 129, 130, 131
Thomas, Leo Kirk, 65
Thomasville, Miss., 144, 241
Thompson, Bob, 249
Thompson, Carolyn, 39
Thompson, H. Leroy, 35, 36-37, 38, 39, 40, 50, 55
Thompson, Tommy, 216
Thrift plan, 146-47, 245
Tiblier, Don, 87

PHOTOGRAPHY AND ART CREDITS

The art on pages 2, 12–13, 66–67, 134–135, and 198–199 is from mixed-media paintings by William Dunlap. These paintings were commissioned for this book and are the property of Mississippi Chemical Corporation. The title page illustration is by Dugald Stermer.

Mississippi Chemical Corporation is grateful to the following individuals and organizations for providing photographs on the pages indicated.

Mack Barber, 243
James Bell, 145 (bottom)
ChemFirst,Inc., 121
Owen Cooper Collection, Mississippi Department of Archives and History, 24, 44, 90, 120, 130 (bottom), 162
Louise Dean, 124
Paul Lacy, 79, 112 (right), 156
U.S. Senator Trent Lott, 244
Mitchell Memorial Library, Mississippi State University, 22 (top)
New York Stock Exchange, 204, 222, 223
Tom Parry, 179
The Potash and Phosphate Institute, 20
Lois Roberts, 157 (left)
Ephraim Smith, 21, 22 (bottom)
The White House, 129
Eudora Welty Collection, Mississippi Department of Archives and History, 18
Yazoo Historical Society, 106

Most photographs in this book are from Mississippi Chemical's corporate archives. Individual photographers and photographic studios, when known, are noted below with page numbers of their respective photographs.

Stanley Beers, 36, 44 (upper left), 47, 50, 51
Marion Brown, 177 (right), 252
The Chronicle Star-Moss Point Advertiser, 74 (upper left and right)
Stewart Charles Cohen, 207, 214 (upper right)
Cyan Studios, 232, 234, 235
H.J. Davis, 63
Evans Studio, 96 (bottom)
Gil Ford Photography, 196
Larry Franco, 241 (left)
Len Grice, 127
Bob Hand Studio, 107 (top left), 210
Harold Head, 218, 241 (right)
Hiatt Photo Service, 38 (top)
Melinda B. Hood, 247
Tom Joynt, 151 (top), 184, 215 (upper right and bottom), 217, 219, 226, 239 (left), 242 (upper left and bottom)
Al Johnson, 78 (right)
Glen Jones, 92, 97, 105, 107 (bottom), 108 (top left and right), 119
James E. Lubbock, 193 (top)
McLanglin Air Service, 56
Steven Mangold, 88, 140, 150, 153, 167, 170
Norman A. Mott, Jr., 44 (lower right), 45
C. G. Nelson, 87
James Patterson, 48, 86, 152, 253
Frank Phillips, 237, 242 (upper right)

Jo G. Prichard, 58, 78 (left), 95, 108 (bottom), 109, 110 (bottom),112 (left), 114, 132 (top left), 133, 142, 143, 146, 159, 168, 192, 228
Wallace Reeves, 80
Jodi W. Savery, 230
Glenda Shaheen, 238 (upper right), 250 (right)
Clifford Stagg, 76
C.F. Weber Photography, 144
Wendy Weathersby, 214 (upper and lower left), 215 (upper left), 216, 229, 239 (right), 246, 247, 250 (left), 251
Noel Workman, Delta Design Group, 75, 98, 105, 151 (bottom), 174, 183
Yaphoto, 43

JO G. PRICHARD, a management consultant in Jackson, Mississippi, grew up on a family farm in Sunflower County, Mississippi. A graduate of Mississippi State University and the Harvard Business School, Prichard is a former MCC officer and a longtime observer of Southern agri-business.

WILLIE MORRIS has written sixteen books and countless articles about the South and America over a span of forty years. The former editor of *Harper's Magazine*, Morris grew up in Yazoo City and now lives in Jackson, Mississippi.

WILLIAM DUNLAP, a native Mississippian, is an acclaimed painter who lives in McLean, Virginia. His work is in the Metropolitan Museum of Art, Corcoran Gallery of Art, Mississippi Museum of Art, and many other museums and private collections.